DESIGN GRAPHICS

DESIGN
GRAPHICS

C. LESLIE MARTIN

PROFESSOR OF ARCHITECTURE

College of Design, Architecture, and Art

University of Cincinnati

THE MACMILLAN COMPANY · NEW YORK

DEDICATED TO

MILDRED MARTIN

WHOSE COOPERATION AND HELP

MADE THIS BOOK

POSSIBLE

CONTENTS

PART FIVE

Shadows on Drawings

PART SIX

Rendering Techniques

Preface

The principal methods by which thoughts of one person can be conveyed to another are, first, by means of oral or written speech, and second, by means of drawings or pictures. It is a well-known saying that "one picture is better than a thousand words." Speech has its limitations as well as its advantages. It introduces the elements of imagination with differences of visual interpretations of word descriptions. These interpretations vary with the training, environment, and temperament of the individual. Two persons who have listened to the same speech may interpret the information in entirely different ways. There may be wide variations in their visual conceptions of an object which has been described to them by words alone. Drawings supplement speech in describing objects. They give more precise descriptions which permit little variation in interpretation.

Graphics is the process of drafting and representation through which designs are developed, explained to others, and finally translated into information from which the finished objects are produced. In most design work the graphical representations are the drawings and renderings of some object which is to be made. The drawings may be larger, the same size, or smaller than the object represented. A drawing is usually made smaller than a large object in order to keep it at a reasonable size. Tiny objects are frequently shown with enlarged drawings in order to make the designs clear.

Drawings are used to develop, present, and explain in detail the designer's creations. First, they are used in the creative process in developing the design from the ideas of the designer. Second, drawings are used to present the design in terms that the client can understand, criticize, and approve. Third, working drawings and specifications are made to explain all details of shapes, sizes, materials, and workmanship to the persons who supervise and perform the work of making the finished object. Drafting is the principal medium of expression which is used to convey the ideas of the designer to others. These ideas should be expressed as simply, clearly, and attractively as it is possible to present them. This requires that the designer and the draftsman must be able to (1) choose the type of drawing best suited to the purpose, (2) do effective layout work, (3) make neat, clean-cut, expressive drawings, (4) add tones, textures, colors, and shadows when these are appropriate to the use of the drawings. In order to do these things expertly it is necessary for the designer and draftsman to acquire knowledge and skills in graphical representation. They must learn to coordinate mind, hands, and eyes to produce the best results of which they are capable.

Graphical representation is important to many persons of greatly varied interests. Some are interested in architecture, city planning, engineering, commercial designing, interior decorating, or industrial designing. Many others are interested in less formidable and often very modest projects. Many of these persons who use graphics, whether as professionals or amateurs, need to be able to draw well in order to explain their designs clearly. They also need a general knowledge of all methods of representing objects by drawings in order to be able to select the best type of drawing for each purpose. It is hoped that this general graphics text will be helpful to many persons in different types of design work.

Acknowledgment

One of the greatest experiences which comes from writing is the feeling of gratitude and appreciation for the many persons who have either directly or indirectly helped to make the publication possible. The author wishes to express his special appreciation to the following persons for their highly valued aid in this project.

To Dr. Ernest Pickering, Dean of the College of Design, Architecture, and Art, of the University of Cincinnati, for very valuable practical advice and help.

To Mildred C. Martin for listening to innumberable explanations without ever seeming to be bored, for cheerfully and conscientiously typing and retyping the text, and for always being a willing party to discussions of problems in the contents and composition of the manuscript.

To Professor Robert A. Deshon for his initiative and skillful aid in the preparation and standardization of drawings and for his cooperation and assistance in providing examples of student renderings.

To Associate Professor Robert Gebhart for reading and criticism of the typed manuscript and suggestions concerning the relations of text and drawings.

To Assistant Professors John M. Peterson and Bruce E. Goetzman for illustration material from their classes.

To four students of the College of Design, Architecture, and Art—Roland T. Docter, Brocky C. Eustice, Byong Hee Jon, and Dennis S. Malone—who inked and finished a large proportion of the drawings. Their skill, interest, and intelligent cooperation were a great help in completing this work.

To the professional designers and delineators who furnished illustrations providing the valuable link with professional practice.

To the students whose work is reproduced here, to David E. Thomas and Philip J. Joehnk who helped with photography, and to many other students of the College of Design, Architecture, and Art whose problems and needs suggested much of the information presented here.

To the preceding writers on the subjects treated here for their creations which provided a foundation of knowledge for compiling and developing this manuscript.

C. Leslie Martin

DESIGN GRAPHICS

PART ONE

Elements of Drafting

CHAPTER 1

An Approach to Graphics

Drafting requires the coordinated efforts of mind, hands, and eyes. Acute vision and skillful hands help to produce excellence of drafting technique. However, the resulting drawing may be of little value unless a great deal of thought and study have gone into producing it. Intelligent thinking is just as necessary for fine and useful drafting as for satisfactory performance in mathematics, science, and other subjects.

Eventually the procedure in drafting becomes automatic for a large proportion of the work. However, the really good draftsman never stops thinking out solutions which will make his work speedier and more accurate. The amateur automobile mechanic who takes a motor apart for the first time does a lot of worrying, scheming, and planning. The experienced mechanic does most of the work automatically. The same things are true of the beginner and the trained draftsman. The experienced draftsman often proceeds confidently and automatically without conscious mental effort for a large proportion of his work. The beginner must do a great deal more thinking and planning in deciding on the order of work and in solving in the most efficient, easy, and accurate manner the problems which arise as his work progresses. A beginner with no graphics training should not be discouraged by inferior performance on his first drafting projects. If he works conscientiously he will discover as time goes on that he has become as proficient as those who have had previous training. He should also remember that he probably has advantages in other subjects which were not studied by people who took drawing.

In drafting, the easiest method is the best if it is accurate. An intelligent system of procedure, which provides planned progress step by step, is essential to good drafting results. This requires constructive thinking. No book, however large, can provide detailed solutions for every problem the draftsman will encounter. It is essential that the reader understand not only the illustrations and accompanying text of this book, but also the principles used. Then he can apply the information to other objects and other problems. This requires effort on the part of the reader, insight into the theory used, and vision to see its possible applications. Drafting is essential to the development and manufacturing of a design. To the creative designer a thorough knowledge of the mechanics of drafting; the mastery of a precise, clean-cut, interesting technique; and a working knowledge of all systems of representing objects by drawings are of great importance. This knowledge and skill will enable him to present his ideas in a manner which can be understood and appreciated by others. A careless, dirty, fuzzy, inaccurate drawing is not attractive to any client.

Few clients have the patience and tolerance to continue with a designer who is not producing interesting and understandable sketches and polished presentation drawings. Designers in many fields are proud of a knowledge of drafting methods and a mastery of drafting technique. It is a great source of personal satisfaction to be able to draw easily, systematically, and expressively; to see the drawing develop to serve efficiently the purpose for which it is being made.

1

CHAPTER 2

Instruments for Drafting

The beginning draftsman may be bewildered by the variety of equipment which he sees in the display cases and on the shelves of the dealer. It is the purpose of this chapter to describe the commonly used items of drafting equipment and explain the type of work which is done with each. After reading this material the beginner should be able to make a better selection of instruments for his use.

The quality of the equipment used determines to a great extent the quality of the student's work. It is possible to do good work in spite of the handicap of poor equipment. It is possible to do better work and do it more easily with good tools. High quality instruments will last longer, require less sharpening and adjusting, and operate more smoothly and accurately than cheap instruments. The person who expects to do drafting over a period of years should buy fine instruments.

A list of instruments and materials for drafting work is given below. Suggested sizes are given in parentheses for some items. However, the sizes should be varied to suit the work to be done. Smaller boards and T-squares may be adequate in some cases.

ESSENTIAL EQUIPMENT FOR DRAFTING
Illustrated in Fig. 1 I

1. Set of drawing instruments.
2. Drawing board (23 in. x 31 in.).
3. T-square (30 in.).
4. 30° x 60° triangle (10 in.).
5. 45° triangle (6 in.).
6. 12 inch triangular scale.
7. Refill pencil and 4H, 3H, 2H, H, F leads (or drawing pencils).
8. Sandpaper pad.
9. Erasers for cleaning, pencil, ink.
10. Pens for lettering and freehand.
11. Penholder and penwipers.
12. Erasing shield.
13. Drafting tape or thumb tacks.
14. Bottle of black drawing ink.
15. Paper as required.

USEFUL ADDITIONS TO THE ABOVE LIST
Illustrated in Fig. 1 II

A. Adjustable triangle.
B. Pencil pointer.
C. Sharp knife.
D. Irregular curves.
E. Dusting brush.
F. Rule.

The Set of Drawing Instruments. The most important and expensive item of drafting equipment is the set of instruments, Figs. 1 III and IV. The various pieces are contained in a case made especially to fit them. There is a great deal of variation in the quality of case instruments and also in the number of pieces in a set. There may be as few as two major items with a few attachments, or as many as twenty major pieces. The essential operations performed by any set whether large or small are: (1) the inking of straight lines with a ruling pen, (2) drawing of pencil and ink circles with compass, (3) dividing and transferring spaces with the dividers. Any set, however small, which will perform these three operations in a satisfactory manner is adequate. It is not always possible to judge performance by appearance of equipment. Some compasses and ruling pens which lack polish and refinement in appearance do very precise work. Others may be made to sell on sleek appearance but do not have the precision of manufacture and high quality materials to do good work. It is a pleasure to have instruments which are graceful in design and which have a good feel when handled. This is especially true if they are accurate and durable also.

Ⓘ E S S E N T I A L   D R A F T I N G   E Q U I P M E N T

Ⓘ Ⓘ   A D D I T I O N S

Ⓘ Ⓘ Ⓘ A   S M A L L   S E T

O F   D R A W I N G

I N S T R U M E N T S

I L L U S T R A T I O N   B Y

C O U R T E S Y   O F   T H E

E U G E N E   D I E T Z G E N   C O.

Ⓘ Ⓥ A V E R A G E   S E T

O F   D R A W I N G

I N S T R U M E N T S

I L L U S T R A T I O N   B Y

C O U R T E S Y   O F   T H E

E U G E N E   D I E T Z G E N   C O.

F I G. I   I N S T R U M E N T S   A N D   M A T E R I A L S   F O R   D R A F T I N G

FIG. 2   LARGE   DRAFTING   INSTRUMENTS

A. The ruling pen is an essential part of a set of instruments. The smallest set has one ruling pen, medium sized sets have two pens, and large sets may have several. Although it may be convenient at times, it is not necessary to have more than one ruling pen. The ruling pen is made to draw ink lines along the ruling edge of a T-square, triangle, or irregular curve. The points on some ruling pens are narrow in the direction of the line drawn, others are quite broad. The narrow ones are easier to use for exact beginning and ending of lines. The broad detail pens hold more ink for long lines. Both are satisfactory for general use. Quick-opening devices for easier cleaning between the blades are provided on many ruling pens.

The compass is used for drawing circles in pencil and ink. There may be either a single compass for general use or several compasses for specific purposes.

The large bow compass and large friction joint compass are made for general use. They are satisfactory for a rather wide range of circle sizes. They will make circles from ¼ inch or less minimum up to 10 inch or greater maximum diameter and with extension bar up to 15 or 20 inch diameter. There are some compasses which are made for very small, and others for very large circles.

B. A large bow compass which can be used for circles of a wide range of sizes is sufficient for some draftsmen. Such a compass is usually made with a center adjusting screw and is provided with attachments for either pencil or ink. Some have an extension for larger circles and some include two needle points so the instrument can be used as a somewhat clumsy dividers. The adjusting screw holds the instrument from either opening or closing. The instrument is usually sufficiently rigid for drawing dark pencil lines. The adjusting screw operates rather slowly for extreme changes of radius.

C. The large compass with friction joints can be adjusted to radius quickly. A hairspring is sometimes provided on one side for tiny adjustments. This style of compass has knee joints which can be adjusted to keep the points perpendicular to the paper. These joints are easier to adjust when they are both at the same distance from the handle. When one is nearer the end of a side than the other, adjusting seems more awkward. This type of compass is likely to change radius when pressure is exerted for dark pencil lines. For light pencil lines and ink work it is usually quite satisfactory.

D. Dividers are not always included in the smallest sets of case instruments. They are useful in transferring sizes from one drawing to another, enlarging and reducing sizes of drawings, measuring a repeating distance accurately, and dividing a straight or curved line into equal segments. Dividers are of two types, the bow dividers (F) and the large friction joint dividers (D). The latter may have a hairspring for more accurate final setting.

E. Proportional dividers are made for reducing or enlarging measurements to a chosen ratio. The person who has to make many large drawings from small ones or vice versa will find this instrument a useful addition to the set. However, there are also drafting methods of accomplishing the same results and they sometimes require less effort. The length of the points of a proportional dividers must not be changed. Any change of length of one or more of the four points makes the proportional scale on the instrument inaccurate since it is based on a definite length for each point.

F. Small bow compasses are made for the specific purpose of drawing very small circles. There are usually separate bows for pencil and ink. However, some small bow compasses are made with interchangeable pencil and ink points. The bow pen or pencil will draw circles from ⅛ inch or less diameter up to about a 3 or 4 inch maximum. They are more delicate than the large compasses and are more accurate and easier to use for the small work for which they are intended.

G. Drop compasses are made for very small circles. They are so designed as to be most efficient for this specialized work. A drop compass is so constructed that it is easy to keep uniform pressure on the drawing surface with both the needle and marking points and also easy to rotate the marking point.

H. The beam compass is used for drawing large circles in pencil or ink. It consists of a metal or wood beam to which the needle point and the marking point are clamped with a screw device. The radius is changed by moving the units containing the points closer together or farther apart on the beam. There is usually a screw adjustment in the mechanism of one point for small changes of radius. There may be complete separate devices for pen and ink, or a single element with interchangeable sets of points. The beam compass may include either beams of different lengths or extensions which add on to the length of the original beam.

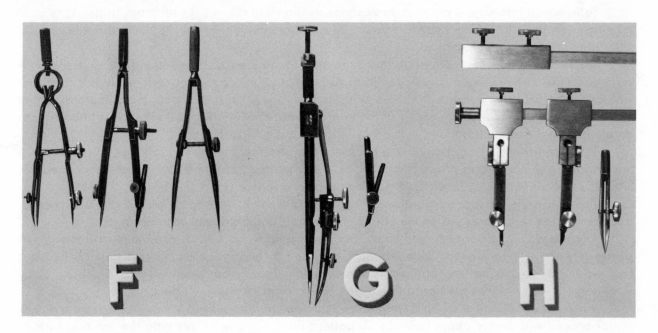

FIG. 3 SMALLER AND LESS USED INSTRUMENTS

6

(A) WOOD CROSS STRIPS AT ENDS

(B) BATTENS ON BACK OF BOARD

(C) METAL DOVETAILED STRIPS AT ENDS

(D) BUILT-UP BOARD—PLYWOOD FACE

FIG. 4 VARIATIONS IN DRAWING BOARDS

Other Drafting Materials. Drawing boards, T-squares, triangles, and other drafting materials vary in design and quality. Brief information about these essential items of drafting equipment will be given in the following paragraphs.

The drawing board should be made of some firm wood having a uniform close grain. White pine and basswood are two good materials for boards. A drawing board should have straight edges and perfectly smooth, plane working surfaces. It should not become warped or crooked from changes in humidity.

Solid wood boards are made in three styles as shown in Fig. 4:(A) with cross strips at the ends forming a continuation of the board surfaces, (B) with battens applied on the back of the board, (C) with dovetailed metal end strips.

The first style has the advantage that both sides can be used. However, it has several disadvantages. (1) It is more likely to warp, split, or to have crooked edges on the long sides. (2) Expansion and contraction may cause the cross strip joints to open. (3) It may also leave the cross strips either longer or shorter than the center of the board so that they interfere with the use of the T-square on the long sides of the board.

The second style with battens on the back makes a stronger board, which is less likely to warp. It has uniform expansion and contraction over its entire surface, and has four good working edges. It takes up more room in a locker and may be used on one side only.

The third style has the advantages of both the other two. The metal braces allow expansion and contraction. All four edges of the board are straight and both sides can be used.

Anyone making a board should know that good solid wood boards are made of a number of pieces of wood so turned as to minimize warping caused by expansion and contraction; furthermore that cross pieces and battens are not fastened rigidly throughout their lengths, but have some arrangement which allows the board to expand and contract without splitting.

Built-up wood boards of light weight are manufactured in various styles. Some have a hollow center braced with heavy paper honeycomb pattern filler. On one of this type the working surface is made of a single layer of veneering; on another each flat surface is made of about 1/8 inch plywood composed of three layers of veneering, Fig. 4 D. These boards are much lighter than

BEVELS FOR LIFTING

(I) STANDARD TRIANGLE

HOLES FOR SPACING LINES

(II) LETTERING TRIANGLE

PROTRACTOR

(III) ADJUSTABLE TRIANGLE

HEAD

WORKING EDGE

TRANSPARENT PLASTIC

BLADE

WOOD CENTER

(IV) A WIDELY USED TYPE OF T-SQUARE

FIG. 5 DESIGNS OF TRIANGLES AND T-SQUARES

solid boards. The one with the three-ply veneering seems to be quite stable in dimensions so that all four edges remain straight.

Triangles of tough transparent plastic are the most satisfactory ones. High grade triangles are usually thicker than the inexpensive ones and they are made with bevels on the inside edges, Fig. 5 I. The fingernails can get under the beveled edges to take hold of the triangle. When the triangle has a square edge all around the open inside it is very difficult to lift. But it can be beveled with a file, a piece of sandpaper over a strip of wood, or more crudely with a knife. The edges of the inside of the triangle should be beveled equally from both sides. This does no damage since the inside edge is not intended for drafting use. Some triangles are made with a series of regularly spaced small holes to be used for spacing guide lines for lettering, Fig. 5 II. This device is especially useful when lettering several lines of the same height.

Adjustable triangles which can be set to a scale of degrees on the triangle or set to match a given angle on a drawing are very useful in some drafting work, Fig. 5 III. The draftsman will find such a triangle a decided convenience in making dimetric, oblique, and perspective drawings and in casting shadows at angles not given on the fixed triangles.

Special drafting devices are often used in professional drafting rooms. The parallel rule is frequently used instead of a horizontal T-square. It is a straightedge which is controlled with cords and pulleys so that all of its positions are parallel as it is moved up and down the board. The drafting machine is a combination of scale, adjustable straightedge, and protractor.

The T-square should have straight edges on the blade and a straight working edge on the head. The head should be fastened rigidly to the blade so there is no movement between the two parts. T-squares are made of wood entirely, of wood having transparent plastic edges to the blade, of metal with plastic edges to the blade, and of solid stainless steel, plastic, or other materials. Wood is not entirely satisfactory for the drawing edges. It is likely to have slight imperfections, irregularities in grain, or other defects which cause uneven lines. The edges are easily damaged so that the T-square is ruined or must be repaired. Good plastic edges have the advantage of being tough, close grained, and transparent. Wood T-squares with plastic edges to the blades are most generally used, Fig. 5 IV.

8

Scales are used to measure distances on drawings. Drawings of the same object can be made at different sizes by using different scale divisions. It is possible therefore to choose a numerical scale which will give the desired size drawing. There are three types of scales which are in general use: (1) The *architect's scale* is divided for measuring in feet and inches. (2) The *mechanical engineer's scale* is divided for measuring inches and fractions of an inch. It looks very much like the architect's scale but usually includes a 50 divisions to the inch scale instead of one of the fractional scales. (3) The *civil engineer's chain scale* is divided into decimal divisions ranging from 10 to 60 divisions to the inch. Be sure to get the type of scale which will be most useful.

Scales are made of a number of different materials and in several different shapes, Fig. 6. The white plastic materials can be kept clean and bright so the scale divisions and numerals are easy to read. The wood surfaces used for numerals and divisions should have a good varnish finish or they will become dirty, worn, and indistinct from use. The triangular shape is the only one which gives the six edges needed for all the commonly used divisions on one scale. If flat shapes are used it may be necessary to have two or three scales since only two sets of divisions can be placed on each working edge. Some flat scales have two working edges, some have four.

Drawing pencil leads are graded from hard to soft as follows: 9H, 8H, 7H, 6H, 5H, **4H, 3H, 2H, H**, F, HB, B, 2B, 3B, 4B, 5B, 6B. The draftsman seldom has use for a harder lead than 4H, or a softer one than H. Pencils with long filler leads have the advantages of remaining constant in length and of eliminating the use of a knife or pencil sharpener to remove wood.

Pencil Sharpeners for writing pencils give too blunt a point for drafting use. A drafting pencil should have a long, thin, conical point. A sharp knife can be used for trimming the wood from the common drafting pencil and a sandpaper pad can be used to grind the lead to a point on any type pencil. There are special pencil lead pointers made for use on either refill or common drafting pencils. One widely used type is shown in Fig. 7. There are also special pencil sharpeners made for wood pencils which remove the wood and point the lead for drafting use.

Erasers are of three general types: (1) cleaning erasers, (2) pencil erasers, (3) ink erasers. An eraser should not discolor or make a smudge on the paper. Ink erasers should not be so coarse as to roughen and scratch the paper. Old erasers are often hard and smear instead of erasing.

Penholder and pens are used for lettering and freehand forms. Pens are needed to provide a good variety of line widths. There are many pens made for fine line work. Ball point pens are used for medium lines and "Speedball pens" for medium to very wide lines.

The erasing shield is a thin rectangular sheet of metal or plastic having a number of perforations of various shapes and sizes. It is used to protect the drawing and paper near the place being

6 — SCALE FACES EACH
TRIANGULAR SCALE SHAPES

TWO BEVEL
2-SCALE FACES

OPPOSITE BEVEL
2-SCALE FACES

FOUR BEVEL
4-SCALE FACES

DRAFTSMAN'S MECHANICAL POINTER GIVES A LONG POINT

FLAT SCALE SHAPES

FIG. 7 PENCIL

FIG. 6 SHAPES OF DRAFTING SCALES   POINTER

erased. The erasing is done through one of the openings. An old erasing shield worn thin around openings is better than a new one.

Paper fasteners are a necessary nuisance. They are used to hold the paper securely in place on the board. They are a nuisance because all types form an obstruction to movement of T-squares and triangles.

The paper may be fastened to the board with thumb tacks, drafting tape, or staples. Glue is sometimes used for mounting paper for rendering but very seldom used for drafting problems. Thumb tacks should have points which are small enough so they can be pushed into the board and removed from it easily. The head of the thumb tack should be shaped so the T-square and triangle will slide over and not bump against it.

Drawing paper, which may be detail paper or other opaque drawing paper, is used for drawings which are to be drawn and inked on the same paper and for drawings which are to be traced onto tracing paper or cloth. It should have a white or light colored surface which is tough and thick enough to stand erasing and then take ink without having the lines blur.

Tracing paper should be tough enough to stand some wrinkling and folding without breaking. It should withstand pencil erasing. Some thick tracing paper will take ink erasing. Tracing paper may be too transparent. The kind which is clear as glass looks attractive but it is difficult to work on it. Unless there is some particular reason for using them, avoid oily, glassy, brittle, or grainy surfaced tracing papers. It is convenient to have two rolls of tracing paper, a narrow roll for sketches and small drawings and a wide roll of correct width to make the largest sheets required.

Irregular curves are used as guides in drawing curved lines other than circles or arcs of circles. There are two general types of irregular curves: (1) the rigid type which is made in a variety of shapes and sizes of a transparent material like that used for triangles, Fig. 8 I, and (2) the flexible type which can be bent to fit the curve to be drawn (called an adjustable curve), Fig 8 II, III. The flexible type is made of a combination of steel, rubber, and lead or other materials which will retain the shapes into which they are bent, or can be held in position with weights. A piece of soft heavy wire either bare or insulated with an enamel finish can be used for an adjustable curve. The rigid curves are most useful for sharp curves. The ship curves and adjustable curves are best for medium shape and length curvature of lines. The flexible spline is especially useful for very long gradual curves.

The dusting brush is useful in removing eraser particles, dust, and lint from the drawing.

Marking instruments with name or initials for identification is a precaution which should be taken as soon as the student is sure that his instruments and equipment are to be kept.

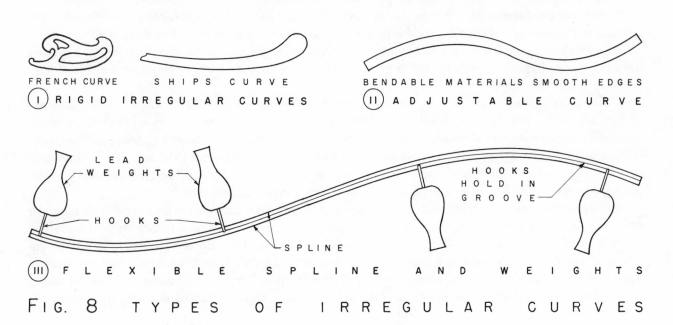

FRENCH CURVE   SHIPS CURVE   BENDABLE MATERIALS SMOOTH EDGES

(I) RIGID IRREGULAR CURVES   (II) ADJUSTABLE CURVE

LEAD WEIGHTS   HOOKS HOLD IN GROOVE   HOOKS   SPLINE

(III) FLEXIBLE SPLINE AND WEIGHTS

FIG. 8 TYPES OF IRREGULAR CURVES

CHAPTER 3

Efficient Use of Drafting Equipment

It is very important that the draftsman learn and employ the best methods of using his drafting equipment. The methods enumerated below have been developed to give the most accurate results and to avoid mechanical errors.

1. The hand doing the drawing is kept over the triangle or T-square along which the line is drawn and not rubbed over the drawing. As lines are drawn, the T-square, triangle, and hand are moved away from the new lines, not smeared over them.

2. The hand which holds the pencil or pen is turned so the line is visible as it is drawn. The hand is not between the line being made and the eye of the draftsman.

3. The pencil is held so that it will not extend under raised places on T-square or triangle and make crooked lines.

4. The pencil is so sharpened and used that it will make many uniform fine lines before it needs re-sharpening.

5. The top edge only of the T-square blade is used for drawing purposes because, (A) the hand is in a better position to draw there, (B) the two edges may not be exactly parallel, (C) the operation of drawing along the two edges may throw the lines out of parallel.

6. The T-square is used on one edge of the drafting board only because triangles are more accurate and more dependable than drawing boards in giving perfect right angles.

7. The triangle is turned one direction only for vertical lines, (A) so that lines will be parallel even though the triangle may not have an exact right angle, (B) so that the hand is over the triangle, not rubbing over the paper and newly drawn lines.

Working Conditions. The drawing table should be large enough to provide space for the board, for spreading out the instruments, and for any necessary books or papers. The drawing table and stool should be of correct heights so that the draftsman can work either standing up or sitting down. Most draftsmen prefer to sit down part of the time and stand up part of the time while working, since it is less tiring to change position at intervals.

Instructions for use of instruments are given for right-handed persons. For those who are left-handed the word right should be read left, and the word left read right in this chapter.

Light should come from the left front for the right-handed person to avoid confusing shadows from the hand, T-square, and triangle. It is most convenient to have both daylight and artificial light from the same direction.

The board should be tilted toward the draftsman by placing a block of wood, books, or other steady support under the farther edge. The board should not be slanted so much that the triangle and other equipment will slide down the inclined surface. Tilting the board has these advantages: (1) The line of sight is more nearly perpendicular to the drawing surface. (2) The scale is tilted at a better visual angle. (3) It is easier to reach the top of the board. (4) If the T-square extends beyond the right edge of the board it will clear most materials placed on the table.

Instruments and materials should be arranged in the most convenient and orderly manner on the clean table top near the right edge of the board, Fig 9. Practically all instruments and materials are first handled or used entirely by the right hand. They should be placed on the right side of the board where they can be reached easily. Try to make each object accessible without moving another object. The T-square is operated almost entirely by the left hand. When it is removed from the board it may be placed to the left or above the board. Keep the board as free as possible of instruments

FIG. 9 ARRANGING THE DRAFTING EQUIPMENT

EQUIPMENT ARRANGED FOR LEFT HANDED PERSON

and materials. Although the draftsman normally works from the bottom edge of the drawing, which is the low edge of the board, he may when drawing on some areas find it convenient to take his position on the left side of the drawing.

Pencils. Sharpen all pencils before beginning to draw. The blank ends of the wood pencils should be sharpened so that the letters and numbers indicating the grades of the pencils remain on the opposite ends. In sharpening a pencil the wood should be removed in a neat cone shape, with either a sharp knife or a special pencil sharpener until about one half inch of the lead is exposed. Take very small shavings when using a knife. Do not take big gouges of wood. The lead should be ground to a needle point on the sandpaper pad or file. Hold the length of the lead almost parallel to the grinding surface so the point will be long and thin. If the angle between the axis of the lead and the surface of the sandpaper is too great the point will be blunt and will dull rapidly when used. Rotate the pencil when grinding the lead so the point will be perfectly round. After the point is shaped remove the black dust by wiping it with a piece of cloth or by polishing it on a scrap of paper. Keep the pencils sharp. A sharp pencil makes neat, accurate lines.

When sharpening the lead on a refill drafting pencil with a sandpaper pad be careful not to grind the metal end of the pencil which holds the lead. If necessary extend the lead farther than the position where it will be clamped for use, then return it to the use position after pointing.

The grade of pencil used has considerable influence on the neatness of the work. Too hard a pencil requires heavy pressure to make a mark. This pressure makes a groove in the paper with the mark at the bottom of the groove. It is difficult to erase the pencil mark made with a hard pencil. When the mark is erased the groove may still remain to disfigure the paper. Never use a pencil which is so hard that it ruins the paper.

When a pencil is too soft it soon becomes dull from use. The lines smear when the instruments are moved over them and the paper becomes dirty in a short time.

The best rule is to use the softest pencil which will give a neat, fine line. The paper and the weather have some influence on the grade of pencil used. Slick paper requires a softer pencil than soft, grainy, or rough paper. In damp weather it is necessary to use a softer pencil than when the atmosphere is dry. The grades on the list of materials provide a sufficient range for most work.

FIG. 10 THREE COMMONLY USED DRAFTING SCALES

The Scale. The word scale is applied to the entire instrument and also to any series of divisions on the instrument. The scale is used primarily to measure distances in making drawings.

The architect's scale is designed for measuring in feet and inches. By using the ⅜″ = 1′-0″ scale, ⅜″ on the drawing represents a distance of one foot on the object. For convenience in the use of the scale the first space is divided to give parts of a foot on the architect's scale, Fig. 10 A. Where possible these small divisions give inches and in the larger scales, where space permits, various fractions of an inch. In the smaller scales the smallest subdivision may represent two inches. In all cases the total distance divided into small divisions represents one foot on that scale. It is then simple arithmetic to determine what each division represents.

In using the architect's scale to measure a distance in feet, the measurement starts not at the end of the scale but at the 0 point which is in the position shown in Fig. 10 A between the divided space and the next adjoining undivided space. To measure 7 feet 5 inches the feet are measured in one direction from the 0 point and the inches in the opposite direction as shown in Fig. 10 A. Both the architect's and mechanical engineer's scales have two scales on one edge. One begins at the 0 on the left end and the other at the 0 on the right end. Each of the two scales has a sequence of numbers beginning at the 0 point. These numbers overlap. Care must be taken to use the correct set of numbers for a given scale.

The mechanical engineer's scale is designed for measuring in inches and fractions of an inch. The basis for the small divisions is the common fractions of an inch such as ⅛, 1/16, etc. The divided space usually represents one inch. This scale is useful to the designer of furniture and other small objects where the common fractions of an inch are used.

The mechanical engineer's scale is used to measure inches and fractions of an inch in the same way that the architect's scale is used to measure feet and inches. The scale in Fig. 10 B shows the dark line to be 4⅜ inches long.

The engineer's chain scale is a simple decimal scale. The divisions vary from 60 to the inch to 10 to the inch. There are no smaller divisions of a unit such as those on the architect's and mechanical engineer's scales. The scale along one edge has equal divisions throughout its length, Fig. 10 C.

When drawing to scale a great variety of numerical scales is desirable so that a drawing may be made as large or as small as required. If ½" scale is used in making a drawing, the drawing is a certain size. By using ¼" scale the drawing can be made only half as large, and by using 1" scale it can be made twice the size of the ½" scale drawings, Figs. 11 I, II, III.

In laying out measurements with the scale the points of measurement may be marked by dots, V-shaped marks, or by short straight lines perpendicular to the length of the scale. The latter method is the best, but sometimes different markings may be used to help distinguish between lines. Keep the marks light enough so they do not disfigure the drawing.

Most people have a tendency to make measurements either too large or too small. If this slight error is repeated a number of times, the total distance may be appreciably in error. The effects of this tendency can be minimized either by keeping the scale in one position for a number of measurements or by measuring from a base point.

Measurements should be laid out vertically at the left ends of horizontal lines and horizontally at the bottom ends of vertical lines, with the scale held perpendicular to the lines to be drawn. It is then quite convenient to draw the lines in the correct directions for T-square and triangles.

Ⓘ SCALE ½" = 1'-0"

Ⓘ Ⓘ SCALE ¼"= 1'-0"   Ⓘ Ⓘ Ⓘ CABINET AT SCALE   1" = 1'-0"

FIG. 11 MAKING SCALE DRAWINGS OF AN OBJECT

14

Ⓐ MOVING T—SQUARE   Ⓑ HORIZONTAL LINE   Ⓒ VERTICAL LINE

FIG. 12 RIGHT HANDED DRAFTING ABOVE—LEFT H. BELOW

The T-Square. The T-square is used for drawing parallel lines across the paper from left to right, and as a rest for the triangles in drawing vertical and slanting lines. The top edge of the T-square is called the working edge. It is used for drawing lines and supporting the triangles. Lines drawn across the board with the T-square will be called horizontal lines. Lines perpendicular to the horizontal lines will be called vertical lines.

To draw a line with the T-square, use the left hand first to move and then to hold the T-square, leaving the right hand free to draw the line from left to right, Fig. 12 A, B. Place the head of the T-square in contact with the left edge of the board. Then slide it up or down until the working edge of the blade is in proper position for drawing the line. Grip the T-square by the head when moving it, then slide the hand along the blade to the holding position. Hold the T-square in position with the left hand placed partly on the paper and partly on the blade of the T-square, Fig. 12 B.

For drawing lines along the ruling edge of T-square or triangle, the pencil is held in a plane perpendicular to the paper through the line to be drawn, Fig. 12 B, C. The tip of the tapered pencil point and the line are then a small distance from the T-square. The top of the pencil is inclined in the direction in which the line is drawn. Hold the pencil about ¾ inch from the point with the thumb, forefinger, and middle finger. The tips of the other two fingers can steady the hand in placing the pencil and then slide along the surface of the T-square or triangle as the line is drawn. Rotate the pencil slowly in one direction when drawing so that the point will remain symmetrically shaped and will give a thin even line for a long time. The side of the pencil point must be brought against the ruling edge without touching the paper or the top surface of the straight edge, then pushed down along the ruling edge into contact with the paper.

The experienced draftsman uses a little more pressure to make the beginning and end of a line definite. Form the habit of drawing the line once and leaving it alone. If necessary, erase and redraw, but never go back and forth over lines. The working edge of the T-square and the outside edges of the triangles are the only guiding edges to be used in drawing straight lines.

When there are several lines to be drawn with the T-square, start at the top and draw the lines in

Ⓓ MOVING T—SQUARE   Ⓔ HORIZONTAL LINE   Ⓕ VERTICAL LINE
LEFT HANDED USE OF T—SQUARE AND TRIANGLE

Ⓘ A 15° POSITION   Ⓘ POSSIBLE ANGLES   Ⓘ A 75° POSITION

FIG. 13 ANGLES GIVEN BY TRIANGLES ON T—SQUARE

order from top to bottom of the drawing. Thus the lines drawn remain visible and each new line, as it is drawn, can be seen in its relation to the completed lines. Furthermore, working back and forth over lines is reduced to a minimum and the drawing is kept cleaner. Always start at the left and draw towards the right along the T-square. Two T-squares do not ordinarily make identical lines. Use only one T-square on a drawing. The T-square is used in one direction, across the board, and against only one edge of the board, the left edge.

Triangles. All lines perpendicular to those drawn with the T-square are drawn along the triangle resting on the T-square. The triangle is turned with the vertical edge to the left, Fig. 12 c. The line is drawn from bottom to top, that is, away from the draftsman. The pencil is inclined with the top farther away from the T-square. Do not start to draw at the corner of the triangle which is against the T-square. Leave room so the line begins a short distance above the T-square.

In drawing lines with the triangle the left hand holds the T-square and triangle together and keeps them from slipping along the board. This can be done by dividing the holding surface of the left hand between the triangle, T-square, and board so that part of the surface of the hand rests on each.

When drawing a long vertical line with the triangle it is usually best to start near the T-square at the bottom end of the line and draw up nearly to the tip of the triangle. Then move the triangle and T-square up higher to start at the end of the line just drawn and continue it. Repeat as many times as necessary. The triangle will probably have to be shifted to the left or right so do not attempt to hold it in the same relation to the T-square when moving up to continue a line.

When drawing a series of vertical lines, draw the left line first then draw each line in order toward the right. Thus the triangle does not rub over the lines drawn and all lines remain visible. When the lines are longer than the triangle draw the bottom parts of all lines before moving the T-square up to continue the height of the lines.

The draftsman will find that it is sometimes better to make exceptions to the above rules for sequence of lines. For example, when several horizontal lines extend between two verticals it is better to draw the verticals first.

The various angles obtained with the triangles on the horizontal T-square used singly and in combinations are shown in Fig. 13 II. It should be noted that all lines which slant up and to the right are drawn up, that all lines which slant down to the right are drawn down except in the one case of the 75° combination when the line is drawn up and to the left to keep the hand over the triangle as the line is drawn. When all possible lines are drawn through a point with the single and combined triangles resting on the horizontal T-square the lines will be spaced 15° apart. The draftsman should shift his position whenever it will help him to draw lines in different directions easily and naturally. It is usually sufficient to move a little to the right or left and twist around to a more comfortable relation to the drawing. The position below the drawing should be maintained when possible. Drawing the object upside down should be avoided.

The Ruling Pen. The quality of an ink drawing usually depends on the correct use and mechanical excellence of the ruling pen more than on all other instruments combined. The ruling pen is used for inking straight lines along the edge of the T-square or triangle. It is never used free-hand. However, it is used to ink along the edge of the irregular curve as a guide. The widths of lines obtained with a correctly sharpened pen vary from the very finest to about 1/16 inch, which is the approximate maximum for a single stroke of the pen. The ruling pen is held with the adjusting screw on the side away from the ruling edge. The inside flat surfaces of the point must be parallel to the line being drawn.

The pen should be held in a plane perpendicular to the paper and through the line to be drawn. It can be inclined slightly in the direction of the motion or be held perpendicular to the paper. If it is inclined too much the edges of the points will not be parallel where they touch the paper. The line will then vary in width and its edges may be uneven.

Before starting to ink a drawing be sure that the pen is clean and that the paper, T-square, and triangles are free from lint, dust, and particles of eraser. Use the dusting brush on the paper and a clean cloth for rubbing dust from the T-square and triangles. Any tiny bit of lint or eraser may catch on the point of the pen as it is used and cause the lines to blur. It will continue to cause trouble until the pen is cleaned. When cleaning the pen be sure not to leave any lint on it.

The ruling pen is filled with ink by touching the tip of the filler which is in the stopper of the ink bottle between the blades of the upright pen and allowing the ink to run down into the point between the blades, Fig. 14 A. Care should be taken to see that there is no ink on the outside surfaces of the pen. If there is too much ink in the pen it will run out rapidly causing the lines to spread and making a blot. The pen can usually be safely filled about 1/4 inch or 3/8 inch from the point.

Do not fill the pen until it is to be used, since the ink dries rapidly. Form a habit of cleaning the pen with a penwiper before laying it down and before refilling it when it is used continuously. If the penwiper is moistened slightly it will work more efficiently. If the ink should dry in the pen, do not scratch it out with a knife, but open the pen and clean it by rubbing with a moist cloth.

The ruling pen should make neat, fine lines of uniform width having perfectly straight true edges on good inking paper. Draw the lines once and in the same directions that pencil lines are drawn, Figs. 14 B, C. It is impossible to make good lines by going back and forth over them. If the pen does not make good lines, there is something wrong with it or with the way in which it is used. Find out what is wrong and correct it.

Faulty lines, other than those due to conditions of the ruling pen, may be caused by one of the following technical mistakes:

1. Too much pressure against the ruling edge will bend the spring blade of the pen and cause the space between the points to vary or will hold them together. This may cause a line of varying width, or a thin wiry line, or the ink may stop flowing from too much pressure.

2. The points of the pen may be held tightly together by the adjusting screw so that the ink cannot flow between them easily and reach the paper. This may cause a line of uneven width which is thin and wiry or no line at all.

3. Touching the top surface of the ruling edge with the tip of the pen may cause the ink to run down between the pen and ruling edge and make a blot.

4. Ink left on the outside surfaces of the pen may run down the ruling edge to make a blot.

5. When the pen is tilted out of the plane perpendicular to the paper through the line drawn, one point may not touch the paper. This will cause a ragged edge on that side of the line. When the pen is tilted so the point is in the angle between the paper and ruling edge, blots result from the ink getting onto the ruling edge.

6. Blots are sometimes caused by sliding the T-square or triangle into the wet line. However, the lines should be allowed to dry without the use of a blotter.

7. When the blades of the pen are not held parallel to the line being drawn, the pen will make a scratchy line when turned at a slight angle in one direction. It will either run away from the ruling edge when turned in the other direction or make an uneven line.

(A) FILLING THE RULING PEN   (B) DRAWING LINES HORIZONTALLY   (C) DRAWING LINES VERTICALLY

FIG. 14 INKING WITH THE RULING PEN

8. Too much ink in the pen causes bulbs at the ends of lines and sometimes causes the ink to spread and make uneven lines or blots.

Dividers. The right hand alone is usually sufficient to hold, open, adjust, and use the dividers. The friction joint instrument is opened by pressure of the thumb and middle finger on the bevel or against the inside edges of the sides of the instrument as shown in Fig. 15 D. In adjusting the instrument it is pressed together by the thumb and forefinger and opened by the outward pressure of the middle (second) and third fingers. The pressure on the friction joint should be so adjusted that the dividers can be opened and closed easily, but with sufficient resistance to movement so the setting will not change while the instrument is being used.

Dividers are used for dividing spaces, for transferring measurements, and for enlarging and reducing drawings. Dividers are useful in transferring distances from one drawing to another, and for repeating equal spaces through the same drawing. They are more accurate than the scale for this work. Furthermore, since the procedure is mechanical, there is less chance of error.

(D) ADJUSTING A FRICTION JOINT INSTRUMENT   (E) STEPPING OFF DISTANCES WITH THE DIVIDERS   (F) DRAWING CIRCLE WITH THE LARGE BOW COMPASS

FIG-15 OPERATING THE DIVIDERS AND COMPASS

The Compass. The pencil point of the compass should be sharpened to a flat wedge shape with the flat surfaces tangent to lines drawn. The lead can be sharpened while it is in the compass if care is taken not to allow the sandpaper to touch the metal of the instrument. The instrument should be opened and the lead flattened from both sides so that its flat surfaces are perpendicular to a line between the needle and pencil points. Some persons prefer to sharpen the pencil for a compass with a single bevel from the outside. The lead can be sharpened in this manner without changing the radius even when the needle and pencil points are close together. The length of a needle point should be adjusted so that it is always kept just slightly longer than the pencil point.

For very small circles a round pencil point is better than a wedge point. When drawing small circles the legs of the large compass can be kept straight because they are practically perpendicular to the paper. When larger circles are drawn the joints of the compass should be adjusted so that the points are perpendicular to the paper. There are two reasons for this: first, so that the needle point rotates on its axis when circles are drawn; second, so that the radius is unchanged as the lead wears. If the compass were used with the points at an angle to the paper the needle point would gouge a hole in the paper, and the radius would become shorter as the circles were drawn. In using the compass with the pen point, the pen, when properly sharpened, makes a neat line when held perpendicular to the paper but is likely to make an uneven line if the pen is tilted toward or away from the needle point. This is most noticeable when wide lines are drawn.

The friction joint compass is held and adjusted in the same manner as the dividers except that both hands are used in adjusting the knee joints to keep the points perpendicular to the paper.

The lengthening bar is used in drawing circles too large to be drawn without its use. It is placed in the compass at the joint where the pen and pencil points are inserted. One end of the lengthening bar holds the pen or pencil point and the other is attached to the compass.

When drawing lines with a compass the right hand only is used, Fig. 15 F. However, it will be found necessary to use both hands when the lengthening bar is used. In order to get a neat line the instrument should be revolved slowly and leaned slightly in the direction of motion to keep a uniform pressure on the paper.

Bow Instruments. The bow pencil and bow pen are used to draw small circles in pencil and ink. The bow dividers is used for spacing, transferring measurements, and enlarging and reducing sizes when the spaces are small. The pencil lead on a bow pencil can be sharpened to a wedge point for most circles as is done on large compasses. However a round tapered point such as is used on drafting pencils will give better results for very small circles. The bow pen or pencil should have the needle point adjusted so that it is just slightly longer than the pen or pencil point. The bow dividers should have the points of equal length. Small adjustments of radius of the bow instrument are made with one hand with the instrument in position. However, for speedy large changes in radius the side adjusting bow instrument can be approximately adjusted by pressing the sides together with the left hand to relieve the pressure on the threads, then spinning the adjusting nut with the right hand.

Care of Equipment. Drafting equipment requires intelligent care to keep it in good condition. The following information is given to help the beginner understand how to take care of his equipment.

The drawing board should be supported by laying it flat on top of a table or standing on end. If the board is left in a strain, it is likely to warp. Do not leave it supported on opposite corners with two corners up in the air or leaning against the wall on one corner. Never drag a board across the floor or slam it around. The edges may be splintered or roughened by such treatment. Keep the board clean. Never leave it near a hot radiator. Keep the edges smooth and straight.

The T-square should be left flat on the board or suspended by the end of the blade to avoid warping. If the T-square is dropped it may be knocked out of alignment with the drawing on which it is being used. If the head of the T-square becomes loose it should be tightened securely. In extreme cases it is sometimes necessary to remove the head from the blade, clean the contact surfaces of the wood by scraping with a knife or sandpaper, give them a coating of glue or model cement, then replace the head.

The triangles should not be left in warped positions as they are easily deformed by continuous pressure. They become soft when subjected to heat. When a triangle does become warped it can sometimes be straightened by pouring hot water on it and, if necessary, bending it several times in the direction opposite to the warp. In some cases the hot water straightens the triangle without any bending.

The sandpaper on the sand pad should be used as long as it will point the pencil. It is usually too coarse at first and works better after it has been used a while.

Drawing ink dries rapidly. Keep the stopper in the bottle except when filling the pen. Shaking the ink produces bubbles which take the ink from the quill making it difficult to get any ink.

Paper should be kept clean and free from wrinkles, folds and scratches. It is discouraging to start a drawing on a dirty, mutilated piece of paper. It is stimulating to start out on a perfect sheet.

The case instruments are usually made of corrosion-resisting metals. However, the points of the dividers, compasses, and pen blades are sometimes made of steel which may rust if they are not kept clean and dry. The case instruments should be kept in perfect working order. Avoid bending or dulling the needle points. Keep the points adjusted to correct length. Keep the pencil points sharp and the pen points sharp and clean. Adjust the friction joints on compasses and dividers so they will work just right. Leads for the instruments can be obtained by splitting the short lengths of old pencils and removing the lead or using refill leads.

It is much more pleasant to work with equipment which is ready for use than to use equipment which is in poor condition or has to be put in condition while it is being used.

Erasing. A good rule for erasing is to use the softest eraser which will do the work. *The art gum or other soft cleaning eraser* is used to keep the paper clean while the drawing is being made, for erasing light pencil lines, and for cleaning the entire drawing and removing pencil lines after the drawing has been inked. The cleaning eraser is very good for removing pencil lines which have been drawn with a soft pencil using a very light pressure. The paper should be dusted with a clean, soft cloth or dusting brush after using an eraser. When the art gum is used for cleaning a large area, precautions should be taken to avoid getting eraser crumbs scattered over the drawing equipment.

The pencil eraser is used for erasing smudges and pencil lines which cannot be removed easily with the cleaning eraser. It is also used for erasing ink lines when it is desired to avoid scratching or roughening the paper. If the eraser is brightly colored watch carefully to see that it does not discolor the paper. Hard pressure and rapid movement causing the eraser and paper to become heated are likely to cause discoloration when colored erasers are used. The eraser will work more efficiently if the direction of movement is changed frequently.

The ink eraser is made of rubber containing sand, ground glass, or other abrasive grit. It is used for erasing ink lines and blots. It is quite likely to scratch or roughen the paper. Therefore it may be necessary to smooth the paper down in some way before inking over the erased area. The paper can be smoothed by rubbing with the thumb nail or other hard, smooth rounded object which will not discolor the paper. Finishing the erasing with a pencil eraser helps to smooth the paper in some cases. When inking over an erasure have only enough ink in the pen to make the line.

An ideal eraser should remove the lines quickly, leaving the paper in good condition. The eraser should not polish, roughen, or stain the paper. Roughened places in the paper become dirty more quickly than the surrounding surfaces. They will not take the ink well.

The erasing shield is used to confine the erasing to the desired area and protect lines near the erased area. An erasing shield wears down to a thin edge around the openings after it has been used a long time. A worn erasing shield with its sharp edges allows the eraser to work right to the edge of the shield while the new shield will leave a space which the eraser does not reach.

The erasing shield serves another useful purpose by wearing the eraser down and removing its dirty surfaces, thus keeping the surface clean where it comes in contact with the paper and avoiding discolorations of the paper.

A sharp knife, knife eraser, or razor blade is sometimes used to trim the edges or ends of lines when other lines or washes do not have to run over the erased areas. The knife eraser cannot be recommended for erasing lines or areas since it roughens the paper.

CHAPTER 4

Technique of Drafting

The objectives in drafting are (1) to produce a drawing which is made to appear as simple as possible so that it can be easily understood, and (2) to make the drawing attractive and expressive.

In looking through a number of drawings of the same object even the inexperienced person may be impressed with the varied effects produced by different persons. The character of a drawing may be anemic, erratic, delicate, refined, forceful, heavy handed, or brutal. Three of these characteristics are illustrated in Fig. 17. A good drawing is something more than a monotonous repetition of lines. It is a means of emphasizing the forms and divisions of an object, of suggesting materials and textures, of giving an impression suitable to the object depicted. In the example of Fig. 17 ı, the lines are thin and weak. There are no variations in weight of lines to form accents and divisions or to subordinate less important lines. In Fig 17 ıı the lines are all very heavy. There is no feeling of refinement in lines. Although there is some variation in line weight, there are no subdued lines. In Fig. 17 ııı emphasis is given to important divisions and areas by use of heavy lines. Unimportant lines are subordinated. There is both refinement and forcefulness in the drawing.

Drafting has been employed as a tool for artistic expression in the fine arts as well as in the applied arts. Paintings by Mondrian and the drafted art of Josef Albers are two examples of drafting techniques in fine art. Commercial art works in packaging and in advertisements often employ crisp ruled lines and drafted patterns. Drafting is then very often a medium of expression for art work other than the commonly accepted uses such as interior design and architecture.

A person in design work can do better, more expressive, creative designs if he has a good working knowledge of all methods of drawing and is skillful in the techniques of drafting.

SANDRA SCHMIDT–STUDENT

(A) LINES IN DESIGN

STUDENT WORK BY ROBERT MARTIN

(B) LINES A PART OF RENDERING

FIG. 16 DRAFTING IS IMPORTANT IN PRESENTATION

ANEMIC
DRAWING

THIN LINES
THROUGHOUT
PALE AND WEAK

I

BRUTAL
DRAWING

COARSE LINES
THROUGHOUT
HEAVY HANDED

II

REFINED
DRAWING

SUBORDINATION
AND EMPHASIS
OF CHOSEN LINES

III

FIG. 17 EXPRESSION IN DRAFTING

A) INDEFINITE LENGTH LIGHT LINES DRAWN

B) DARK LINES DRAWN BETWEEN LIGHT LINES

C) USED PART OF LIGHT LINES DARKENED

D) MEASUREMENTS FROM CENTER LINES

FIG. 18 ESTABLISHING LENGTHS OF LINES OF A DRAWING

When laying out a drawing it is seldom practical or even possible to draw each line the correct length directly. It is more practical and speedy to (A) draw parallel lines which are very light and extend farther than necessary, (B) draw dark lines between these, then (C) darken the established correct lengths of the original light lines. The unused parts of the light lines should be light enough to be almost invisible on a pencil drawing. When the drawing is to be inked they will be removed when the drawing is cleaned after inking. Fig. 18 shows this system applied to a simple object. The same basic procedure may be used several times on one drawing. Its principles should be adapted to other shapes also.

Center lines are often very useful in laying out a drawing. If the entire drawing is symmetrical on one or both axes, each center line should be used as the beginning of equal measurements on each side. Single center lines should be used for constructing elevation drawings of symmetrical objects such as a lamp or fireplace, Fig. 18 D. Intersecting vertical and horizontal center lines should be used to locate centers of circular or other forms such as radio dials which are symmetrical on the two axes.

Many persons have a tendency to minimize contrasts of spacing of parallel lines and of free form curved shapes. This produces monotony and a lack of character in a drawing. It is usually better to exaggerate contrasts slightly. Small spaces cannot always be measured accurately. It is sometimes more practical to divide them by eye. In such cases the relations of sizes should be noted and contrasts of size clearly maintained.

An orderly system of laying out a drawing or series of drawings is one phase of technique in drafting, Fig. 19. In layout work the whole drawing is more important than any of its parts. Major divisions of the drawing are more important than minor ones. Better, more accurate, and more speedy results are obtained by laying out (I) the limits of the entire drawing, (II) the major divisions of the area of the drawing, (III) minor divisions, (IV) small details and surface treatments.

This procedure provides an automatic means of checking accuracy and will prevent cumulative errors. It first assures that the drawing is located in the best position on the paper, then that successively smaller divisions fit correctly in the larger spaces. The reverse of this procedure is to start at one edge, perhaps the bottom, and add one small area at a time. Since practically everyone makes individual measurements either too small or too large, the final resulting size may be appreciably in error. Unless some system of checking at intervals is used, an error in measurements may not be discovered by the draftsman until the entire drawing is completed. Furthermore, the drawing may not be well placed on the sheet of paper when it is completed.

Speed in drafting is related to some phases of technique. Speed in obtaining results does not depend so much on actual hurrying as on the system used in drafting and on the correct, accurate, and efficient use of equipment. The person who works from large areas to small detail in a progressive order, who thinks as he works, who checks each step carefully once and then proceeds, will get results in a short time. The person who works frantically, uses incorrect procedure, or fails to check by appearance and mechanical means will make errors and have to erase and start over so often that he accomplishes little. Confidence in the accuracy of equipment and in the correctness of the developing drawing are essential to rapid progress with the drawing. An alert and attentive mind in searching out and using the best means of constructing the drawing is an essential part of speed in drafting.

(I) ENTIRE DRAWING OUTLINED FIRST

(II) MAJOR DIVISIONS MADE SECOND

(III) MINOR DIVISIONS DRAWN THIRD

(IV) SMALL DETAILS ADDED LAST

FIG. 19 SYSTEM USED IN LAYING OUT A DRAWING

24

Pencil technique in drawing includes a wide variety of effects in line work and in rendering. It is easy for anyone to draw with a pencil and obtain mediocre results. It is not so easy to produce first-rate work. One very simple and obvious problem is that of keeping the paper clean. Dirt from the hands and equipment will transfer to the paper. Cleanliness is therefore a major problem in drafting. The draftsman can help to keep his drawing clean by (1) keeping equipment clean, (2) working in such an order as to prevent rubbing over lines as much as possible, (3) covering all parts of the drawing and paper except for the area on which he is working, (4) using a light coating of powdered eraser particles on the surface of the paper when making pencil drawings.

Sharp, uniform, clean-cut lines are essential for precision in drafting. Use the best grade of pencil for the purpose, keep the pencil point sharp, rotate the pencil as you draw to keep the point symmetrical and the lines uniform. Draw the finished lines with one stroke for neat clean work. Start and finish pencil lines with pressure to make the ends sharp and distinct, not indefinite fadeouts.

Lines are basic elements of drawings made in pencil or ink. Their correct treatment is essential for polished drafting work. Lines should meet precisely at corners, or cross slightly, not fall short of meeting. Minor variations of line weight are often confusing rather than helpful. They may seem to be caused by errors and inaccuracy in drafting rather than by intention. To obtain a noticeable contrast in line weight a greater variation is required than most persons would assume. A one to two ratio is about the minimum and a one to three ratio is better for effective contrast of line weight in ink.

Broken lines which are made with dots, dashes, or combinations of the

BAD   GOOD   GOOD
HANDLING OF LINES AT CORNERS

LIGHT   MEDIUM   HEAVY
VARIATIONS IN LINE WEIGHTS

THE DRAWING OF BROKEN LINES
(A) TECHNIQUE OF DRAFTING LINES

HEAVY   BETTER
(B) TREATMENT OF MINOR DETAIL

(C) EMPHASIZING NEAR ELEMENTS

FIG. 20 CHARACTER IN LINE TECHNIQUE

(I) SILHOUETTE EMPHASIZED

(II) OUTLINING OF CUT AREAS

(III) SHADE LINE DRAFTING

FIG. 21 SOME USES OF HEAVY LINES IN DRAFTING

two should be as mechanically precise as it is possible to make them, Fig. 20 A. Choose a good relation of space and lines and stick to it with a dotted line or a dash line. When dots and dashes are both used in the same line use a very definite contrast of length of dot and dash.

Overemphasis of repeating minor details is a common mistake in drafting. Divisions of materials such as stone, brick, or tile may appear harsh and offensive when made prominent. Such elements can be treated in a conventionalized manner or, when drawn completely, be subordinated by using thinner or lighter lines, Fig. 20 B.

Darker lines are sometimes used throughout nearer elements to emphasize them and make them appear closer to the observer, Fig. 20 C.

Good judgment of weight of lines for different parts of a drawing is very important. Do not be afraid to use some heavy lines. They add life to the drawing and when correctly used make it more easily understood. Heavy lines can be used as a silhouette around the entire drawing, Fig. 21 I; to separate the visible areas of the object from the hidden structure when the drawing cuts through the object, Fig. 21 II; for shade lining to emphasize the shadow casting edges of the object and make projecting areas more obvious, Fig. 21 III. Usually the lower projecting edges and those at the right are used for this purpose. However, some other system may be employed if it is more effective on a given object.

Heavy lines are almost always used at the base or ground line of an object. They can frequently be used effectively to emphasize the edges of overhangs and to separate different materials and major elements.

The draftsman should decide what he wishes to accomplish with different line weights and then use those which are most effective for each drawing.

CHAPTER 5

Lettering on Drawings

Lettering is a necessary part of practically every drawing. It is used for titles, subtitles, names of areas or elements, and notes. The sizes of lettering used on a single drawing may vary from a very large size for the title to the smallest readable size for minor notes. The size, location, and quality of the lettering used have a great influence on the appearance and usefulness of the finished drawing. Well-placed lettering can make a drawing seem simple and easy to understand. Bad design in layout and details of lettering text will cause even a good drawing to be confusing and difficult to comprehend. Since lettering is a necessary and important element of graphical representation, the draftsman should learn to do clear, polished, attractive lettering, as speedily as he can. Bad lettering will spoil any drawing while good lettering will add to a drawing.

Lettering procedure varies with the individual and type of work. Whenever it is practical to do so, ink lettering is done directly in ink. This can often be done with notes and minor titles which do not have to begin and end at fixed points or center on a given center line. Some experienced draftsmen may also do titles and other important lettering directly in ink. However, most draftsmen prefer to do all lettering other than very small and minor material in pencil first. This gives

FIG. 22 BASIC PRINCIPLES OF FINE LETTERING

26

ABCDEFGHIJKLMNOPQRSTUV

Ⅰ THE THIN OR COMPRESSED ALPHABET
GIVES MANY TALL LETTERS IN A SMALL SPACE

ABCDEFGHIJKMI

Ⅱ NORMAL OR AVERAGE WIDTH ALPHABET
GIVES PLEASING PROPORTIONS FOR MOST USES

ABCDEFG

Ⅲ THE WIDE OR EXPANDED ALPHABET
COVERS WIDE SPACE WITH FEW LETTERS

FIG. 23 WIDTH VARIATIONS IN LETTERS

an opportunity to work out spacing. Sizes and locations of the lettering can also be checked before inking. Whenever lettering is done in pencil, the same grades of pencils should be used as those for other drafting purposes. It is more difficult to letter with ink than with pencil, so do not plan to improve crude pencil lettering when it is inked. Make the pencil lettering as perfect as possible before inking. Whether pencil or ink is used, form the habit of going over a line once only. Good lines can seldom be made by scratching back and forth over them. A number of guesses at the form of a letter will not produce precise and polished letter shapes, Fig. 22 A.

Horizontal lines called guide lines should always be used at the top and bottom of each line of lettering. Intermediate guide lines are useful on some styles of lettering. The letters are drawn exactly to the top and bottom guide lines except in cases of optical correction described later. Lettering triangles and other spacing devices are useful in spacing the guide lines uniformily.

Attractive lettering is not made by using individual letters which are ordinary, crude, or uninteresting in shape, Fig. 22 B, C. It is essential that each letter be beautiful. The person who hopes to do fine lettering must study his A B C's in detail and learn the characteristics of each letter from the example which he is following. When he designs an alphabet of his own, he must take infinite care to polish each letter to as near perfection as possible. Each letter must be coordinated with all the other letters of the alphabet.

Proportions of letters vary in different alphabets. In most alphabets one group of letters including B, H, and E have the horizontal divisions above center. Another group which includes A, P, and Y have the divisions below center. This helps to produce good proportions and gives a feeling of unity in the alphabet, Fig. 22 C. Horizontal divisions on center are usually considered unattractive. For style effect the horizontal division is sometimes made either above or below center on all letters. The widths of letters can be made to vary greatly and still be perfectly legible. Fig. 23 Ⅱ shows letters of normal or average width. Figs. 23 Ⅰ and Ⅲ show thin and wide letter shapes.

A THE SIMPLEST BACKGROUND AREAS OF LETTERS

B MORE COMPLEX LETTER EDGE SHAPES

C SPACING WITH VERTICAL LINE EQUIVALENTS

NORMAL LETTER WIDTHS   COMPRESSED L   OVERLAPPING EDGES

D DECREASING THE SPACE FOR TWO LETTERS

E MINIMUM SPACING DETERMINED BY LA

FIG. 24 THE CORRECT SPACING OF LETTERS

The Correct Spacing of Lettering. After selecting an interesting alphabet for use, the next problem is spacing the letters to produce the most pleasing optical effect. The first idea of most beginners is to make an equal distance between the extreme edges of all letters. Unfortunately the shapes of letters vary. If all had identical edge forms, equal distances between all edges would give good spacing. However, some edges of letters are vertical, some are inclined, some curved, and others have projecting horizontal members. The problem is to space the letters so as to make them appear to be the same average distance apart. In other words, the apparent background area between each two letters in a word must be equal in order to give a smooth and pleasing pattern. Extremely irregular spacing of letters in words will make the text difficult to read. It may even suggest word divisions which do not exist.

The background area between letters is obvious with some letter shapes. With others it is not so readily apparent. The simplest background shape between letter edges is a rectangle such as that between an ND combination. Slightly more complex is the triangular area between a slanting edge and a vertical edge as with AN, Fig. 24 A. This space can easily be expressed in a rectangle of equal area by using the average width of the truncated triangle as the width of the rectangle. The mechanically correct spacing of the word AND is then simple. The average width of the horizontal space between the AN must equal the width of the ND space to give equal background areas.

A similar analytical procedure can be followed with other letter forms by the person who likes to work in a mechanical way. In order to do this it is necessary to make a straight line equivalent at the edge of each letter, Fig. 24 B. This straight line should cut from an irregular letter edge the same amount of area that it removes from the background. Thus in the letter O the crescent shape cut from the edge of the O by the vertical line should equal in area the sum of the two small pointed background areas, one at the top and one at the bottom of the O.

Some letter shapes partially enclose an area. Only a part of this area seems to be background and the remainder belongs to the letter form. The letters C and G are the most extreme ones of this type. A curving area extending into the open edge of the C is considered as background. The amount of this area varies with the distance across the ends of the curved line of the C. With a large opening the background extending into the letter includes a large proportion of the entire space within the C, Fig. 24 B. A small opening will reduce the amount of the area included in the space between the open side of the C and the next letter. The system of mechanical analysis of areas between letters now becomes less precise because it depends on the judgment of the individual making the lettering. It will be found that the same procedure as that used for the C will apply to the E, F, L, and other irregular letters. An allowance must be made because only a part of the area at the irregular edge of a letter seems to be background. This amount varies with the thickness and length of the horizontal members of a letter such as E. In the case of an L most of the area will be background, since the form does not make much of an enclosure. In the lettering of the word PLACES in Fig. 24 C the background area between each two letters has been expressed by a rectangle.

The closest spacing of letters in a word is limited by the amount of area necessary for the two adjacent letter edges which require the largest space. The LA combination requires the most space in the word PLANED, Fig. 24 E. The horizontal part of the L can be shortened and the edges of the L and A pushed close together. However, this reduction of space is limited by clear separation of letters and the necessity of maintaining a distinct form for the L which will not be out of character with other letters used. In some work it is satisfactory to have the L and A overlap. However this is rarely done. The minimum area between each two letters in the word PLANED is set by the amount required between the L and A, Fig. 24 E. Furthermore other words used in the same title or continuity of words should conform to this spacing. It is impossible to space letters satisfactorily when straight line edges such as those of NE in PLANE are close together. The large spaces of such combinations as TT, LA, and TY determine the minimum working space between each two letters of words.

Words should be spaced far enough apart to make word divisions clear but not so far as to give a spotty disconnected effect, Fig. 25. A commonly used rule is that the space between two words should be the amount obtained by omitting an average width letter from a word. Even this amount may in some cases seem excessive for clear separation of words, Fig. 25 II.

LEND   IS   A   TERM   OF

(I) WORDS TOO FAR APART — SPOTTY

LEND WAS A TERM OF

(II) GOOD SPACING OF WORDS

FIG. 25   SPACING OF WORDS IN LETTERING

FIG. 26 THREE TYPES OF LETTERS

Mechanically Constructed Letters. Titles and other large lettering used on drawings are often made with instruments. The straight lines of these letters are made with T-square, triangles, and ruling pen. The curves are made with the compasses. All of the lines should be made mechanically. Mixing of freehand and mechanical lines in the same lettering is not satisfactory. The freehand lines waver and are not as precise in their width as the lines which are drawn with instruments. This gives a ragged, uneven effect to the lettering which has neither the precision of mechanical lettering nor the charm of good freehand lettering.

The slanting lines of letters can rarely be made with the triangle resting on the horizontal T-square. The triangle must be twisted to secure the best slant for each letter. Care should be taken to assure that the same letter is made the same shape throughout a given plate with the exception of minor variations for more satisfactory spacing. The vertical balance or symmetry should be carefully maintained in letters which use V shapes. These include A, V, Y, M, W, and X.

Centers for semicircles can be located quickly by using the 45° triangle to draw intersecting diagonals and determine the positions of the lines on which the centers are located. The diameters of all semicircles should be drawn as construction lines which will remain very light or be removed when the drawing is cleaned, Fig. 26 A, B. They locate with accuracy the ends of the arcs and beginnings of the connecting straight lines. Their correct use will prevent bumpy transitions which are caused by making the arcs extend too far or stop short of their correct lengths. When a semicircle connects to two tangent straight lines always draw the semicircle first. It is much easier to draw the straight lines one at a time to meet the semicircle than to make the ends of the semicircle connect perfectly to the ends of the two straight lines.

The thickness of line made with a single stroke of the ruling pen and compass is often satisfactory for mechanical lettering. The same thickness is used for every letter and every line in most cases. When the lettering is not extremely large a combination of heavy and light lines can be worked out within the line thickness limitations of the ruling pen, Fig. 26 B.

Shaded letters should have a standard set size for all thin lines, and another size for all the thick strokes, Fig. 26 B. When these two sizes are used throughout all letters, there is a feeling of unity. When the size of a wide or thin stroke is allowed to vary, confusion may result. It is important to locate the thin and thick strokes according to some system and not just by chance. The shaded Roman lettering was developed from pen lettering with a flexible freehand pen. The pen made thin upward

ⓘ SERIFS EMPHASIZE ENDS OF LINES

ⓘⓘ PLANNED VARIETY IN LETTER SHAPES

ⓘⓘⓘ OPTICAL REFINEMENTS IN LETTER SHAPES

FIG. 27 DETAILS OF LETTER SHAPES

and horizontal strokes, and spread on the down strokes to make heavy lines. Most shaded lettering follows this system.

Built-up letters are used when a single stroke of the pen will not give the required width of lines. This is usually done by outlining each black area and then filling in with a small brush or speedball pen. Built-up letters are made either with a uniform width of all the elements or with a combination of wide and narrow elements, Fig. 26 c.

Serifs are the small cross strokes made at the ends of lines and used as extensions at corners, Fig. 27 I. It is a common error to use these on the I and J when the other letters of the alphabet do not have them. When serifs are used, they should be used throughout the alphabet on all letters wherever they can be used appropriately. They are not used at the angles of A, V, W, the center of the M, or on the bottom angle of the N. Serifs look better when they are kept rather small. It is a mistake to allow the curves of the serifs to extend so far that they destroy the straight lines which they terminate.

The shapes of letters are usually made similar throughout a title or plate. Thus all letters used appear to be narrow, or all appear to be wide. Futhermore it is usually considered best to keep the same general characteristics of letters in so far as possible throughout the entire alphabet. If a circular O is used then other curves are made circular. When an oval or angular form is used in the O then other letters keep the same characteristic. This system gives harmony of form and proportions throughout all the lettering. It is most widely used and is satisfactory for many lettering uses.

Planned dissimilarity of form of letters is sometimes used to create contrast and attract attention. The contrasting shapes should produce an interesting and satisfactorily balanced pattern. This device is most frequently used in trademarks and advertising matter, Fig 27 II.

Optional corrections are made in some lettering. They are more common on large than on small lettering. The purpose of these corrections is to make letters of various shapes at the top and bottom seem to be exactly the same height, Fig. 27 III. A letter such as an E, which is horizontal at the top and bottom seems higher than the point of an A at the top and lower than a W at the bottom. Points of letters are extended slightly beyond the horizontal guide lines to correct the illusion of their being too short. Circular shapes at top and bottom usually require a smaller correction than the pointed forms. It is better for most beginners to ignore these refinements and bring all letters exactly to the horizontal guide lines at the top and bottom.

ABCDEFG
HIJKLMNO
PQRSTUV
WXYZ

(A) CAPITALS MADE WITH COMPASS AND RULED LINES

abcdefghijklmn
opqrstuuwxyz

(B) LOWER CASE LETTERS USING A SINGLE RADIUS

ABCDEFGHIJKLMNOPQ
RSTUVWXYZ

(C) COMPRESSED LETTERS WITH RULED AND COMPASS LINES

FIG. 28 SINGLE STROKE MECHANICAL ALPHABETS

I SHADE LINE LETTERING

II OUTLINED LETTERING

III BUILT-UP LETTERING

FIG. 29 SOME VARIATIONS IN LETTER FORMS

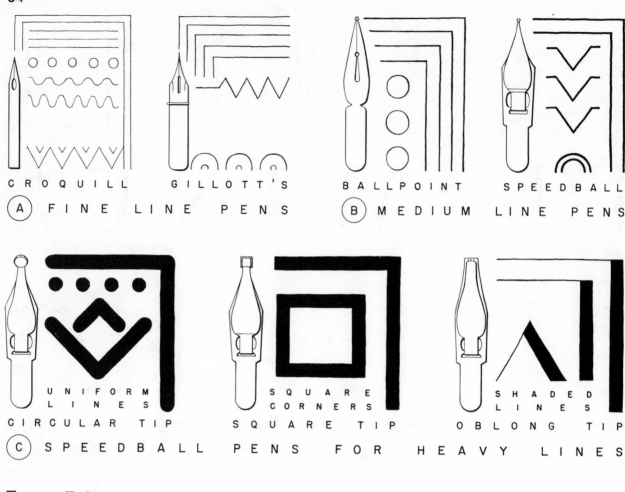

FIG. 30 PENS FOR FREEHAND LETTERING

Freehand Lettering. On many drawing plates all the lettering is done freehand. On others the main titles are constructed mechanically and small lettering made freehand. By using lettering devices such as the Wrico and Leroy pens and templates all lettering small and large can be done mechanically. Although some offices and schools encourage or require all lettering to be made with a mechanical lettering device on some projects, the ability to do good freehand lettering is expected of students, draftsmen, and designers. Style of lettering is limited when using mechanical lettering guides.

A wide variety of lettering pens is available at stationery and drafting supply stores. The draftsman should select a number of these which will give line widths ranging from the finest available to the largest he expects to use. The first step in using the pens should be to try all of them in order to become familiar with the type of line obtained from each one. Most new pens are protected from corrosion by an oily film. This film should be removed by use of soap and hot water, by rubbing with a damp cloth, by filling with ink and wiping vigorously, or in some other manner. After the oil is removed the ink will flow to the point of the pen and it can be used.

Fine line pens are most difficult to use, Fig. 30 A. The point must be sharp and if the pen is pushed toward the point it will stick in the paper. Therefore only strokes away from the point and to the side are possible. Too much ink in the pen will cause wider lines, and when the pen is almost dry the lines will be thin. It is necessary to refill the pen frequently and keep a moderate amount of ink in it. Since the point is small, the nibs of the pen are flexible. The least pressure spreads them apart making a wider line. A very delicate sense of touch and good coordination are necessary to

ABCDEFGHIJKLM
NOPQRSTUVWXYZ
1234567890
abcdefghijklmnopqr
stuvwxyz

(I) SIMPLE SINGLE STROKE ALPHABET

ABCDEFGHIJKLMNO
PQRSTUVWXYZ

(II) ALPHABET WITH SHADING AND SERIFS

FIG. 31 FREEHAND LETTERING ALPHABETS

get uniform thin lines from a lettering pen. A good rest for the arm all the way from the fingers to the elbow gives better control of the pen. Better results are obtained by allowing the fingers and muscles of the arm to relax than by being tense and taking a "death grip" on the pen. Some persons can letter with an arm movement and get very good results. There is a great deal of variation of ability between individuals to do good small lettering. It is encouraging for the person who is having difficulty to see the work done by someone who does very perfect lettering. It is astonishing to find how many draftsmen have such perfect control of a pen that they can make letters which are easily read at $\frac{1}{32}$ inch high and can put style and polish into lettering $\frac{1}{16}$ inch high. Lettering is rarely used less than $\frac{1}{16}$ inch to $\frac{3}{32}$ inch high on drawings.

Pens for medium to heavy lines are comparatively stiff, Fig. 30 B, C. Their points do not spread sufficiently under normal use to widen appreciably lines made with them. Some pens have a restraining device which limits the spread of the nibs. Most pens other than the finest line ones have reservoirs which hold the ink and keep it from feeding to the point too rapidly. Some of these open for cleaning. Pens should always be cleaned before the ink has an opportunity to solidify in them.

Practice is necessary in order to become skillful in freehand lettering. Effort with the hands and eyes alone may produce skill in handling pens. However, mental effort is essential to any real progress in producing polished and artistic lettering. The mind must know just what each shape will be, precisely where each stroke goes, in order to provide the confidence necessary for excellent lettering. The mind must analyze each letter, almost each stroke, to see if it is exactly right. To the word practice we must add intelligent and painstaking if real progress is to be made in lettering.

Titles. The design and composition of titles and subtitles is a major division of lettering on drawings. The size, weight, style, and location of this lettering are important design elements. The draftsman designer should choose lettering which he thinks will not detract from but will help his drawing. Heavy black lettering may overpower and distract attention from delicate and refined drawings. Heavy lettering may be in character with a drawing which has heavy lines and black areas. Ornate and elaborate titles are not often suitable for simple drawings. Lettering may intentionally be made to contrast wih a drawing for design purposes. However, it is usually more satisfactory to have a similar character in the lettering and drawing. Vertical lettering is in better harmony with the predominately horizontal and vertical lines found in most drawings than inclined lettering with its emphasis on oblique lines in one direction.

In laying out a title there are two common conditions: (1) wherein the exact length of the title is not important, and (2) wherein the title should be a definite established length.

When the exact length is not important the center line of the title may be located and the horizontal guide lines drawn to establish its height. The center letter or space is located by counting the letters and spaces between words in the title. The title is then lettered from the center out. The last half may be completed first and then the first letter of the title located at the same distance from center as the last letter. This method works rather easily and accurately, although some minor adjustments may be required, Fig. 32. The lettering may be worked out completely at the required size on scrap paper and then transferred to the final paper of the drawing. This method requires a repetition of the lettering.

When the lettering is made to fit a given space the height and length of the lines of lettering

STEP A - ESTABLISH HEIGHT - BEGIN LETTERS AT CENTER

STEP B — LETTER LAST HALF — THEN LOCATE BEGINNING

STEP C - FILL IN FIRST HALF — MAKE MINOR ADJUSTMENTS

FIG. 32 TITLE WHICH CAN VARY IN LENGTH

should first be outlined precisely. There are two general procedures which can be followed to fit the letters into this space: (1) The lettering can be drawn directly in place by a system of dividing the distances. (2) The lettering can be laid out on scrap paper then transferred to position on the plate with any necessary increase or decrease of space size between letters and words to fill the given space.

In using the first method the number of letters in the title is counted and each space between words counted as a letter. In the title A MODERN ROOM of Fig. 33 there are 13 letters and spaces combined. In lettering this title, first letter the A on the left and the M on the right. Letter R which is number 7 will be in the exact center of the title and O and R which are numbers 4 and 10 respectively will be the center letters of each half of the title. After breaking up the space in this manner, the remaining small spaces are filled in as shown in step III to complete the title. Titles are not always as accommodating in dividing so easily as the one just used. When the number of elements is more difficult to divide some ingenuity is necessary in developing a workable method of spacing letters. The title at the bottom of Fig. 33 A WALNUT CABINET has 16 letters and spaces. It does not have a letter or space between words on center. Furthermore it is slightly unbalanced with an I on the right side of center. Different methods could be used to space this title; some persons may prefer to use one system, some another. The important thing is to think out a logical procedure which will get good results. A suggested procedure which locates center lines of letters is: place A at the beginning of the title, then add an A beyond the end of the title estimating spacing for the location of this letter. There are now 17 elements instead of 16. Number 9, a space, is in the center and a light X may be used to suggest the space. Now the spacing will divide to single letters.

STEP I — END LETTERS AND CENTER UNIT LOCATED

STEP II — CENTER LETTERS OF EACH HALF DRAWN

STEP III — LETTERS FILLED IN AND ADJUSTMENTS MADE

WHEN LETTERS DO NOT DIVIDE ON CENTERS

FIG. 33 TITLE TO FIT IN A DEFINITE LENGTH

The second method of fitting a title into a given space requires that the lettering be executed on practice paper at the size to be used, Fig. 34 B. It is then transferred to the final drawing with any necessary adjustments. The preliminary lettering should be spaced correctly but the letters need not include all refinements of the final title. The preliminary will probably occupy too much or too little space and this error should be divided proportionately by counting one unit for each space between letters, and two units for each space between words. In the title MOLDED PLASTIC WARE there are 14 spaces between letters and 2 spaces x 2 = 4 unit spaces between words—a total of 18. One eighteenth of the error should be added to each space between letters, and two eighteenths to each space between words to increase the distance for the title. These amounts should be subtracted if the preliminary was too long.

A second procedure for obtaining an approximately correct spacing of the finished title from a trial title will seem simple to an experienced draftsman. Draw the vertical center line of each letter in

FIG. 34 TITLE SPACING FROM A TRIAL TITLE

I SPREAD TITLE TO INCLUDE DRAWINGS TITLED

II THE CORRECT LOCATION FOR SUB TITLES

FIG. 35 COMPOSITION OF TITLES FOR DRAWINGS

the preliminary, Fig. 34 B. Lay out the vertical center lines of the first and last letters of the finished title, Fig. 34 A for longer final title and Fig. 34 C for shorter final. Use a straight edged strip of paper. If the final is to be longer than the preliminary, mark off the distance a-g between the centers of the first and last letter of final on the edge of the paper strip. Slant this across the lines through centers of preliminary lettering and adjust until the two marks fit the end center lines. Transfer spacing of center lines of letters to strip and thence to final where strip is used horizontally to locate the center line of each letter as shown in Fig. 34 A. When the final is shorter than the preliminary, take measurements off the preliminary with horizontal strip, then slant strip between verticals through centers of the end letters of final. Dot off centers and draw vertical center lines of letters from dots to letter positions. The letters of the preliminary study are now drawn or traced in position on their center lines on the final title, Fig. 34 C.

Large distances between letters make the work of spacing much easier than when a minimum space is maintained. Widely spaced letters are easy to read and give an attractive appearance. The wide spacing spreads a title out so that it may refer more clearly to a long object or a series of drawings without overemphasizing the lettering with excessive height, Fig. 35 I.

The correct relation of a number of subtitles to the drawings to which they refer is essential to easy and correct reading of a plate. The titles should be so placed that there is no slightest possibility of an error as to which drawing is referred to by each title. This is one of the most important phases of composition of lettering, Fig. 35 II.

CHAPTER 6

Types of Drawings

When classification is based on the general characteristics and the visual effects obtained, there are three basic types of drawings. They are (A) multi-view orthographic drawings, (B) paraline drawings, and (C) perspective drawings.

Multi-view orthographic shows in one drawing a single face of an object as it would appear if the observer could look perpendicular to the principal plane of that face at every point, Fig. 36 A. The result is a two-dimensional drawing which may show the top, end, front, or other view of the object. However, a single view of this type is not enough to explain the nature of a three dimensional object. At least two views are necessary to explain even a simple form, and six or more views may be necessary to describe a more complex shape clearly. Since a number of views are usually required, the term multi-view orthographic drawing is used for this method of representing objects.

Multi-view drawing has this important advantage: in one of the views the true shape of every plane figure part of the object can be shown. This type of drawing is therefore the best for giving precise shape and size information about an object. The principal disadvantage of multi-view drawing is that it is difficult to visualize the actual object from views of its different faces, since each drawing gives only two sets of dimensions.

Paraline drawings include all the parallel line pictorial types. These are isometric, dimetric, trimetric, and oblique drawings. They have the common characteristic of showing three adjacent faces of an object in a single drawing. For example the top, front, and one end of a desk may be shown in one drawing. This gives the effect of a view toward one corner of the object. It produces a drawing which represents all of the three dimensions and is therefore easily understood, Fig. 36 B.

Since all lines which are actually parallel on the object are made parallel the drawings of this type are easily constructed. Because the lines are drawn parallel, an artificial effect is obtained. Lines on the near parts of the object are made the same length as similar more distant lines. This makes measuring on the drawing easy but makes the more distant parts appear too large.

Perspective drawing gives the truest picture of the object but is the most difficult type of drawing to construct, Fig. 36 C. Since the more distant parts of the object are smaller, few measurements can be made directly to scale on the drawing. A perspective drawing which is correctly made is just as true a picture of the object as is a photograph.

Drawing classification according to the relation of the projectors to the picture plane is commonly used. This system also gives three types: (1) orthographic drawing with projectors perpendicular to the plane of projection includes multi-view, isometric, dimetric, and trimetric; (2) oblique drawing having parallel projectors oblique to the picture plane; and (3) perspective drawing with projectors converging to the eye or station point position. This system does not group the resulting drawings logically according to appearance and use, important factors to the designer.

Projectors are the imaginary lines of sight of the observer which would enable him to see the object as it is represented in a drawing. They are an element of the basis of the theoretical background of each method of representing objects by drawings. In some methods of perspective drawing they are actually traced to locate points on the drawings. They have no practical use in constructing other drawings. The theoretical bases of each drawing type explain why drawings appear as they do. This theory is not necessary for the construction of most drawings. In fact it is often confusing to the beginner rather than being helpful. It is not emphasized in this text.

A M U L T I — V I E W   D R A W I N G

B P A R A L I N E   D R A W I N G

C P E R S P E C T I V E   D R A W I N G

FIG. 36 THREE MAJOR TYPES OF DRAWINGS

PART TWO

Multi-View Drawing

CHAPTER 7

Principles of Multi-View Drawings

In multi-view drawings of a simple box shape, each view will show only one face of the box. When the front is drawn on a picture plane parallel to it, the projectors are parallel to the sides, top, and bottom. The observer is assumed to be looking parallel to these surfaces which are perpendicular to the picture plane and appear as lines in the drawing, Fig. 37 A. Since each view gives only two of the three sets of dimensions, two or more views are necessary to explain an object, Fig. 37 A, B, C.

The Six-View Standard Arrangement of Multi-view Drawings. When a picture plane is used parallel to each side of a box-like object, these six planes meet to form a box enclosing the object. By projecting onto each side of a transparent picture plane box, a drawing of each face of the object is obtained, Fig. 38 I. If the top, bottom, and two sides of the picture plane box are hinged to the front and if the rear is hinged to the left side, all the views can be unfolded into the plane of the front, Figs. 38 II, III. This is the American standard arrangement of views.

The multi-view drawings of objects such as chairs or radio cabinets which have definitely different characteristics in different views are relatively easy to understand. They have different shapes in side, front, top, and other views. It is usually easy to tell whether the drawing is turned correctly for the normal position of the object. The drawings of such objects can be easily understood even when they are not arranged according to the American standard.

SIDE   FRONT   SIDE   FRONT   SIDE   FRONT

SAME FRONT VIEW FROM THREE DIFFERENT FORMS

FIG. 37 TWO OR MORE VIEWS NEEDED TO EXPLAIN SHAPES

FIG. 38 SIX—VIEW STANDARD DRAWING ARRANGEMENT

Other objects such as parts of mechanical devices have no familiar forms by which the top, front, etc. can be determined. A standard arrangement of the views of such an object is essential in order that its design may be understood.

Variations from the standard arrangement of views are often made in some fields of drawing. The following are some of the reasons for such variations. (1) The views may be so large that they cannot all be presented on one sheet. (2) Different scales may be used on the views of the same object. Usually one important view is drawn at a larger scale. (3) Composition in presenting a design may be improved by variations from standard. (4) Custom in the field of drawing may require variation from the American standard arrangement. It is customary in architectural drawing to have all views on horizontal planes (called plans) turned with the principal entrance to the bottom of the drawing.

When drawing an interior the views are most appropriately considered as being hinged to the rear of the transparent box and rotated into its plane. As in architecture it may be preferable to consider the ceiling turned the same way as the floor plan. The ceiling is then either shown as seen from above and represented by hidden lines, or assumed to be seen in a mirror on the floor, represented with visible lines, and called a reflected plan. Its relation to the floor plan is more easily understood when both drawings face the same direction.

FIG. 39 HORIZONTAL AND VERTICAL CONSTRUCTION LINES

The construction of multi-view drawings is made easier by their relations to each other in the standard arrangement of views. Heights which are common to front, rear, and sides are carried across with the T-square for all four of these views. Widths are transferred between the front, top, and bottom drawings by vertical construction lines drawn with the triangle on the T-square. These alignments horizontally and vertically simplify construction, reduce the possibility of errors through variation of heights and widths, and make the interpretation of drawings easier, Fig. 39. Measurements can be transferred from top or bottom views to side or rear views in different ways. A scale, dividers, or a straight edged strip of paper can be used for this purpose.

Geometric construction methods can also be used to transfer dimensions from top and bottom to the side views. These constructions require the tracing of the sizes around a right angle. This can be done either with 45° intersections as shown in Fig. 40 A, or with arcs as shown in Fig. 40 B. In using either of these methods of transferring sizes around a right angle the draftsman must be alert to see that the final spacing is correct and accurate. The arcs should be tangent to the horizontal and vertical projectors. The points of tangency are located accurately by drawing the horizontal and vertical lines through the center of each arc. These lines are the perpendiculars to the tangents. The 45° turning lines continue the spacing correctly around the corners on this example because they are the bisectors of 90° angles. By turning the 45° lines in the opposite direction the sequence of spaces is reversed, and the drawing is incorrect, Fig. 40 C. To transfer widths with construction lines from top, front, or bottom view to the rear view it is necessary to turn the measurements through 180°. This is usually done by turning two right angles with two 45° lines or two quarter circles. However, semicircles can be used for this purpose when the drawing space is available.

The procedure in laying out multi-view drawings may vary with the object drawn and the draftsman. The usual procedure is to construct the front and top together, then construct the sides, rear, and bottom from these first two drawings. To locate the position for the side view, measure any desired distance A-B to the side of the front view and draw a vertical line through B. Draw a horizontal line from the lowest edge of the top view to meet the vertical line at C. Point C is then used as the center of arcs or the beginning of the 45° turning line, Fig. 40 B.

A CONSTRUCTION WITH BISECTORS OF ANGLES TURNING THE MEASUREMENTS

REAR

LEFT SIDE FRONT RIGHT SIDE

TOP

BOTTOM

B CONSTRUCTION WITH ARCS

REAR L. SIDE FRONT R. SIDE

TOP

BOTTOM

CORRECT SPACING

REVERSED SPACING

C CHANGING 45° LINE REVERSES SPACING

FIG. 40 CARRYING SPACING AROUND CORNERS

ROOF PLAN

NORTH ELEVATION   WEST ELEV.   SOUTH ELEVATION   EAST ELEV.

(A) COMPASS DIRECTION NAMES OF VIEWS

ROOF PLAN

REAR ELEVATION   LEFT ELEVATION   FRONT ELEVATION   RIGHT ELEVATION

(B) STANDARD ARCHITECTURAL NAMES OF VIEWS

FIG. 41 VARIATIONS IN NOMENCLATURE OF VIEWS

The nomenclature of views varies in different types of design work. The system of naming views which has been used on previous pages is the one of engineering drawing. In Fig. 41 two other common systems are shown.

The number of views required to explain an object will vary with its design. Two views are often enough for simple objects such as a cylinder or box. If each face of a box-like object differs in detail then it is necessary to have drawings of all six faces to explain the differences. When two opposite faces of an object are identical only one need be shown.

Hidden lines, which would not be visible in the drawing because they are between a part of the object and the observer, are shown with evenly spaced dots. Hidden lines in one view may give a clear explanation so that a view where these lines are visible can be omitted. In the drawings of a television cabinet the shapes and positions of the legs of the object can be shown with dotted lines in the top view and the bottom view can be omitted, Fig. 42 III. In some work all hidden lines are shown in all drawings. In other work parts which are explained with visible lines are not shown with hidden lines. In sectional drawings hidden lines are used for parts which have been removed in making the drawings as well as for lines which are hidden by a visible part of the object.

TOP

FRONT   R. SIDE

I SMALL RADIO CABINET

TOP   L. SIDE

FRONT

II TRAY FOR A DESK

TOP

LEFT SIDE   FRONT   RIGHT SIDE

III FOUR VIEWS OF A TELEVISION CABINET

FIG. 42 EXAMPLES OF MULTI—VIEW DRAWINGS

CHAPTER 8

Auxiliary Views

Some objects have plane surfaces which are not parallel to any of the six picture planes of the glass box, Fig. 43 A. These oblique planes of an object are not shown in true shape in any of the standard multi-view drawings. In order to represent the true shape of an oblique surface it is necessary to assume an oblique picture plane parallel to the surface to be drawn. The lines of the object are assumed to be transferred with projectors perpendicular to the oblique area and to its picture plane. All drawings of this type, which would require picture planes other than those provided by the standard transparent box arrangement in order to show the true shape of an oblique area, are called auxiliary drawings.

Auxiliary drawings can usually be constructed rather easily from two of the standard views. Fig. 43 B gives a top and front view of a wedge shape. The side view when constructed from the first two drawings does not give the correct size or proportions of the slanting area. The horizontal dimension A-B of the side view is correct but the horizontally projected height A-C is shorter than the actual or slant height X-Y of the area. The true height can be transferred to the side view by use of an arc with a center at X and a radius of X-Y. A horizontal tangent to the arc locates D-E, the top edge of the area. A-D-E-B is the required auxiliary drawing. Any means of transferring the distance X-Y to the side view so that A-D and B-E are equal to X-Y will give a correct auxiliary view of this object. A second method of obtaining the auxiliary drawing is to draw perpendiculars to the line X-Y from X and Y to establish the height of the auxiliary drawing and then transfer the width F-G from top, Fig. 43 C. The auxiliary drawing is tilted when the second method is used. It is kept in a vertical position by the first method. It should be observed that the arc used in the second method to transfer the width is greater than 90°. It must be tangent to both the horizontal and the inclined projectors. A 45° turning line could not be used here because the dimension is not turned 90°. The bisector of the angle between the inclined and horizontal projectors could be used to transfer the dimension as shown by the dotted line.

(A) THEORY OF USE OF AUXILIARY PLANES (B) FIRST METHOD (C) SECOND METHOD

FIG. 43 THEORY AND CONSTRUCTION OF AUXILIARY VIEW

I AUXILIARY WALL PLANE — PROJECTING ONTO PLANE

II DRAFTSMAN'S METHOD — TOP, TOP VIEW TURNED, FRONT, AUXILIARY

III INCLINED AUXILIARY — TOP, FRONT, AUXILIARY

IV HORIZONTAL AUXILIARY — TOP, FRONT, AUXILIARY

FIG. 44 VERTICAL PLANE AUXILIARY DRAWINGS

Vertical Plane Auxiliary Drawings. Fig. 44 illustrates construction of vertical plane auxiliary drawings. The pictorial drawing I shows the relation of the object, transparent box, and auxiliary plane while the remaining drawings explain three methods of working out the auxiliary view.

The draftsman's simple method is to turn the top with the oblique wall planes in a horizontal position as shown in II. The vertical projectors from top and horizontal projectors from front view locate the lines and points for construction of the auxiliary elevation. When the top is available on a separate piece of paper it can be turned to correct position and attached to the board for this use instead of making a new drawing of the top view.

Methods of descriptive geometry and engineering drawing for constructing auxiliary views are shown in Figs. III and IV. In III the projectors are drawn perpendicular to the line representing the auxiliary surface in top view. The heights are then transferred to these projectors and the auxiliary drawing constructed in the inclined position. In IV the projectors from top have been turned into a vertical position with arcs. The heights are carried over from the front view with the T-square. This second method brings the auxiliary view into horizontal alignment with the front view. This may seem logical since this auxiliary is a wall auxiliary or oblique side view and is normally in a horizontal position. In the examples the slant areas to the right and left of the true shape areas have been included in the auxiliary drawing. However, these oblique areas may be either shown attached to the true shape area but unfinished, or omitted entirely.

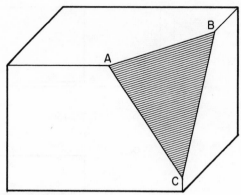

A PICTORIAL DRAWING OF INCLINED OBLIQUE AREA

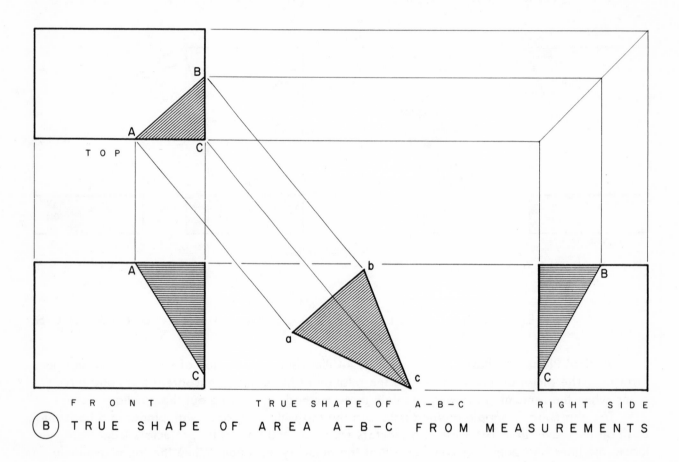

TOP

FRONT   TRUE SHAPE OF   A−B−C   RIGHT SIDE

B TRUE SHAPE OF AREA A−B−C FROM MEASUREMENTS

FIG. 45 DRAWING OF AN INCLINED OBLIQUE AREA

Inclined Oblique Auxiliary Planes. When the auxiliary surface is not seen as a line (is not perpendicular to any standard plane) in any of the six standard views, the auxiliary view cannot be constructed by direct projection from two of these views as in the two preceding examples. Fig. 45 A illustrates this condition. In Fig. 45 B the true length of one side of the triangular area is located from the top view, one from front, and one from right side. The triangular area is then constructed from these three dimensions as shown in Fig. 45 B. Line a-b is projected from *A-B* in the top view with projectors perpendicular to *A-B*. With a center at *a* and a radius *A-C* an arc is drawn to inter-

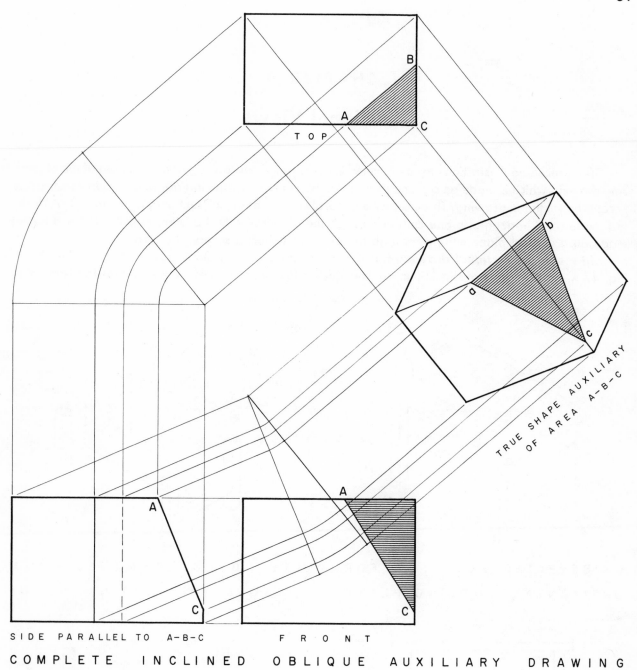

TOP

B

A

C

TRUE SHAPE AUXILIARY
OF AREA A-B-C

b

a

c

A

C

SIDE PARALLEL TO A—B—C

A

C

F R O N T

COMPLETE   INCLINED   OBLIQUE   AUXILIARY   DRAWING

FIG. 46 CONSTRUCTION   OF   AN   AUXILIARY   DRAWING

sect an arc with center at *b* and radius *B-C* from right side view at point *c*. *a-c* and *b-c* are then drawn on the true shape area.

Fig. 46 shows a method of constructing the complete auxiliary view from the top view, front view, and an auxiliary side view which is projected parallel to the auxiliary plane *A-B-C* and shows it as a line. Projectors perpendicular to *A-B* in top view and perpendicular to *A-C* in the side view parallel to area *A-B-C* are used to construct the true shape auxiliary of *A-B-C*. When the entire auxiliary drawing is made it is an axonometric pictorial drawing with one true shape area.

CHAPTER 9

Sectional Views

The preceding illustrations for multi-veiw drawing are views looking at the outsides of the objects. Any drawing which is made on a plane through an object to show the interior and hidden construction is called a sectional drawing. There are two general classifications of sectional drawings: (1) A drawing made on a horizontal plane cutting through the object is called a *plan*, Fig. 47. (2) A drawing made on a vertical plane cutting through the object is called a *section*, Fig. 48.

In making a sectional drawing it is assumed that a cutting plane passes through the object, Fig. 47 A, that the part of the object on one side of the plane is removed, and that the remaining

(A) SELECTED POSITION FOR HORIZONTAL CUTTING PLANE

(B) OBJECT REMOVED FROM ABOVE THE CUTTING PLANE

ELEVATION

PLAN AT A—A

(D) METHOD OF SHOWING PLAN POSITION IN ELEV.

(C) PLAN ON PLANE A—A OF PART BELOW PLANE

FIG. 47 DRAWING A PLAN THROUGH AN OBJECT

part is projected onto the plane with projectors which are perpendicular to the plane, as shown in the pictorial view of Fig. 47 B. The multi-view drawing obtained according to this theory then appears as shown in Fig. 47 C. The legs of the table were cut by the plane. They are drawn in heavy outline and are also shaded to classify them as cut areas. The visible parts beyond the cutting plane are drawn with light solid lines. Parts which are considered as being removed can be shown with dotted lines if this is necessary. In this plan the edges of the table top are shown with dotted lines. The method of showing the cutting plane position for the plan on the multi-view elevation with dot dash line is illustrated in Fig. 47 D. The ends of the line and arrows turn to point in the direction the observer looks in making the drawing. The letters A-A, designating the cutting plane, should be placed at the ends of the arrows as shown and used in the title of the sectional drawings made on this plane. In architecture and interior design floor plans are made through doors and no cutting line for the plan is required on elevations. The line of the cutting plane should be shown when it is necessary or helpful in understanding the sectional drawing.

The theory for sectional drawings made on vertical planes (sections) is the same as for the plan example shown in Fig. 47, and described above. The only difference is that the plane is vertical instead of horizontal. The development of a section drawing is shown in the pictorial drawings of Fig. 48 I, II and the section in Fig. 48 III.

Ⓘ SELECTED POSITION FOR VERTICAL CUTTING PLANE

Ⓘⓘ OBJECT REMOVED FROM ONE SIDE OF THE PLANE

PLAN OF TABLE

Ⓘⓥ METHOD OF SHOWING SECTION POSITION ON PLAN

SECTION AT B—B

Ⓘⓘⓘ SECTION ON PLANE B—B OF REMAINDER OF OBJECT

FIG. 48 DRAWING A SECTION THROUGH AN OBJECT

54

(A) P L A N   L O O K I N G   D O W N   O N   F L O O R

(B) P L A N   L O O K I N G   U P   A T   C E I L I N G

(C) H A L F   P L A N S   O F   F L O O R   A N D   C E I L I N G

F I G.   49   T Y P E S   O F   P L A N S   T H R O U G H   A N   O B J E C T

Plan drawings cutting through the object are usually made in one of these three ways: (1) looking down on the part below the cutting plane, Fig. 49 A; (2) looking up at the part above the cutting plane, Fig. 49 B; (3) with one half of a symmetrical object shown looking down and the other half looking up. In this third type of drawing both halves of the plan should face the same direction, Fig. 49 C. In fact, even with complete plans looking up it is often more satisfactory to make a reflected or mirror plan which is turned the same way as the plans looking down. The different features of the two plan types are more easily related to each other in this type of drawing.

(I) T R A N S V E R S E   S E C T I O N   O F   A   C O U C H

(II) L O N G I T U D I N A L   S E C T I O N   O F   A   C O U C H

(III) O F F S E T   S E C T I O N   T H R O U G H   A   C O U C H

FIG. 50 T Y P E S   O F   E N T I R E   S E C T I O N   D R A W I N G S

Sections are classified according to the direction of the cutting plane, Figs. 50 I, II, III. (I) A transverse section shows the width of the object. (II) A longitudinal section shows the length of the object. (III) An offset section uses two or more parallel positions of the cutting plane to show parts of the object which would not be shown on one continuous plane, or on one continuous drawing. Offset sections should be used only when some definite advantage is gained by their use. They are more difficult to work out and understand than continuous plane sections. The transition between planes is sometimes hard to explain clearly in the drawing of an offset section.

56

Ⓐ   S E C T I O N S   T O   E X P L A I N   D E S I G N   O F   A   D E S K

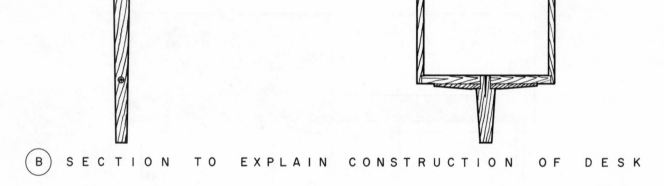

Ⓑ   S E C T I O N   T O   E X P L A I N   C O N S T R U C T I O N   O F   D E S K

F I G. 5 1   V A R I A T I O N   O F   D E T A I L   I N   S E C T I O N S·

The amount of detail shown in a cut area of a sectional drawing depends on the purpose of the drawing and the wishes of the designer. If the purpose of the drawing is to show the visible shapes and surfaces of the object, it is often satisfactory to silhouette the cut areas and leave them blank. This procedure keeps the drawing as simple as possible and avoids confusing distractions from the objective of the drawing, Fig. 51 A. If it is considered advisable or necessary to show the details of the cut areas, these parts of the drawing should be surrounded with a heavy outline to separate the visible from the hidden parts of the object, Fig. 51 B. This clear separation of areas makes the drawing seem much more simple and easy to understand. The really skillful draftsman and designer has the knack of making drawings which separate into divisions at a glance and are readily interpreted.

LEFT ELEVATION   PLAN   RIGHT ELEVATION

Ⓘ SECTIONS SHOWING INTERIOR OF ONE ROOM

PLAN AT C-C

PLAN AT D-D AND E-E

SECTION AT F-F

ⒾⒾ DETAILS ON ELEVATION   Ⓘ Ⓘ Ⓘ ENLARGED DETAILS

FIG. 52 SOME TYPES OF PART SECTION DRAWINGS

Part sectional drawings show a portion, not all of the object. One room in a building may be singled out for special sectional drawings of its floor (ceiling) and walls, Fig. 52 I. In this type of interior drawing it is often more satisfactory to show the visible surfaces as seen from within the room, but to omit any thicknesses to adjoining rooms and avoid showing any of the enclosed cut areas which would not be visible. If the thickness and structural details of the walls are shown, the visible surface should be emphasized with a heavy outline.

Part sectional drawings either on horizontal or vertical planes are sometimes used over the elevation drawing of an object to explain molding shapes, projections, etc., Fig. 52 II. It is sometimes better to make these part sections as separate drawings which may be either at the same scale as the elevation or enlarged in size, Fig. 52 III.

CHAPTER 10

Working Drawings

A set of working drawings provides precise shape and size information for the construction or manufacture of the object described in the drawings. It is usually accompanied by a set of typed or printed specifications describing the materials and workmanship required. It is essential that the working drawings be complete, accurate, clear, and precise in their information. They are an important part of the contract between the owner and the persons who are to perform the work described. As a part of a legal agreement they must avoid errors of interpretation. This chapter gives a small amount of general information on some of the important phases of working drawings.

Although it is the primary purpose of working drawings to provide shape and size description, other information is sometimes included in notes or tables on the sheets of the drawings. The amount of this information varies with the type of object and with the wishes of the individual or practice in the office doing the drawings. Some offices include so much descriptive matter on the drawings that specifications are minimum while others make minimum drawings and detailed specifications.

Working drawings might very well be called construction drawings since the term describes their use. They are often called "The Blueprints" since they are commonly printed in some manner to provide duplicate copies for use by workmen and others so as to protect the originals.

Symbols are widely used on working drawings. Some symbols are pretty well standardized while others may vary with the office and type of work. It is good practice to include on one of the sheets of the drawings a key to symbols used. Symbols avoid repetition of information in a more lengthy form and provide pictorial elements instead of words. Some of the more commonly used symbols are given in Fig. 54. These symbols and Fig. 53 are about ¼" = 1'-0" scale.

FIG. 53 AVERAGE SIZES FOR COMMON FURNITURE

BRICK MASONRY · POURED CONCRETE · CONCRETE BLOCK · CUT STONE · RUBBLE STONE · EARTH · FINISH WOOD · ROUGH WOOD

MATERIALS IN SECTION OR PLAN DRAWINGS

SHEET METAL · BRICK MASONRY · PLASTER OR CONC. · CONCRETE BLOCK · CUT STONE · SMOOTHED STONE · SPLIT STONE · RUBBLE STONE

MATERIALS IN ELEVATION DRAWINGS

DOUBLE HUNG WINDOW · WOOD CASEMENTS · STEEL CASEMENTS · STATIONARY GLASS · DOOR OPENING IN

PLANS OF OPENINGS IN EXTERIOR MASONRY WALLS

DOUBLE HUNG WINDOW · WOOD CASEMENTS · STEEL CASEMENTS · STATIONARY GLASS · DOOR OPENING IN

PLANS OF OPENINGS IN EXTERIOR WOOD WALLS

I ARCHITECTURAL SYMBOLS

CEILING OUTLET · WALL OUTLET · DROP CORD · CEILING FAN OUTLET · WALL OUTLET · CEILING LAMP HOLDER · WALL HOLDER · CEILING PULL SWITCHES · WALL PULL SWITCHES

DUPLEX OUTLET · SINGLE OUTLET · TRIPLEX OUTLET · WEATHER-PROOF OUT · RANGE OUTLET · SWITCH + OUTLET · SINGLE POLE SWITCH · DOUBLE POLE SWITCH · THREE WAY SWITCH

II ELECTRICAL SYMBOLS

SINK WITH L.H. DRAIN BOARD · SINK WITH DISHWASHER · KITCHEN RANGE · WASHER DRYER · LAUNDRY TRAYS

RECESSED TUB · SHOWER · WATER CLOSET · WALL TYPE STALL TYPE URINALS · WL WALL PL PEDEST. C CORNER LAVATORIES

III PLUMBING SYMBOLS

FIG. 54 COMMONLY USED SYMBOLS FOR DRAWINGS

The Dimensioning of Drawings. This is one of the most important phases of working drawings. Dimensions must be given accurately, clearly, and as simply as they can be arranged and shown. It is universal practice to have all dimensions, notes, and titles read from the bottom and right only, never from the left or top. Lines called extension and dimension lines are used to show where dimensions apply on the object, Fig. 55 A, B. These lines are made lighter than the solid lines of the object to avoid confusion between the two sets of lines.

Extension lines continue the lines of the object. They should begin about ⅟₃₂ inch from the ends of the lines to which the measurements are to be given and extend far enough from the drawing so the dimensions can be given clearly between the extension lines. Extension lines should be drawn about ⅛ inch beyond the dimension lines with which they are used.

Dimension lines are the lines on which dimensions are given. They are terminated with arrows which have their points ending exactly on the extension lines to which measurements are given. Dimension lines can be drawn in either of two ways: (1) as continuous lines with the numerals for the dimensions placed just above the lines, Fig. 55 A; or (2) with a part of the center of the line omitted so that the dimension can be given centered on the line, Fig. 55 B. The first method is commonly used for architecture and structural engineering, the second for mechanical engineering. One of the two methods should be used consistently throughout a set of drawings.

Dimensions are given in various ways to suit the convenience of the type of work and the accepted practice in the profession for which the drawings are made. (A) In architecture and structural engineering, dimensions are given in feet and inches with the foot (') and inch (") signs after the numerals and a dash always placed between the numerals for feet and inches, thus 5'–2½", Fig. 55 A. Some offices give any dimension of a foot or more in feet and inches, 1'–0", etc. Others continue measurements in inches beyond one foot with an arbitrary maximum for distances which can be given in inches only. This is convenient in giving spacings of joists and other structural elements. (B) In mechanical engineering all dimensions are given in inches only and the inch sign is omitted. A note to that effect should be given with the scale or as a part of the title.

Fractions are given either as common or decimal fractions. Common fractions are given as half, fourths, eighths, sixteenths, thirty-seconds, and sixty-fourths. Other fractional divisions are seldom used. Common fractions should be given with a horizontal line separating numerators and denominators ($\frac{3}{16}$) and with the numerals about two thirds the size of other numerals. There is less chance of error in reading fractions when the horizontal division is used.

Multiple dimension lines are sometimes necessary on the same side of an object since dimensions should not be given across the object when it can be avoided. Multiple dimension lines should be arranged so that they cross extension lines only where the measurements terminate. In order to avoid confusion and make the simplest arrangement of dimensions, the smaller measurements are kept near the object and larger ones progressively farther away as shown in Fig. 55 C. All dimensions which are either necessary or useful should be provided on the drawing. Give enough dimensions so that other persons are not required to add or subtract to obtain necessary measurements. Unnecessary repetition of measurements is often confusing, not helpful. Avoid useless repetition. It is good practice to locate dimensions between views where their relation to two views can be seen for both, Fig. 55 D. Base line dimensioning is sometimes advisable or necessary. This is especially true for a mechanical contrivance where measurements must be exact from some working surface. In this system distances in one direction are given from the same line, Fig. 55 E.

Small spaces on the drawings may require special treatment in dimensioning, Fig. 55 F.

Circles are dimensioned in various ways for different professions. The method for mechanical engineering is shown in Fig. 55 G. Either the diameter or radius may be given depending on which will be most useful in laying out the construction of the object. In some work it is desirable to give the dimension for a circle in the view where it appears as a circle. When the diameter is given the abbreviation *DIA.* accompanies the numerals of the size when the circle view is not shown. The letter *R* is used with the numerals for a radius, Fig. 55 G.

A) CONTINUOUS DIMENSION LINES NUMERALS IN FEET AND INCHES

SYSTEM USED IN ARCHITECTURE AND STRUCTURAL ENGINEERING

2'-5"

5'- 2½"

DIMENSION LINE

EXTENSION LINES

DIMENSION LINE

B) BROKEN DIMENSION LINES NUMERALS IN INCHES ONLY

THIS SYSTEM IS USED FOR MECHANICAL ENGINEERING

29

62½

DIMENSION LINE

EXTENSION LINES

DIMENSION LINE

C) MULTIPLE DIMENSION LINES

7"   11"   7"   1'-9"   4"   1'-9"   9"   6"

2'-1"   3'-10"   1'-3"

7'-2"

D) DIMEN. BETWEEN VIEWS

4

8½   TOP

2

L. SIDE   FRONT

E) BASE LINE SYSTEM

BASE LINE

6

7

9

10½

F) SMALL SPACE METHODS

⅛   3/16   ¼   ⅛

METHOD 1

¼   ⅛   3/16   1/16

METHOD 2

G) DIMENSIONING OF CIRCLES AND ARCS

3   2

CIRCLE VIEW GIVEN

4 DIA.   5 DIA.   6 DIA.

CIRCLE NOT SHOWN

½ R   2R   ¾ R

METHODS FOR RADII

FIG. 55 THE DIMENSIONING OF DRAWINGS

62

PART PLAN   PART ELEVATION

FIG. 56 PENCIL TECHNIQUE FOR WORKING DRAWINGS

The Technique of Working Drawings. The necessity of making drawings which will print clearly dominates the drafting technique for working drawings. A drawing which will not print so that all the lines and lettering of the print can be seen easily is worthless. Either a transparent tracing paper or tracing cloth is used for working drawings. The cloth is coated with a starchy material and is quite transparent. One side of the cloth is usually very slick and the other dull. Tracing cloth is made with a medium dull surface for ink work and with a very dull velvety surface for pencil drawings. It is stronger, gives clearer prints, will take more erasing, and does not become as brittle with age as paper. Plastic material which looks like tracing cloth is used for the same purpose.

Tracing paper varies a great deal in quality and characteristics. Fragile and easily torn paper should not be used for working drawings. Paper which is extremely slick does not take pencil lines very well. Paper which is very transparent makes lines on the drawing under the paper so clear that there is confusion as to which lines are on the tracing paper. It may actually be more difficult to work on this type of paper than on less transparent material. Some tracing paper is very tough and will stand erasing of ink lines. Since a great deal of time and thought usually go into the making of a working drawing, either a good quality tracing paper or tracing cloth should be used.

Pencil drawings are very widely used as originals from which working drawing prints are made. Dark, clean-cut, crisp pencil lines are necessary for drawings which will print satisfactorily, Fig. 56. It is necessary to keep the paper clean because dirty smears will reproduce and give a mussy appearance to the prints. Some tracing paper becomes opaque where it is bent sharply in a crease or fold. These opaque places print as lines do. Dimension and extension lines should be made less prominent than lines of the object. They may be either thinner or lighter in weight or both so they will not be confused with lines of the object in the print. Outlines of important shapes, divisions of materials, and silhouettes of cut areas should be made quite heavy. All lettering and arrow points should be made dark. It is important that they should be seen clearly. Indication of materials is usually kept somewhat subdued since it is an area treatment and each line or dot is not usually of great importance. When uniform shading is used over areas as a tone symbol for a material the shading can be applied on the back of the paper or cloth. This procedure has these advantages: (1) lines surrounding the areas are not smeared by application of the tone, therefore print more clearly; (2) erasures and changes can be made more readily.

FIG. 57 INK TECHNIQUE FOR WORKING DRAWINGS

Ink drawings either on tracing paper or tracing cloth are used in some offices. It is usually necessary to make a complete preliminary drawing on scrap paper and trace it in ink. Changes are more easily made on pencil drawings than on ink ones. Ink drawings give clearer, brighter prints, Fig. 57. Ink technique provides a more positive variation of darkness of line by the use of diluted and colored inks. Tones can be applied to either the front or back of tracing cloth with a small brush and diluted or colored ink. Use a moist brush. Avoid getting the cloth very wet. Wet spots on tracing cloth become opaque and wrinkled if the water penetrates. Sometimes the surface of tracing cloth repels the ink as though it were oily. Such a condition can be overcome by dusting and rubbing the surface of the cloth with a powder sold for that purpose, or with powdered chalk. The powder should be removed with a clean dusting cloth before inking.

Colors are frequently used on ink drawings and less often on pencil drawings to secure variations of line weight. Whenever possible the draftsman should make sample lines and have them printed as he will have the drawings printed in order to check on the reproduction from colors. Colors sometimes produce surprising results. Yellow prints the same as black on blueprints. It is sometimes used for tones because it does not hide lines on the original. Red ink is sometimes used for dimension and extension lines because it prints lighter than black. The colors help to separate different uses of lines on the originals, and if carefully selected give variations of tones on the lines of the prints, thus producing prints which are more easily read. Colored ink which is too dark can be diluted by adding water to it.

Unnecessary repetition is preferably avoided on working drawings. Needless duplication of the same repeating element in all its details often adds nothing to the clearness of the drawings and causes additional work and expense in making the drawings. The following are examples of ways to avoid repeating details: (1) Continuous bands of details may be drawn completely for a short distance and the remainder drawn more simply or omitted with a note "Continue details". (2) One of a series of units may be drawn completely and all others shown in outline form only with a note stating that the details apply to all the outlined areas. (3) A symmetrical object can be drawn completely on one side of the center line and outlined on the other side.

In all cases where only part of the drawing is finished in detail notes and arrows should be used to make entirely clear where the details are required on the object.

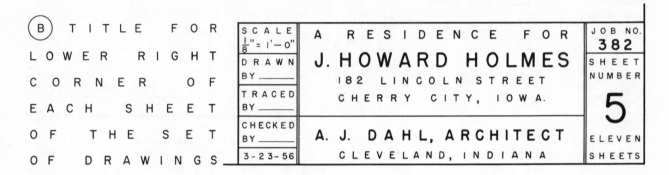

JOB NO. 1192	DESIGNED BY _____	BEDROOM FURNITURE DESIGNS FOR	SHEET
	DRAWN BY _____	MCLEOD FURNITURE CO.	2
SCALE 1½" = 1'-0"	TRACED BY _____	EAGLE ROCK, ARK.	
	CHECKED BY _____		
MAR. 7, 1963	REVISED BY _____	H. J. HANKS DESIGNERS, HILL, OHIO	OF-7

Ⓐ TITLE COMPLETELY ACROSS LOWER EDGE OF EACH SHEET

Ⓑ TITLE FOR LOWER RIGHT CORNER OF EACH SHEET OF THE SET OF DRAWINGS

SCALE ⅛" = 1'-0"	A RESIDENCE FOR	JOB NO. 382
DRAWN BY _____	J. HOWARD HOLMES	SHEET NUMBER
TRACED BY _____	182 LINCOLN STREET CHERRY CITY, IOWA.	5
CHECKED BY _____		
3-23-56	A. J. DAHL, ARCHITECT CLEVELAND, INDIANA	ELEVEN SHEETS

FIG. 58 TITLES FOR WORKING DRAWING SHEETS

The title is an important part of a sheet of working drawings. Usually the set of drawings consists of several sheets and some of the title is repeated on each sheet. Necessary variations are made for items applicable to each individual sheet. The title is usually in a box form in the lower right corner, or extended completely across the bottom of each sheet, Fig. 58. Some of the material usually repeating on each sheet and some of the material which may vary are listed below.

Material on each sheet

1. Name of object
2. Name and address of client
3. Name, address, and profession of office
4. Total number of sheets in the set

Material which may vary

5. Sheet number in the set
6. Date completed
7. Names of authors of drawings
8. Scale on the sheet

The sheet number is usually located in the lower right corner so that it is easily found. The total number of sheets is given to allow a check for completeness of a set. The first sheet of a set may also include a tabulation of all drawings made for this job. In large offices it is often desirable to give complete listing of types of work done by different individuals on each drawing. This may include sketches, drawing, tracing, computations, checking, and other items necessary or important for the particular job. The scale can be given in the title block when all drawings on a sheet are at the same scale. When the scale "varies" that word may be put under scale in the title block and the scale of each individual drawing given with its subtitle.

The set of drawings should include any and all drawings which are necessary to explain the shapes and dimensions of the object shown. It should include multi-view drawings consisting of two or more complete views. Auxiliary drawings, sections, and plans through the object may be necessary. Details at a larger scale are sometimes made to more clearly explain parts of the object which are not sufficiently large and clear on the multi-view drawings. These details may be either sectional drawings, exterior views, or a combination of the two types. Their positions should be clearly designated on the complete views as shown for the sectional details of Fig. 52.

One of the parallel line pictorial drawing types may be used in a set of working drawings to give a three-dimensional explanation of forms which are difficult to understand in the two-dimensional multi-view drawings.

The Reproduction of Drawings. The printing from the original drawings made on transparent paper or cloth is usually done by a commercial blueprinter. Prints can be made in different ways with considerable variety in the results, Fig. 59. In all cases the tracing is placed over a light-sensitive paper and run through a machine which has a strong light shining on the tracing and through it onto the paper it covers. The printing paper is then developed either by use of liquids or vapors.

Blueprints are called negative prints because they have white lines and blue background thus reversing the tone relation of the original drawings. After being exposed they are run through one or more chemical solutions and finally dried. By first making a Van Dyke negative print which has a dark brown background and transparent white lines and using it for the printing, blue-line prints can be made. They reverse the blue and white of the common blueprint. They are more satisfactory for use where drawing on the prints is required since they have white background areas.

Direct positive prints are reproductions giving the same tone relations as the original drawings in one step instead of requiring an intermediate negative (Van Dyke) as in blue-line printing. Black and white prints have black lines and a white background. Ozalids have colored lines. Both are developed with ammonia vapor.

Minor distortions of the original drawing shapes and sizes may appear in any type of prints. Warping may be caused by wetting and shrinking of the printing paper or in other ways. Sometimes the length of the print will be changed in the printing process through defective equipment. Minor variations can be expected in prints. However, appreciable distortion of shape or change of dimension should not occur in good prints. The drawings and/or specifications often contain a statement that where dimensions are given they should be followed. Taking sizes from prints with a scale should be avoided.

Discoloration of prints often occurs when they are brought in contact with perspiration, acid, cement, lime, or other substances. Fortunately it is usually an easy and relatively inexpensive matter to replace prints which are damaged.

Photostat prints are not contact prints. They can be made either smaller or larger than the original. They can be made either as negative prints reversing the tone relation of the originals, or, by using an intermediate negative, as positive prints duplicating the tones of the original. Photostats are expensive and are seldom used for working drawings. Their big advantage is change of size.

Ⅰ   N E G A T I V E   P R I N T

Ⅱ   P O S I T I V E   P R I N T

F I G .   5 9   T Y P E S   O F   R E P R O D U C T I O N S   O F   D R A W I N G S

CHAPTER 11

Geometric Shapes

The simple lines, areas, and solids of geometry are the principal basic forms of design. It is essential that the designer should be able to draw them easily, accurately, and quickly. The simpler geometric forms can be constructed easily when T-square, triangles, instruments, and drafting board are used.

The equilateral triangle can be constructed in four different positions by using the 30° x 60° triangle on the T-square, Fig. 60 A.

A square can be drawn in two ways: (1) by first drawing a circle with diameter equal to a side, then drawing tangents to the circle with T-square and triangle; (2) by using the 45° triangle to draw the diagonal then constructing the square on its diagonal, Fig. 60 B. Squares can be tilted at different angles by using the sloping sides of the triangle and 45° diagonals.

The rectangle which is the most widely used geometric area has no set proportions. It can vary from almost square to a long thin shape which approaches a straight line.

A pentagon can be drawn in a circle by drawing a vertical line through the center of the circle to locate the top point on the circumference, then stepping off the other corners with the dividers,

WITH 30°x60° TRIANGLE

(A) EQUILATERAL TRIANGLES

WITH TANGENTS TO A CIRCLE

FROM ONE SIDE AND A DIAGONAL

(B) SQUARES DRAWN BY TWO METHODS

CORNERS LOCATED WITH DIVIDERS

CONCENTRIC PENTAGONS

CORNERS LOCATED WITH PROTRACTOR

(C) CONSTRUCTION OF A REGULAR PENTAGON

FIG. 60 CONSTRUCTION OF PLANE FIGURES

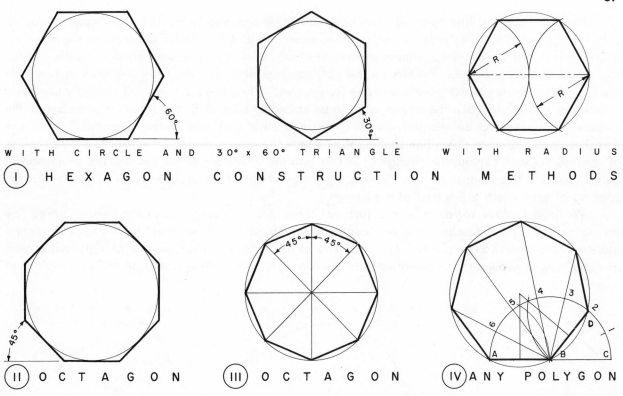

WITH CIRCLE AND 30° x 60° TRIANGLE   WITH RADIUS

Ⓘ HEXAGON   CONSTRUCTION   METHODS

Ⓘ OCTAGON   Ⓘ OCTAGON   Ⓘ ANY POLYGON

FIG. 61 CONSTRUCTION OF REGULAR POLYGONS

by trial and error until five equal divisions are secured. A larger or smaller pentagon can be constructed from this by drawing lines from the center through the corners, then drawing lines parallel to the sides of the first pentagon between these radiating lines, Fig. 60 c. An adjustable triangle or other protractor can be used to locate the corners of a pentagon or other polygon by drawing through the center of a circle.

A hexagon can be constructed around a circle by drawing 60° lines tangent to the circle with horizontal tangents at bottom and top, or with 30° tangent lines to make points at top and bottom and vertical lines at both sides, Fig. 61 I. The hexagon can be constructed in a circle by using the radius of the circle as the length of a side of the hexagon.

The octagon can be drawn around a circle with two horizontal and two vertical sides. The four slanting sides are drawn with the 45° triangle, Fig. 61 II. A horizontal, a vertical, and two 45° lines through the center of the circle locate the eight corners on the circumference of the circle. This construction gives corners at the top, bottom, and two sides as shown in Fig. 61 III.

Any regular polygon can be drawn about a given side A-B in the following manner, Fig. 61 IV. Draw a semicircle of which A-B is a radius and A-C a diameter. Divide the semicircle into the same number of equal parts as the number of sides of the required polygon. Seven divisions have been used in the example. Through the second division draw a second side B-D of the polygon. From the two sides A-B and B-D locate the center of the polygon by drawing the perpendicular bisectors of the sides. Draw the circumscribing circle. The remaining corners of the polygon can be located on the circle by drawing radial lines from B through the divisions on the semicircle. The distance A-B can be used to locate the corners of the polygon as an alternate method.

Any regular polygon can be inscribed in a circle by locating with dividers by trial and error the required number of points on the circle for the corners of the polygon. The corners can also be located on the circumference of the circle by drawing from its center angles equal to 360° divided by the number of sides of the polygon.

The projection of line spacing from one multi-view drawing to another on simple geometric solids is illustrated for a cylinder, cone, and hexagon in Fig. 62. In these illustrations the top view is drawn first and the required number of divisions laid out in top view with dividers on the circular top views and with scale or dividers on the polygon top view. The divisions are then drawn from the top views to the correct positions in the front views. When lines are spaced correctly around a cylinder or cone they make the object seem to be smoothly curved. If the spacing is inaccurate, the surface will appear to be warped. Slanting surfaces such as those of the hexagonal prism are foreshortened and have closer line spacing than where the area is projected in true size. This change of spacing helps to explain the change of planes and the directions of the planes. The projection of equal spaces in this manner is useful in locating the positions of decorative motifs as well as for the spacing of lines which are a part of the design.

Warped surface solids in whose surfaces there are no straight lines have only curved line divisions. The vase and sphere are two examples which have circular cross sections on horizontal planes. These forms can be divided into equal spaces by drawing vertical planes through their centers at equal angles around the circumference of the top view and plotting points on the intersections of

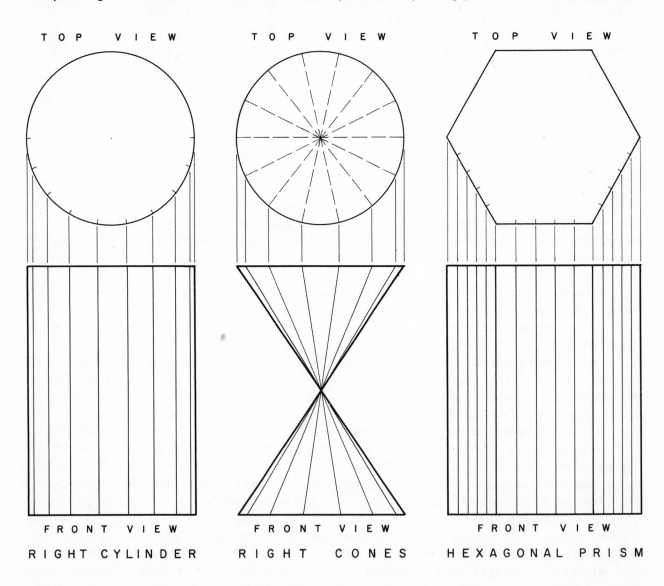

FIG. 62 LINE SPACING ON GEOMETRIC SOLIDS

FRONT VIEW

VASE

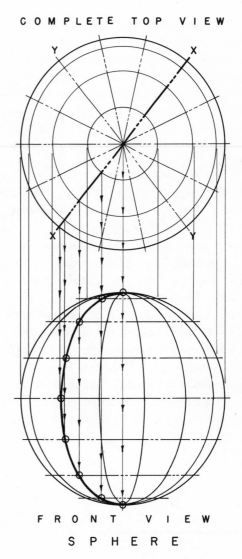

FRONT VIEW

SPHERE

FIG. 63 LINES ON WARPED SURFACE SOLIDS

these planes with the surfaces of the object. In the example of the vase in Fig. 63, points have been located on the 45° plane represented by line B-O in the top view. Horizontal lines have been drawn across the front view wherever it is thought that points will be most useful in drawing the intersection of plane B-O with the surface of the vase. These lines, 1-1, 2-2, etc., represent the front views of horizontal planes through the vase. Their circle intersections are drawn in the top view and labeled 1, 2, etc. These circles must be the diameters cut in the front view by the same planes.

A vertical drawn from the intersection of B-O with circle 1 in top view to line 1-1 in front view locates a point on the intersection of plane B-O with the surface of the vase. The intersections of the other circles give additional points. The curve is then drawn through the points located. Any number of points can be located with this system and the intersections of any number of planes can be located. The same circles 1, 2, etc. and their corresponding planes in front view are used for all vertical cutting planes A-O, B-O, C-O, etc.

It will be observed that the left side of the curve cut by plane X-X on the sphere is visible and the right side is hidden on the back of the sphere in front view. When planes X-X and Y-Y are at the same angle from opposite sides, their complete curves will coincide in front view.

CHAPTER 12

Manipulations and Short Cuts

The student draftsman will remain an amateur if he draws in awkward ways, takes a great deal of time, accomplishes little, and does unpolished drawings. However, he can acquire much of the knowledge and skills of a professional draftsman by the use of a little thought and effort. He can become much more expert in his work by using correct techniques and efficient methods. This chapter is intended to help the amateur to become a more finished and precise draftsman.

Parallel lines at an angle not given with the triangle resting on the horizontal T-square are frequently required in drafting work, Fig. 64 A. The T-square and triangle can be used for this purpose. Keep one edge of the triangle in contact with the working edge of the T-square. Twist them around until the slanting or perpendicular edge of the triangle is parallel to the lines to be drawn, Fig. 64 B. The T-square is held in position and the triangle slid along it to draw the required parallel lines. By using the most satisfactory angle of the triangle the lines can be made for a long distance without moving the T-square. Sometimes it is more convenient to use two triangles than to use the longer and more clumsy T-square for the stationary support for the sliding triangle.

The adjustable triangle can be set at the required angle and used directly on the horizontal T-square to draw parallel lines at any angle, Fig. 64 C.

A) THE PROBLEM PARALLELS TO A—B

B) SOLUTION WITH T-SQ. AND TRIANGLE

C) SOLUTION WITH ADJUSTABLE TRIANGLE

PARALLEL LINES AT ANY ANGLE

D) SETTING THE TRIANGLE AND REST

E) DRAWING THE PERPENDICULARS

F) USING ADJUST. TRIANGLE AND T-SQ.

PERPENDICULAR LINES AT ANY ANGLE

FIG. 64 OTHER USES OF T-SQUARE AND TRIANGLES

Perpendicular lines at any angle require the use of two triangles or a triangle and T-square. When a set of lines is to be drawn at a given odd angle and it is required to draw both perpendiculars and parallels to the given line direction, place the triangle on a rest of T-square or another triangle with a 90° angle on the rest. Twist the triangle and its touching rest so that the acute angle side of the moving triangle lines with the direction given, Fig. 64 D. By sliding the moving triangle the parallels to the given direction can be drawn. By rotating the moving triangle on its 90° corner to bring the other side of the 90° angle in contact with the rest, the same side of the triangle first used will now draw the perpendiculars when the triangle slides along the rest, Fig. 64 E. Remember three things: (1) the moving triangle must be turned on its 90° corner; (2) the two sides of the 90° angle must be used on the stationary rest; (3) the same side of the triangle must be used for both groups of lines. Considerable ingenuity and foresight are required to have the triangles turned so that they cover the required area of the drawing with as little moving of the rest as possible.

The adjustable triangle will also draw perpendiculars to lines at any angle. It is used on the horizontal T-square and set for the given lines. When turned on its 90° angle it will then draw the perpendiculars to the given lines while resting on the horizontal T-square, Fig. 64 F.

The location of center lines with triangles is a routine procedure for an experienced draftsman. The most common problem is to find the center lines of a rectangle which has vertical and horizontal sides. From the bottom corners A and B of the rectangle draw 45° lines to intersect at C, Fig. 65 I. The vertical line through C is the center line of the rectangle. Lines at 45° from the top corners accomplish the same result. Lines at 45° from two corners D and B at one vertical side of the rectangle meet in point E. The horizontal line through E is the other center line of the rectangle. The 45° triangle is ordinarily used for this operation because it is the best for the purpose. However, any other angle can be used if the lines drawn from the two corners make identical angles with the line connecting these corners, Fig. 65 II. The diagonals of a rectangle can be drawn to locate its center at their intersection. This is the simple method of geometry. It is accurate on almost square rectangles and loses accuracy on long thin rectangles.

To find the center line of a space between two vertical or horizontal lines L-M and N-O, draw X-Y perpendicular to the given lines and from the corners X and Y draw intersecting 45° lines to locate a point on the required center line, Fig. 65 III.

The center line between two parallel lines at any angle can be located by the following procedure, Fig. 65 IV. Draw V-W perpendicular to the lines. Place one side of the 90° angle of a 45° triangle on a rest of triangle or T-square and adjust so the perpendicular to the rest is parallel to the given lines R-S and T-U. Slide moving triangle to draw the diagonal of one corner. Reverse the triangle to draw the diagonal of the second corner and locate a point Z on the center line at the intersection of the two diagonals. Use the edge of the moving triangle which is perpendicular to the rest to draw the center line through Z.

(I) CENTER LINES OF RECTANGLE

(II) ANY=ANGLES CAN BE USED

(III) CENTERS OF PARALLEL LINES

(IV) CENTERS OF OBLIQUE LINES

FIG. 65   THE   LOCATION   OF   CENTER   LINES

BEST FOR ACCURACY   ANY SCALE GIVES SAME DIVISIONS

(A) EQUAL DIVISIONS BETWEEN PARALLEL LINES

(B) SIMPLE ALTERNATION   (C) IRREGULAR SEQUENCE

UNEQUAL DIVISIONS BETWEEN PARALLEL LINES

(D) PERPENDICULARS AT ENDS OF LINE

(E) PERPENDICULAR AT ONE END ONLY

(F) LINE ANY ANGLE FROM END OF LINE

METHODS OF DIVIDING A LINE A—B INTO PARTS

FIG. 66 THE DIVISION OF SPACES AND LINES

The division of a space between two parallel lines by using the scale is one of the most useful manipulations that a draftsman can learn. It enables him to do easily, accurately, and speedily work which would take a great deal longer by other methods. Given two parallel lines Fig. 66 A. Required to divide the space between these lines into a number of equal divisions. Seven divisions are used for the example. If the scale used perpendicular to the given lines will divide the space exactly, then the problem is solved. However, this rarely works out. Almost always the space is too large for some scales and too small for others. Use a scale which gives too large a distance for the required seven divisions. Put the zero point on one line and tilt the scale until the seventh division exactly meets the second line. Now mark out precisely the positions of each of the seven divisions and draw through these points parallel to the given lines to make the required divisions. Note that different scales can be used to obtain the same results. However, the scale which is most nearly perpendicular to the given parallel lines will give slightly more accurate results.

Simple unequal divisions can also be laid out in the same manner as equal divisions. A simple alternation of small and large spaces is shown in Fig. 66 B. Here the ratio of size is 1 to 2. Four

FIG. 67 DIVISION OF SPACES ON A DRAWING

large and five small spaces are required. The sum of small spaces is then 2 x 4 + 5 = 13 spaces total. A simple sequence of unequal spaces is illustrated in Fig. 66 c.

The division of a line into parts can be made in the following manner. Draw parallel lines perpendicular to the given line A-B at its end points A and B, Fig. 66 D. The space between the two parallel lines is divided and the divisions extended to line A-B by drawing construction lines parallel to the two lines through points A and B. Only one perpendicular to the line to be divided is necessary for this manipulation, Fig. 66 E. One end of the line A-B can be used as a pivot point and the scale revolved until the required division touches the perpendicular at the other end of the line. In the example B has been used as the pivot point and the perpendicular to A-B has been drawn through A. The line A-C drawn at the end of the line to be divided need not be a perpendicular, Fig. 66 F. It can be drawn at any angle and the result will be the same if the lines from the division points are drawn parallel to A-C. It is usually more convenient to draw the construction line perpendicular to the line to be divided when using drafting equipment. The perpendicular also provides favorable construction line intersections for maximum accuracy.

Duplicating, Reversing, etc. Trace and transfer methods are widely used by designers for duplicating a given drawing or a repeating motif and for the purpose of transferring a design from a rough study to final paper. The given drawing is traced onto the tracing paper and then may be handled in a number of different ways. Whatever the method used, it is almost always necessary to draw over the transfer in pencil or ink in order to get a neat final drawing.

1. When the object is symmetrical the tracing can be made with a medium soft pencil. It is then turned over with pencil lines down, aligned on the final paper, and rubbed to transfer the pencil lines. The rubbing can be done with the thumb nail, a coin, or the edge of the bowl of a spoon. Care must be taken to see that the tracing does not move. Better results can be obtained by placing a piece of tracing cloth, with the slick side down, over the tracing paper and rubbing on the cloth. The cloth helps prevent movement and stretching of the paper drawing. When the transfer is made by rubbing, the texture of the final paper may be changed if very much pressure is used. Usually no serious damage is done.

2. When the drawing is unsymmetrical the tracing can be made in the usual way with a hard pencil. It is then turned over and traced on the back with a medium soft pencil, turned again to its original position, and rubbed to make the transfer identical with the original drawing.

3. A less tidy method is to blacken the back of the tracing with a soft pencil, then attach the paper to the final drawing surface and trace over all the lines with a hard pencil to transfer the design. Much neater results are obtained if the blackened surface is first cleaned of loose pencil dust by rubbing over it vigorously with a piece of cloth or soft paper. The transfer will then be clearer and neater and the paper will not become dirty from the loose black particles of carbon.

Tick strips for transferring measurements can be made from narrow bands of plain paper. Trimmings from drawings are often used for the purpose. The edges of the strips should be straight and smooth. The tick strips are used in transferring measurements from one drawing to another, for marking sizes of repeating elements on the same or different drawings, and for duplicating a preliminary study on final paper. The measurements on the given drawing are marked on the edge of the tick strip and then transferred to the required location, Fig. 68 A. By changing ends of the tick strip the sequence of measurements will be reversed. This is done when transferring between side views, or from front to back, and in other situations, Fig. 68 C. The tick strip method is much simpler, easier, and less likely to permit errors than using a scale or dividers. It reduces the transfer of dimensions to a simple mechanical process. It is one of the important devices of the professional draftsman.

Arcs. An arc can be drawn through three given points, A, B, C, by drawing the perpendicular bisectors of the straight lines connecting point B with A and C. The intersection of the bisectors is the center of the required arc, Fig. 69 I. The center of a given arc is located at the intersection of the perpendicular bisectors of any two chords of the arc.

A tangent to an arc at a given point T can be drawn as a perpendicular to the radius when the center of the arc is given, Fig. 69 II. When the center of the arc is not given, use the point of

(A) DUPLICATING   (B) COMPLETING   (C) REVERSING

FIG. 68 TICK STRIP USED FOR TRANSFERRING SIZES

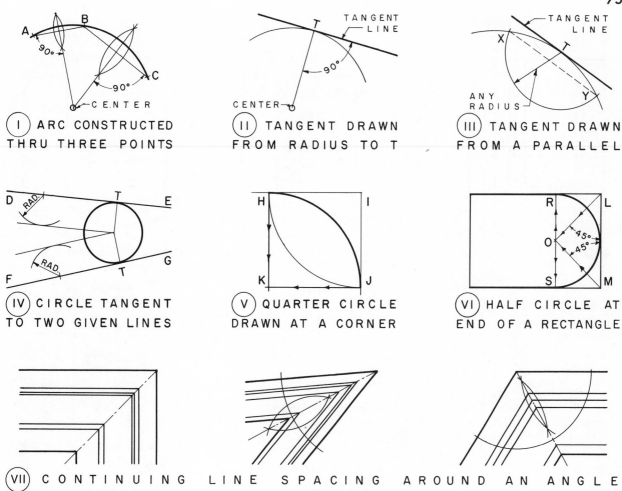

FIG. 69 DRAFTING PROBLEMS OF ARCS AND ANGLES

tangency *T* as a center and lay off equal distances on each side of it with the compass to locate points *X* and *Y*. The required tangent will be parallel to the line *X-Y*, Fig. 69 III.

A *circle tangent to two given lines* D-E and F-G which are not perpendicular or parallel to each other can be drawn in the following manner. With the radius of the required circle and a center on each of the given lines draw an arc on the side toward the other line. Draw tangents to these arcs parallel to the lines used as centers for the respective arcs. The parallels meet in the center of the required circle, Fig. 69 IV. Two arcs can be drawn for each line to give the parallel to that line.

A *quarter circle at a right angled corner* requires for its construction the location of the two tangent points and the center, Fig. 69 V. With the required radius and the corner *I* as a center, draw arcs to intersect the two sides of the corner at *H* and *J*. Draw lines through *H* and *J* parallel to the sides of the corner to intersect in *K*, the required center. The quarter circle terminates at *H* and *J* the points of tangency of the arc and straight lines.

A *semicircle at the end of a rectangle* is constructed as follows. Draw the 45° bisectors of the corners *L* and *M* of the rectangle to locate the required center *O*. Through *O* draw the line *R-S* parallel to *L-M* to locate the ends of the required semicircle at *R* and *S*, Fig. 69 VI.

To continue a set of lines around any angle draw the bisector of the angle as shown in Fig. 69 VII, and change direction of the lines on the bisector. When the angle is 90°, the 45° triangle can be used to draw the bisector. The compass is used to locate bisectors of other angles, as shown in the last two examples of VII.

ENLARGED DRAWING

DRAWING REDUCED IN SIZE

ENLARGED DRAWING

(A) ENLARGING WITH TICK STRIP

GIVEN DRAWING

(B) REDUCING WITH TICK STRIP

GIVEN DRAWING

(C) USES OF RADIALS AND PARALLELS

DRAWING REDUCED FROM ORIGINAL

FIG. 70 ENLARGING AND REDUCING DRAWINGS

Enlarging and Reducing the Size of a Given Drawing. This is a very common procedure for a draftsman. If the given multi-view or paraline drawing is made to scale, the popular method is to use the scale to measure from it and a larger or smaller scale to measure on the new drawing. This is a relatively simple procedure and easy to use. However, it requires many measurements and gives many chances of error in reading, remembering, and transferring correctly. Furthermore the amount of change of size is limited by the available scales.

Simple numerical changes of size of a multi-view or paraline drawing can often be made speedily with the dividers. An enlargement to two times the scale of the given drawing can be made by setting the dividers to the given sizes and using the measurements two times on the enlarged drawing. When making a drawing one half the size of the original, the dividers should be adjusted to one half the given sizes to give correct measurements for the smaller drawing. Other simple relations of size can be handled in the same manner. When the scale relations become complex the amount of effort required is excessive. The dividers method is a more mechanical system than using the scale. It is less likely to cause error in measurements. Both methods require a great deal of detailed work and are limited to simple size relations. The proportional dividers is very convenient for changing the scale of a drawing. It can be adjusted for a wide range of sizes.

The tick strip method of enlarging and reducing multi-view drawings any amount desired is a very convenient device. With one dimension the height *A-B* of the enlarged drawing established and marked on the tick strip, the strip is slanted to fit these marks between the correct lines of the given drawing, Fig. 70 A. Each of the heights is marked on the edge of the tick strip where it crosses the lines. The tick strip is then used vertically to transfer the heights to the enlarged drawing. The widths should be marked on the second tick strip which is placed at 90° to the position of the first tick strip on the given drawing. The widths C-D are then transferred to a horizontal line on the final drawing.

When the size of the drawing is reduced, the tick strips E-F and G-H are used vertically and horizontally on the given drawing and slanted to give the sizes on the final drawing, Fig. 70 B.

In using this method the draftsman should be sure the main dimensions of the new drawing are correct. The remainder of the construction is a mechanical process which can be done speedily.

Radial and parallel lines can be used to enlarge or reduce the size of a given straight line drawing of any type. This method is particularly good for perspective drawings. The change of size can be any desired amount.

Choose a corner X which will be common to both the given and the new drawing. All lines of the given drawing which radiate from X will coincide with the same lines of the new drawing as far as the lengths extend on both of the drawings. When the length of any one of these lines radiating from X is established for the new drawing all other lines are determined by drawing radiating and parallel lines. Radial construction lines from the common corner X through intersections of the given drawing pass through the same intersections on the new drawing. All of the lines of the new drawing are drawn parallel to those of the given drawing. In Fig. 70 C, X-Y is the line of the given drawing and X-Z is the length chosen for the new drawing. The relative lengths of X-Y and X-Z determine the relative sizes of the two drawings. In the top example of Fig. 70 C, X-Z has been made 1 ½ times the length of X-Y. The new drawing is therefore 1 ½ times the size of the given drawing. The lines of the enlarged drawing have been numbered in the order in which they were drawn. The radiating lines have not been numbered. They were drawn as they were needed to determine ends of lines of the enlarged drawing.

These last two methods of using radials and parallels and of using tick strips to enlarge and reduce the sizes of drawings are devices which an expert draftsman would use automatically and accurately. Both methods have the advantage of allowing any size ratio between the drawings.

Irregular forms can usually be most efficiently reduced and enlarged in size by using a cross section paper grid. The grids must be identical in pattern but varied in size to suit the two drawings. There are two methods of making the grids: (1) A uniform spacing is used, Fig. 71 I. (2) The spacing is varied to produce intersections at important points on the drawings, Fig. 71 II. The first method requires judgment in locating intersections of drawing and grid. It is often quite satisfactory. The second method locates points with greater accuracy, but requires more thought and effort.

(I) WITH A UNIFORM GRID   (II) WITH SELECTED OFFSETS

FIG. 71 ENLARGING AND REDUCING IRREGULAR SHAPES

PART THREE

Paraline Drawing

CHAPTER 13

Characteristics of Paraline Drawings

A pictorial drawing gives a three-dimensional view of an object from which it is easy to visualize the forms represented. The term paraline drawing includes all the parallel line pictorial drawing types. As the name indicates, all divisions of this group use parallel lines in the drawings to represent the parallel lines of the objects.

There is an impression of distortion in any paraline drawing because the more distant parts of the object are drawn the same size as the nearer parts, Fig. 72 A. The eye expects more distant parts to appear smaller as they do in an actual object, a perspective drawing, or a photograph. The amount of distortion varies with the shape of the object and the specific arrangement of drawing used. It does not prevent these drawings from being easily understood. It merely makes them seem more or less warped or out of proportion.

Axis lines are used for scale measurements in all paraline drawings. Three adjacent planes which are perpendicular to each other meet in a corner of an object and are visible in all types of paraline drawings. The three edges formed by the intersections of the planes of the object which meet at a corner are called axis lines, Fig. 72 B. These planes and edges are those of a box.

Paraline drawings are easy to construct because measurements are laid out to scale on the axis lines and all lines parallel to them. Lines in other directions can seldom be used for scale measurements. When the object is not made of plane surfaces which are all perpendicular to each other, a box form and axis lines are used to construct points and lines on the irregular shape, Fig. 72 D.

True shapes are rarely shown in any pictorial drawing either paraline or perspective. One set of planes in oblique drawing, and one set in one-point perspective, are shown true shape. It is very unusual for a true shape to be shown elsewhere in any pictorial drawing. It can be expected that representations of rectangles and squares will not have right angles in most paraline drawing planes, Fig. 72 B. Circles will usually be represented as ellipses, Fig. 72 C. These are characteristics of all pictorial drawings. They are necessary results of showing three dimensions of an object.

To summarize: paraline drawings sometimes seem distorted to the observer. However, they are (1) easily constructed, (2) easily understood, and (3) offer variety in pictorial effects.

In order to use paraline drawings intelligently and to obtain the best results with them, it is necessary to have a good working knowledge of each type. Then the draftsman can select the type best suited to his particular problem and get the best results from that type for his purpose.

Paraline drawings are used for advertising illustrations, explanatory diagrams for catalogues, working drawings, design drawings, and for many other purposes. They are much easier to construct than perspective drawings. Contrary to popular belief, perspectives are not always the best drawings for representing the shapes of an object. Some irregular objects are not explained as clearly in perspective as in the most suitable type of paraline drawing.

(A) TYPICAL PARALINE DRAWING

(B) 90° ANGLES APPEAR ACUTE OR OBTUSE   (C) CIRCLES USUALLY APPEAR ELLIPTICAL   (D) TRUE SHAPES ARE SELDOM SHOWN

APPEARANCE OF SHAPES

FIG. 72 CHARACTERISTICS OF PARALINE DRAWINGS

CHAPTER 14

Types of Paraline Drawings

There are three commonly used types of paraline drawings. They are: (1) isometric drawing, (2) dimetric drawing and, (3) oblique drawing, Fig. 73 A, B, C. In both isometric and dimetric drawing, the projection lines are perpendicular to the picture plane and the object is turned in an inclined position so that all three of its sets of planes are visible. Oblique drawing is different in theory and in results. The object is turned so that one of its sets of planes is parallel to the picture plane. The projection lines are oblique to the picture plane so that three faces of the object can be shown.

(A) I S O M E T R I C   (B) D I M E T R I C   (C) O B L I Q U E
D R A W I N G   D R A W I N G   D R A W I N G

FIG. 73 THREE PRINCIPAL TYPES OF PARALINE DRAWING

Isometric Drawing. The object is turned so that all three axis lines are at the same angle with the picture plane in isometric drawing. They are therefore all foreshortened equally and will be the same scale in the drawing. Since the three axis lines are mutually perpendicular their projections will make equal angles with each other in an isometric drawing. The three equal angles are then each one third of a complete circle of 360° or 120°. In most cases one axis is vertical and the other two are drawn at 30° to the horizontal, Fig. 74 I. With one axis vertical either the top or bottom of the exterior of an object can be shown. With one axis horizontal either the right or left end of the exterior of the object can be shown. These four commonly used isometric positions are shown in Fig. 74 II. They can all be drawn with 30° x 60° triangles. The axes of the object can be inclined in any way if they are spaced 120° apart. However, there is seldom any advantage to tilting the object so that none of the three axes are either horizontal or vertical.

The only variations possible in isometric drawing are those obtained by varying the directions of the axes as shown in Fig. 74 II. Regardless of the directions of the axes, the three visible faces of the object are always turned at the same angle to the picture plane. When a cube is drawn all three faces will be exactly the same size and shape whatever the directions of the axis lines.

Isometric drawing gives one picture only. No variation of the picture effect is possible. Blank uninteresting planes must be given the same importance as more attractive or more complex ones. If the elements of the object are in an unsatisfactory relation to each other the picture effect cannot be improved in an isometric drawing. Another paraline type can be used to avoid the difficulty.

80

TOP VIEW ARRANGEMENT

Ⓘ SPACING OF AXES

Ⓘ POSITIONS WITH 30°× 60° TRIANGLE

FIG. 74 COMMON POSITIONS OF THE AXES IN ISOMETRIC

FIG. 75 ISOMETRIC DRAWING OF A ROOM

Dimetric Drawing. The object is turned so that two of its axes make the same angle with the picture plane and the third axis a different angle in dimetric drawing. When the odd axis is vertical the drawing is a symmetrical dimetric, Fig. 77 A. When the odd axis represents one of the two sets of horizontal lines of the object the drawing is an unsymmetrical dimetric, Fig. 77 B. The two axes which make the same angle with the picture plane are foreshortened equally. They are at the same scale in the drawing and the third axis is at a different scale. It is therefore necessary to use two scales on a dimetric drawing. The larger scale, whether it be for the two equal axes or the single axis, is expressed as 1 in diagrams giving the proportionate scales and their accompanying angles for dimetric drawings. The smaller scale is given as a fraction. Scale relations of 1 to ¾, 1 to ⅔, 1 to ½, and 1 to ⅓ can usually be found on available divisions of standard scales. For example, the scales ⅛ to ³⁄₃₂ are in the same proportion as 1 to ¾ and ³⁄₃₂ to ¹⁄₁₆ are the same proportion as 1 to ⅔. There are also other divisions of the scale having the same relative proportions of 1 to ¾ and 1 to ⅔. These simple fractional scale relations are the most easily used ones and are given on the data supplied for dimetric drawing layouts. Certain set angles must be used with each pair of scales. These angles are seldom ones which can be drawn with the standard triangles on the horizontal T-square. It is therefore necessary to use odd angles for most dimetric drawings. The simplest procedure in drawing at the odd angles is to use an adjustable triangle which can be set to any angle by using the protractor on the instrument.

When an adjustable triangle is not available for use the angles can be laid out for each axis with a protractor and lines drawn parallel to these established directions. Horizontal and vertical measurements are given in Fig. 76 to enable the draftsman to lay out the angles required by the different dimetric arrangements given here when a protractor is not available.

Symmetrical dimetric is similar to isometric in having both sides seen and drawn at the same angle, Fig. 77 A. The variation is that the object is either tilted backward so that less of the top is visible or tilted forward more than isometric in order to show a greater amount of the top. The object can be shown tilted backward or forward as much as desired. The top area at one extreme almost disappears and at the other extreme the front and side become very small and the top large. Like isometric drawings, symmetrical dimetric drawings are symmetrical on a vertical center line or axis when the object is symmetrical.

Unsymmetrical dimetric drawings are not symmetrical on a vertical axis, Fig. 77 B. They can be turned so that either of the two visible sides can be given a smaller or larger area than the other. This allows either subordination or emphasis of one of the sides of the object. The dimetric arrangements which are most distinctively different from isometric and oblique drawings and are therefore the most useful have been shaded on all surfaces in the diagrams of Fig. 77.

The unsymmetrical dimetric arrangements can be reversed left to right to face the other direction when that is most suitable for the object drawn. Since either top or bottom can be shown, there are four possible positions for each arrangement of scales and angles. The scale and angle relations given were computed by using a formula. Changing them will distort the drawing.

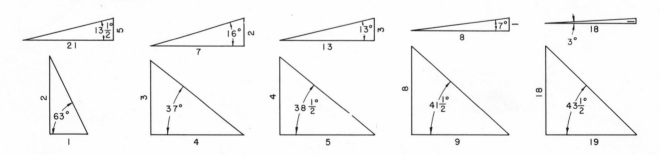

FIG. 76 MEASUREMENTS FOR SOME DIMETRIC ANGLES

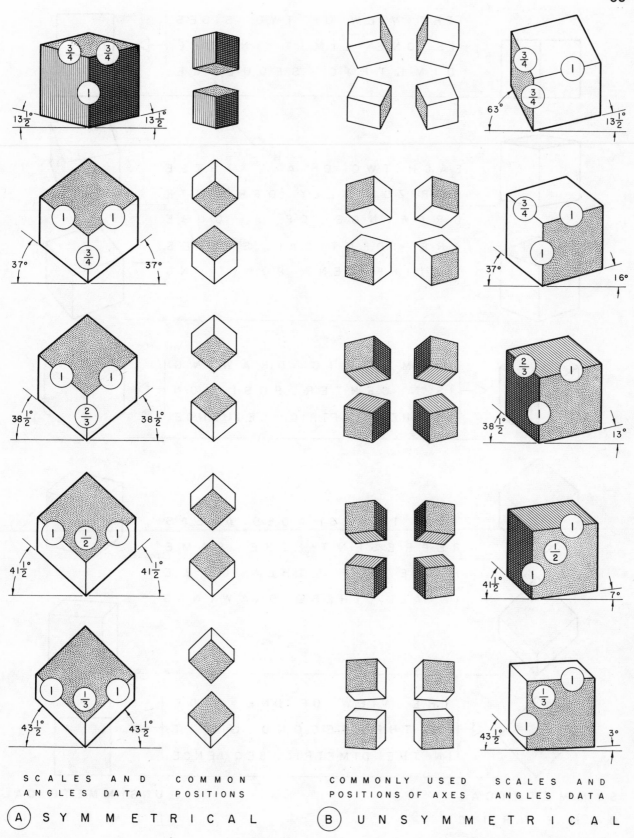

SCALES AND ANGLES DATA   COMMON POSITIONS

(A) SYMMETRICAL

COMMONLY USED POSITIONS OF AXES   SCALES AND ANGLES DATA

(B) UNSYMMETRICAL

FIG. 77 DIMETRIC SCALES - ANGLES - AXIS POSITIONS

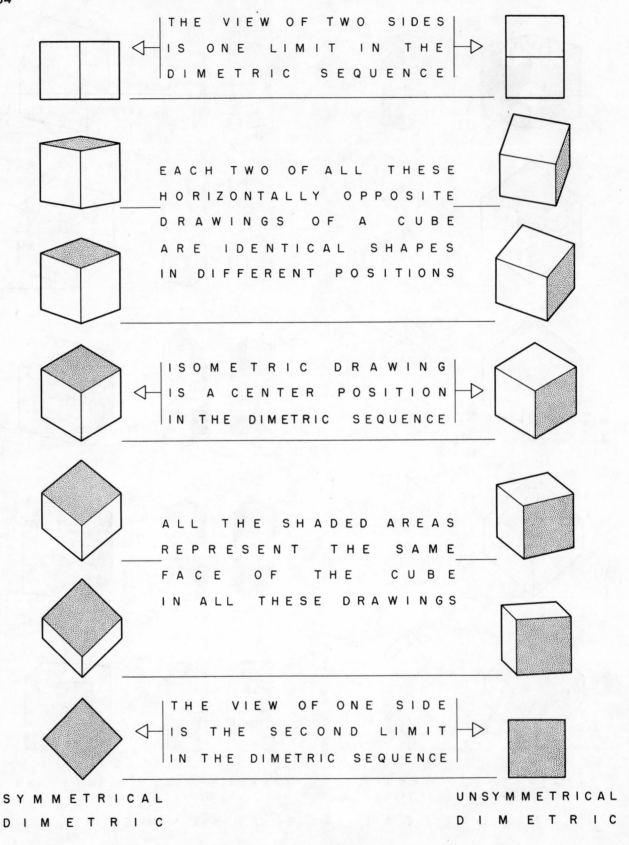

THE VIEW OF TWO SIDES
IS ONE LIMIT IN THE
DIMETRIC SEQUENCE

EACH TWO OF ALL THESE
HORIZONTALLY OPPOSITE
DRAWINGS OF A CUBE
ARE IDENTICAL SHAPES
IN DIFFERENT POSITIONS

ISOMETRIC DRAWING
IS A CENTER POSITION
IN THE DIMETRIC SEQUENCE

ALL THE SHADED AREAS
REPRESENT THE SAME
FACE OF THE CUBE
IN ALL THESE DRAWINGS

THE VIEW OF ONE SIDE
IS THE SECOND LIMIT
IN THE DIMETRIC SEQUENCE

SYMMETRICAL
DIMETRIC

UNSYMMETRICAL
DIMETRIC

FIG. 78 THE SEQUENCE OF DIMETRIC POSITIONS

Ⓐ ONE SET OF VERTICAL PLANES EMPHASIZED

Ⓑ HORIZONTAL AREA SUBORDINATED

FIG. 79 EXAMPLES OF DIMETRIC DRAWING

Oblique Drawing. One set of planes of the object is always presented in its true shapes in oblique drawing. From these true shape areas parallel lines can be drawn at any angle to represent the perpendiculars to them. These lines which represent the perpendiculars to the true shape planes are called the *receding lines*. In Fig. 80 A the front is true shape and the lines where sides, top, and bottom meet and all the lines parallel to them are the receding lines. In the large illustration these receding lines are drawn up and to the left, thus showing the left side and the top of the object. The four small drawings show the possible combinations of top, sides, and bottom which can be shown attached to this front.

All planes parallel to the picture plane are true shape areas and all are drawn at the same scale on a drawing. However, planes which are different distances away, although connected directly in front and side views, are offset to show the perpendicular connecting surfaces as shown in Fig. 80 B.

Oblique drawing is divided into two major divisions: (1) elevation oblique, and (2) plan oblique.

Elevation oblique drawing represents one set of vertical planes of the object in their true shapes. By varying the angle of the receding lines as shown in Fig. 80 C the proportions of the oblique drawing can be changed. One of the receding planes can be subordinated and the other

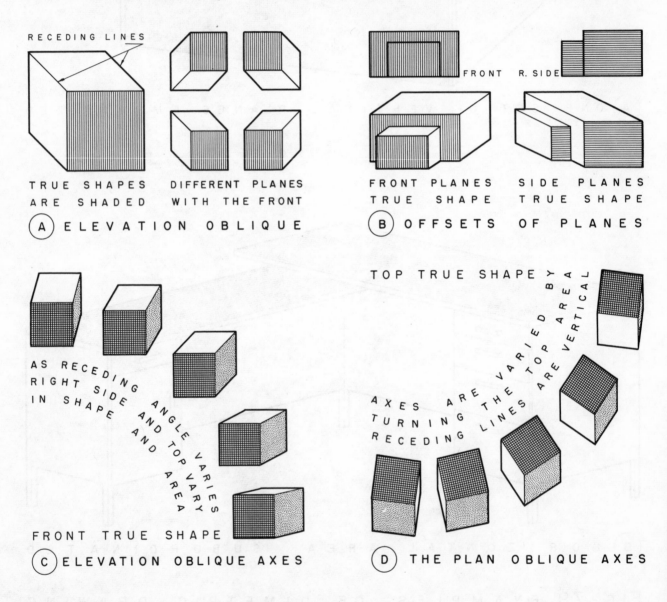

FIG. 80 PICTORIAL VARIETY IN OBLIQUE DRAWINGS

emphasized. Both can be made of equal importance by using a 45° angle for the receding lines.

Plan oblique drawing represents the horizontal planes of the object in their true shapes. In making a plan oblique drawing the vertical lines of the object are the receding lines of the drawing. The receding lines are kept vertical and the plan areas turned to various angles to change the pictorial effect as shown in Fig. 80 D.

The scale of the receding lines can be made the same as that of the two axis lines of the true shape areas. This simplifies the construction of the drawing by using one scale for all three axes and is called *cavalier oblique*. However, the proportions do not seem correct. The object seems to be too long in the direction away from the observer, Fig. 81 I. When appearance is important, better proportions are obtained by using ¾ or ⅔ scale on the receding lines, Fig. 81 II. These two scale ratios are equally good. Use the one which can be found at correct size on the drafting scale for the drawing to be made. Since there are several scale ratios giving proportions of 1 to ¾ and 1 to ⅔, these scale relations can be easily found and used. *Cabinet oblique* drawings are made with the receding lines at ½ the scale of the other two axes, Fig. 81 III. Their proportions seem too thin for most purposes.

I FULL SCALE OF CAVALIER OBLIQUE IS TOO LONG FOR GOOD PROPORTIONS

II THREE FOURTHS OR TWO THIRDS SCALE ON THE RECEDING LINES GIVES THE BEST PROPORTIONS FOR THE OBJECT

III THE HALF SCALE OF CABINET OBLIQUE IS TOO SHORT FOR GOOD PROPORTIONS

PICTORIAL EFFECT OF SCALE OF RECEDING LINES

RECEDING LINES ARE ANY OBLIQUE ANGLE

A VERTICAL FACE IS PARALLEL TO THE PICTURE PLANE AND IS TRUE SHAPE

ELEVATION OBLIQUE DRAWING

HORIZONTAL PLANES ARE PARALLEL TO THE PICTURE PLANE AND ARE TRUE SHAPE

RECEDING LINES ARE ALWAYS VERTICAL

PLAN OBLIQUE DRAWING

FIG. 81 DIRECTION AND SCALE OF RECEDING LINES

(A) BAD—EXAGGERATES
DISTORTED APPEARANCE

(B) BETTER — LESSEN S
EFFECT OF DISTORTION

(C) BAD—DRAWING OF
CIRCLES DIFFICULT

(D) BETTER—DRAWING OF
CIRCLES IS VERY EASY

(E) BAD—COMPLEX SHAPE
IS SHOWN DISTORTED

(F) BETTER—TRUE SHAPE
FOR COMPLEX FORM

FIG. 82 PREFERRED PRACTICE IN OBLIQUE DRAWING

The principal advantage of oblique drawing is that true shapes are shown in one set of planes of the object. This may (1) simplify the drawing of circular or complex forms, and (2) it may also more clearly explain the design of the object than would be possible with any other type of drawing. There are two general rules concerning the best way to lay out oblique drawings. Whenever it is possible and practical to do so, better results will be obtained by following these rules. (A) The largest dimension of the object should be in true shape planes to avoid exaggeration of the distortion common to all paraline drawings. (B) The most complex set of planes of the object should be made true shape to simplify construction of the drawing and explain the object clearly, Figs. 82 c, D, E, F. When used correctly for shapes for which it is adapted, oblique drawing is a very valuable member of the paraline drawing group.

(I) PLAN OBLIQUE DRAWING SHOWING INTERIOR SPACE

(II) ELEVATION OBLIQUE DRAWING OF AN EXTERIOR

FIG. 83 EXAMPLES OF OBLIQUE DRAWING

CHAPTER 15

Selecting A Paraline Drawing Type

Unsatisfactory relations of lines and areas in the representation of an object may appear in any type of pictorial drawing. Some of these pictorial defects are unpredictable chance relations. They can usually be improved by varying the perspective, dimetric, or oblique setup. Other pictorial defects are due to the use of a type of drawing which is basically unsuited to the object drawn. The following paragraphs should help the delineator to avoid mistakes of this nature by helping him to choose the most effective type of paraline drawing for a specific use.

Symmetrical Forms. A drawing type in which the two visible wall planes of an object are turned at the same angle to the observer is said to be symmetrical. The three symmetrical paraline drawing types are isometric drawing, symmetrical dimetric drawing, and 45° plan oblique drawing. They are practically never satisfactory for representing a symmetrical object, or an object which has prominent symmetrical details. Symmetrical forms are shown most effectively in (1) unsymmetrical dimetric, (2) elevation oblique, and (3) unsymmetrical plan oblique (not 45°). These are the three unsymmetrical paraline drawing types, Fig. 84 A.

Equal projections on both sides of a forward corner form segments of one continuous vertical line in any symmetrical paraline drawing thus producing an un-natural effect. These details give a more natural appearance in any unsymmetrical paraline drawing type, Fig. 84 A.

A pyramid shape which has equal slopes on all sides has the front and rear corners vertical in symmetrical paraline drawings. This vertical corner divides the form into two equal and reversed areas. This object shape gives a better appearance in any unsymmetrical paraline drawing type as shown in the roof areas of Fig. 84 A.

Octagonal wall surfaces which are 45° vertical planes of an object do not appear satisfactorily in symmetrical paraline drawings. In these drawing types two of the 45° wall surfaces of an octagonal form will be horizontal and two vertical producing a stiff appearance. A more natural effect will be obtained by using an unsymmetrical paraline drawing type. This applies to 45° vertical planes on other plan shapes as well as to octagon forms, Fig. 84 B.

Horizontal areas of a paraline drawing can be made either a relatively large or small proportion of the drawing space, Fig. 84 C.

Emphasis and Subordination of Areas. Any paraline drawing shows one horizontal plane and two vertical planes of a box shaped object. Isometric drawing gives all three of these sets of planes equal emphasis. Other symmetrical paraline types allow variation in the importance of the horizontal areas. Unsymmetrical types permit emphasis on one wall plane and subordinaton of the other, Fig. 84 D.

Vertical areas can be made equally important or one set can be emphasized and the other subordinated in paraline drawing. The vertical areas can be made equally important by using any symmetrical paraline drawing type. By using elevation oblique, unsymmetrical dimetric, or unsymmetrical plan oblique one set of vertical areas can be emphasized and the other subordinated, Fig. 84 D. Each of these three types allows variation in emphasis.

Unusual shapes which lie in one set of planes may be difficult to visualize and understand when warped from their true forms in isometric, dimetric, or perspective drawings. They can sometimes be more easily understood in oblique drawings, Fig. 84 E.

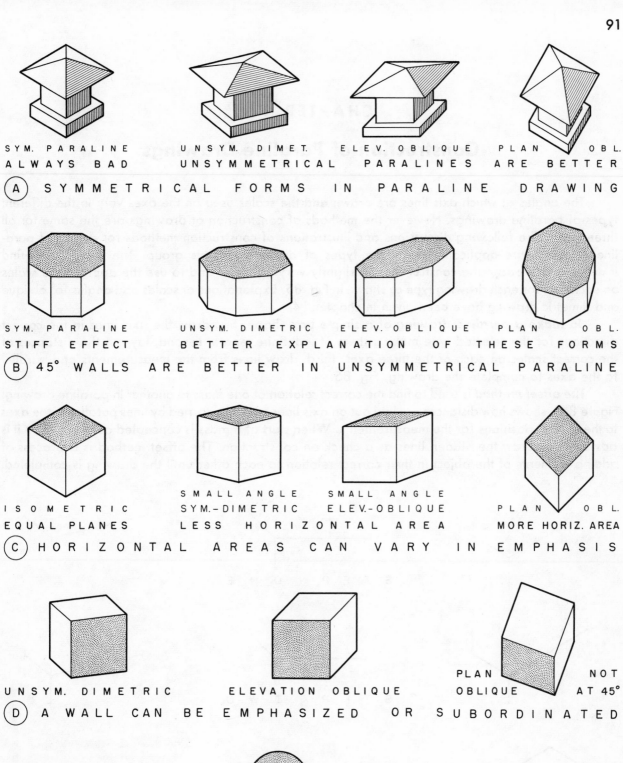

SYM. PARALINE   UNSYM. DIMET.   ELEV. OBLIQUE   PLAN OBL.

ALWAYS BAD   UNSYMMETRICAL PARALINES ARE BETTER

(A) SYMMETRICAL FORMS IN PARALINE DRAWING

SYM. PARALINE   UNSYM. DIMETRIC   ELEV. OBLIQUE   PLAN OBL.

STIFF EFFECT   BETTER EXPLANATION OF THESE FORMS

(B) 45° WALLS ARE BETTER IN UNSYMMETRICAL PARALINE

ISOMETRIC   SMALL ANGLE SYM.-DIMETRIC   SMALL ANGLE ELEV.-OBLIQUE   PLAN OBL.

EQUAL PLANES   LESS HORIZONTAL AREA   MORE HORIZ. AREA

(C) HORIZONTAL AREAS CAN VARY IN EMPHASIS

UNSYM. DIMETRIC   ELEVATION OBLIQUE   PLAN OBLIQUE NOT AT 45°

(D) A WALL CAN BE EMPHASIZED OR SUBORDINATED

(E) IRREGULAR SHAPES MAY BE BEST IN OBLIQUE DRAWING

FIG. 84 CHOOSING THE BEST PARALINE TYPE

CHAPTER 16

Construction of Paraline Drawings

The angles at which axis lines are drawn and the scales used on the axes vary in the different types of paraline drawings. However the methods of construction of drawings are the same for all three types. The following discussions and illustrations of construction methods for details of paraline drawings are applicable to all the types of drawings of this group. The student will find it necessary to adapt the constructions to slightly varying forms and to use the appropriate scales on each axis for each drawing type as shown in Fig. 85. Explanations of scales and angles for oblique and dimetric drawing have been given in chapter 14.

To make a paraline drawing of a simple box shape, first draw the axis lines in the correct directions for the selected type making them of indefinite length; second, lay out the distances at the correct scales on each of the three axes; third, draw lines from the measurements and parallel to the axes to complete the drawing, Fig. 85.

The offset method is used to find the correct relation of one mass to another in paraline drawing. Figure 86 A shows how distances are laid out on axis lines and then carried by lines parallel to the axes to the correct positions for the measurements. When part of a mass is concealed as in Fig. 86 B it is advisable to draw the hidden lines as a check on construction. The offset method is a process of adding elements of the object in their correct relation to each other until the drawing is completed.

STEP ONE

STEP TWO

STEP THREE

IN ISOMETRIC   IN OBLIQUE   IN DIMETRIC

FIG. 85 CONSTRUCTING A PARALINE DRAWING

MULTI-VIEW DRAWINGS

TOP

A B C D
FRONT

D E F G
R. SIDE

TOP

M P
N O
J K
L. SIDE

R O S T
K L
FRONT

FIRST STEP

SECOND STEP

THIRD STEP

(A) ON VISIBLE SURFACE

(B) ON HIDDEN SURFACE

FIG. 86 TWO EXAMPLES OF OFFSET CONSTRUCTION

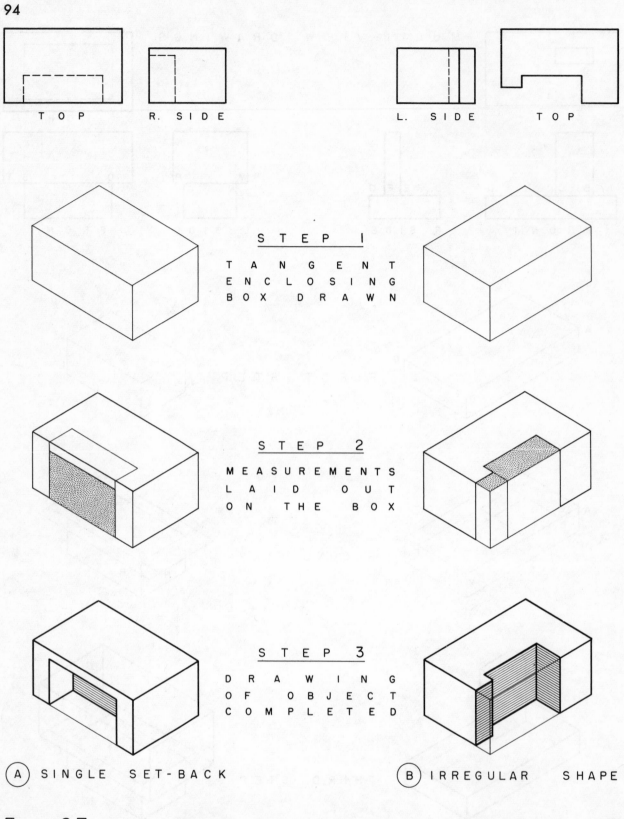

TOP   R. SIDE   L. SIDE   TOP

STEP 1

TANGENT
ENCLOSING
BOX DRAWN

STEP 2

MEASUREMENTS
LAID OUT
ON THE BOX

STEP 3

DRAWING
OF OBJECT
COMPLETED

Ⓐ SINGLE SET-BACK   Ⓑ IRREGULAR SHAPE

FIG. 87 THE BOX CONSTRUCTION METHOD

The box method of first drawing the smallest box shape which will enclose the entire object and then removing the unnecessary forms from it is the best construction method for many object

TOP

FRONT ELEV.

PARALINE DRAWING

C OBLIQUE WALL PLANES ON AN OBJECT

FRONT ELEVATION

RIGHT SIDE

TOP

FRONT

D INCLINED PLANE SURFACES

E PYRAMID

FIG. 88 OBLIQUE SHAPES IN PARALINE DRAWING

shapes. Its applications to a single set-back area, an irregular plan shape, oblique vertical planes, and inclined planes are shown in Figs. 87 and 88.

ELLIPSE CONSTRUCTION FOR PARALINE DRAWING

FOUR—CENTER OVALS FOR PARALINE DRAWING

FIG. 89 REPRESENTING CIRCLES IN PARALINE DRAWING

Circles in paraline drawing appear as circles only when they are in true shape planes, Fig. 89 A. This occurs in oblique drawing but not normally in other paraline drawings. In all other planes of oblique drawings and in isometric and dimetric drawings circles are seen as true ellipses. In isometric the ellipses representing circles in any of the three coordinate planes are always the same proportions. In both dimetric and oblique drawings the ellipses may vary from very thin to almost circular forms.

The ellipse representing a circle in a paraline drawing is commonly constructed by plotting points with offset measurements. The circle is first drawn in multi-view at the scale of the paraline drawing. Pairs of construction lines parallel to the two adjacent sides of the tangent square around the circle are drawn on the multi-view drawing to intersect in right angled corners on the circle. These lines are then drawn on the paraline drawing to locate the same points on the ellipse, Fig. 89 A. After a sufficient number of points is located the ellipse is then drawn through these points either freehand or with an irregular curve. If one axis line of the paraline drawing is reduced in scale, the measurements in that direction for the ellipse construction must be reduced the same amount. One method of reducing the scale for the small scale axis direction is shown in Fig. 89 B.

Four-center ovals are sometimes used in paraline drawing when the draftsman has difficulty getting a smooth freehand ellipse. However, the four-center oval is only an approximation of an ellipse and should not be used when precision of appearance is important. The four-center oval construction will work only when the representation of the square around the ellipse has equal sides in the paraline drawing — that is, when the same scale is used in both of the axis directions of the construction of the square and the figure is a rhombus in paraline drawing. The shape of the four-center oval is most satisfactory when the corresponding ellipse is almost circular and least satisfactory when the ellipse is very thin. Extreme precision in drawing the construction to locate centers, setting the radii on the compass, and drawing the arcs is necessary in order to make a good four-center oval. The perpendicular bisectors of the four sides of the diamond shape (rhombus) reprsenting the square around the circle in the paraline drawing, Figs. 89 c, d, e, intersect at the four centers of the oval. They also define the beginning and end of each arc. In isometric drawing two centers always fall on the corners of the short diagonal of the rhombus, Fig. 89 c. Furthermore the perpendicular bisectors of the sides can always be drawn with the 30° x 60° triangle whenever one axis of the drawing is horizontal or vertical (not necessarily one of the two used). For other proportions of the rhombus two of the centers lie either outside the rhombus for thin ovals, Fig. 89 d, or all four are within the rhombus for almost circular ovals, Fig. 89 e.

Irregular curves are constructed in paraline drawings by the method of plotting points by offsets as used in Fig. 89 a for the ellipse representing the paraline drawing of a circle. Either a uniform cross section can be used over the entire area, Fig. 90 i, or construction lines can be used to intersect at selected points, Fig. 90 ii. The first method requires good judgment in locating points on the curve since lines rarely cross at intersections of construction lines.

Curves which do not lie in one of the three coordinate planes can be located on a paraline drawing by plotting points on section planes through the curves. In Fig. 90 iii horizontal planes through the object are used to plot points on the curved form.

Dimensioning on a paraline drawing is most satisfactory in appearance when the extension lines, dimension lines, arrowheads, and numerals are all a part of the plane of the drawing for which the dimension is given. The extension and dimension lines parallel the axis lines of the drawing. The numerals and arrows are shaped to conform to the paraline drawing forms, Fig. 90 iv.

I UNIFORM SPACING METHOD   II SELECTED POINTS METHOD
CONSTRUCTION OF PLANE SURFACE CURVES

III HORIZONTAL SECTION METHOD
FOR THREE—DIMENSIONAL CURVES

IV PARALINE DIMENSIONING

FIG. 90 CURVES AND DIMENSIONS IN PARALINE DRAWING

PART FOUR

Perspective Drawing

CHAPTER 17

Characteristics of Perspective Drawings

Perspective gives the most natural appearance of any type of drawing. It represents the lines, surfaces, and masses of the object as they would appear to the eye of an observer from one selected station point. A photograph and perspective can be made of the same object and compared. If the lens position of the camera coincides with the location of the station point of the perspective, and film and picture plane positions are parallel, the two illustrations will be identical in lines, areas, and masses. A correctly constructed perspective drawing is therefore a true picture of an object. Since perspectives are the only pictorially accurate drawings they are widely used for design and illustration purposes.

The basic theory of perspective drawing assumes that straight line projectors extend from the *SP* through points on the object which is to be drawn in perspective, Fig. 91. The *SP* is the position of the eye of the observer. The intersections of the projectors with a transparent picture plane give points on the perspective drawing of the object. These points are connected to complete the drawing.

A line from *SP* perpendicular to the picture plane is called the *CV* or center of vision of the

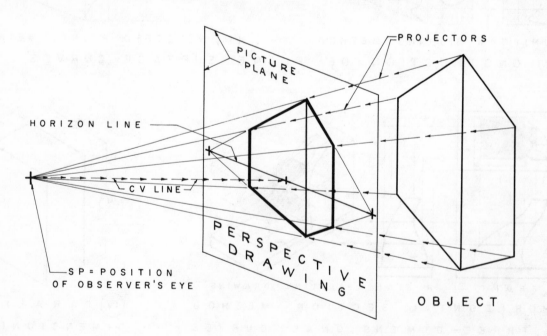

FIG. 91 BASIC THEORY OF PERSPECTIVE DRAWING

PLAN AUXILIARY DRAWING
SHOWS THE TWO SETS OF THE
HORIZONTAL LINES OF OBJECT

PROJECTORS
PICTURE PLANE
C V LINE
S P
PROJECTORS
VL
VR HORIZON LINE
C V S P

PERSPECTIVE DRAWN FROM   VERTICALS SHOWN
TWO AUXILIARY DRAWINGS   ON ELEV. AUXILIARY

FIG. 92 AUXILIARY DRAWINGS IN PERSPECTIVE

perspective. In one-point and two-point perspective this CV line intersects the vertical picture plane at a point on the horizon line. The horizon line is then a horizontal line on the picture plane at the height of the SP, Fig. 91.

A sketch perspective can be made on a window glass or other transparent vertical picture plane. The object sketched is viewed through the transparent plane and the sketch made using a single eye which remains in one fixed position for the drawing.

Since such a sketch perspective is a relatively crude drawing, and the object is not always available for use in this manner, drafting methods based on the above theory are used to construct perspective drawings. Perspectives of objects which are not available and of designs of proposed objects which do not actually exist can be made by these methods.

Mechanical methods of constructing perspective drawings have several variations. All of these methods accomplish the same result of a true picture of the object if they are used correctly and accurately. Multi-view orthographic drawings are usually required to give shape and size information for the construction of the perspective. In some methods they are also used as auxiliary drawings for a part of the construction where they are employed in locating the positions of perspective lines. It is therefore essential that the draftsman have a clear understanding of multi-view drawings before he attempts to make perspective drawings.

The auxiliary plan of Fig. 92 is used to trace the two sets of horizontal lines to the picture plane and then vertically to the perspective drawing. The auxiliary elevation is used to trace the vertical lines into perspective position directly when they are in the picture plane.

There Are Three Types of Perspective Drawing. Each type has a different relation between the lines of the object and the picture plane. Figure 93 gives a paraline drawing of a box shape. This shape has the three sets of mutually perpendicular lines which are found on most objects. In this figure the lines of one horizontal set are labeled X, the second set of horizontal lines is labeled Y, and the lines of the vertical set are labeled Z. In perspective drawing any one of these sets of lines may be parallel, perpendicular, or oblique to the picture plane.

Lines which are parallel to the picture plane remain parallel in perspective. The vertical lines of Fig. 94 A and B, and the one set of horizontal lines of Fig. 94 A are parallel to the picture plane and are actually drawn parallel in the perspective drawings.

A set of lines which is either perpendicular or oblique to the picture plane vanishes to a vanishing point in perspective. The names of the three types of perspective drawings are derived from the number of vanishing points required for each type for the X, Y, and Z groups of parallel lines, Fig. 94.

One-point perspective has two sets of lines parallel to the picture plane and the third set perpendicular to it. Since a set of lines not parallel to the picture plane converges to a vanishing point this arrangement requires only one VP and is called one-point perspective, Fig. 94 A.

Two-point perspective requires two VPs, one for each of the two sets of lines which are oblique to the picture plane. The third set of lines, usually vertical, is parallel to the picture plane, Fig. 94 B.

Three-point perspective has all three sets of lines oblique to the picture plane, thus requiring three VPs. Three-point perspective is rarely used because it is very difficult to construct, Fig. 94 C.

It should be emphasized that every line in any direction not parallel to the picture plane has its vanishing point in perspective. However it is not necessary to find the vanishing points of all such lines for practical perspective construction. The standard vanishing point or points shown in the three illustrations of Fig. 94 A, B and C can be used to locate a line in any direction without having its VP. This construction as well as the location and use of additional VPs will be discussed in later pages.

A person standing in a room can from one position see parts of the room as one-point, two-point, and three-point perspectives merely by looking in different directions. When the center of vision of the observer is horizontal and perpendicular to a wall the room will be seen as a one-point perspective. When looking horizontally at a corner of the room it will be seen in two-point perspective. When looking obliquely either up or down at a corner of the room it will appear as in three-point perspective.

THESE ARE THE BASIC LINES OF PERSPECTIVE DRAWING

FIG. 93 THE THREE SETS OF PERPENDICULAR LINES

VERTICAL LINES — Z
AND HORIZONTAL SET — X
ARE PARALLEL TO
THE PICTURE PLANE

(A) ONE — POINT PERSPECTIVE HAS 1 VP

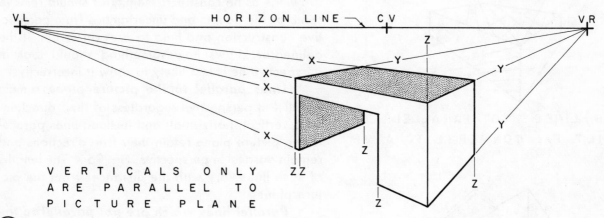

VERTICALS ONLY
ARE PARALLEL TO
PICTURE PLANE

(B) TWO — POINT PERSPECTIVE HAS 2 VPS

ALL LINES ARE
OBLIQUE TO THE
PICTURE PLANE

(C) THREE — POINT PERSPECTIVE HAS 3 VPS

FIG. 94 THE THREE TYPES OF PERSPECTIVE DRAWING

A LINES PARALLEL TO PICT. PL. ARE PARALLEL IN PERSPECTIVE

B LINES NOT PARALLEL TO PICT. PL. CONVERGE TO A V.P.

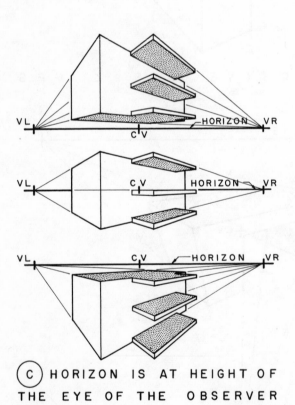

C HORIZON IS AT HEIGHT OF THE EYE OF THE OBSERVER

FIG. 95 LINES AND AREAS IN PERSPECTIVES

Characteristics of Lines and Areas in Perspective. Since perspective is the most important of the pictorial drawing types, the draftsman should obtain a thorough working knowledge of the subject. A preliminary survey of some of the important pictorial characteristics of perspectives will give the reader a clearer understanding of their basic features before the technical construction of drawings is begun. The remainder of this chapter will describe the general behavior and appearance of lines and areas in perspective drawings. The person who understands this relatively simple material will be better able to visualize the appearance of perspective drawings as he constructs them. This should remove some of the doubts and uncertainties from perspective construction and help to prevent errors. If the delineator knows how something should look in perspective he is less likely to draw it incorrectly.

Lines parallel to the picture plane remain parallel in perspective regardless of their direction. Thus vertical, horizontal, and inclined lines parallel to the picture plane retain their true directions and remain parallel in perspective, Fig. 95 A. The lengths of such lines vary with the distances from the picture plane.

Parallel lines which are not parallel to the picture plane converge to a common vanishing point. Each set of parallel lines has its vanishing point, Fig. 95 B. The vanishing points of all horizontal lines are on the horizon.

The horizon is located where the horizontal plane, through the eye of the observer, intersects the picture plane. The horizon is therefore always at the height of the eye position or station point of the perspective. As the eye moves up or down the horizon moves with it, Fig. 95 C. The horizon is also the vanishing line of all horizontal planes.

Horizontal surfaces above eye level are visible from below and those below eye level (the horizon) are seen from above. A surface at eye and horizon level is seen in edge view as a line. When the horizon is below the object only bottom surfaces are seen, Fig. 95 C top drawing. When the horizon is above the object only top surfaces are seen, Fig. 95 C bottom drawing. When the horizon passes through the object both the bottom surfaces of horizontal areas above eye level and the top surfaces of horizontal areas below eye level appear in the same drawing, Fig. 95 C center drawing. This last condition never occurs in paraline drawing.

The more distant parts of an object are smaller in a perspective drawing. Areas which are actually equal in size on the object are larger near the observer and decrease in size as they get farther away. Vertical lines which represent equal heights are longer near the observer and become shorter as the distance away increases. Lines to a vanishing point when divided into equal segments on the object show progressively smaller segments as the line approaches its vanishing point, Fig. 96 D. Obviously then, a scale cannot be used on all lines of a perspective drawing.

Scale size occurs in a perspective drawing only where the lines of the object lie in the picture plane, Fig. 96 E line C-D. Since the projectors converge to the station point, lines behind the picture plane are reduced in size at the picture plane by the decreasing space between the projectors as shown by line E-F. Lines in front of the picture plane are increased in size because the projectors from the object diverge and become farther apart on their way to the picture plane, line A-B.

True shapes are seldom shown in perspective drawings. Areas which parallel the picture plane retain their true shapes in perspective, Figs. 95 A and 96 F. Areas which are not parallel to the picture plane are drawn as they would appear from the station point. A square which is not parallel to the picture plane can be seen as a straight line or an irregular four-sided figure. This figure may be very thin, almost square, or any form between a straight line and a square, Fig. 96 F. In most cases a circle which is not parallel to the picture plane will appear as an ellipse in the perspective drawing. The proportions of the ellipse vary with the angle from which it is seen, Fig. 96 F. A perspective drawing shows the lines and areas of the object depicted as they must be to appear correctly from the SP of the drawing, not as they actually are.

D MORE DISTANT LINES AND AREAS ARE SMALLER

E SCALE SIZES OCCUR AT THE PICTURE PLANE ONLY

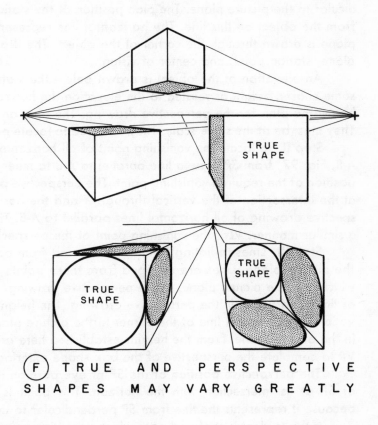

F TRUE AND PERSPECTIVE SHAPES MAY VARY GREATLY

FIG. 96 SIZES AND SHAPES IN PERSPECTIVE DRAWING

CHAPTER 18

Two-Point Perspective

Two-point perspective is used for approximately nine-tenths of all perspective work. For this reason it is presented first in this text. The method employed throughout this chapter is widely used in offices and schools. It is called the Common Method and also the Office Method. When ease of use and understanding are important it is a very good method. Any method of perspective drawing locates intersections with the picture plane of imaginary lines from the SP to points on the object. These intersection points on the picture plane are connected to make the perspective of the object. There are several methods by which this construction is accomplished. Just as there is "No royal road to geometry", so also there is no extremely easy method of doing perspective drawing. Although persons with a thorough knowledge of perspective may prefer another method, the common method is a very satisfactory one for the beginner. Other methods are described in chapter 21.

For the advantage of clearer explanation the development of a simple exterior and interior example of perspective drawing has been divided into three steps in Fig. 97.

Step I. The plan is drawn with the sides at an oblique angle. A line called the *center of vision* (CV) is drawn from the center of the plan. It represents a horizontal line through SP and perpendicular to the picture plane. The plan position of the station point is located at a reasonable distance from the object on this line. The horizontal line representing the plan view of the vertical picture plane is drawn through the corner of the object. The drawing now shows a plan of object, picture plane, station point, and center of vision.

An elevation of the object is drawn below the station point and to one side of the plan. At some chosen height as related to the elevation the horizon line is drawn and extended indefinitely below the plan for the perspective drawing. The plan and elevation are called auxiliary drawings. They must be at the same scale. They are used to locate points and lines of the perspective drawing.

Step II. To locate the vanishing point of all horizontal lines of the object in the direction of line A-B, Fig. 97, from SP draw a line parallel to A-B to meet the picture plane at X. Point X is the plan position of the required vanishing point. The perspective position of the vanishing point VR is located at the intersection of the vertical through X and the horizon. VR is the vanishing point in the perspective drawing of all horizontal lines parallel to A-B. The second vanishing point VL is located in a similar manner. VL is the vanishing point of the perspectives of all horizontal lines parallel to A-C.

Step III. Lines radiating from SP are traced from points on the plan of the object to intersect the picture plane. Lines are dropped from these points of intersection, and from the near corner which is in the picture plane, to the perspective drawing. These lines provide the horizontal spacing of lines and points in the perspective drawing. The height is carried over horizontally from the elevation to the vertical line of the corner in the picture plane. This line is scale height because it lies in the picture plane. From the heights established here at points D and E lines are drawn to VL and VR to complete the perspective of the box shape exterior and from VL and VR for the interior.

The perspective position of the SP or eye position is located on the vertical through the plan of SP at its intersection with the horizon. This point is also called CV or center of vision here because it represents the line from SP perpendicular to the picture plane as well as the SP.

If the student is confused as to which vanishing point to use he should remember the following. Any horizontal line which is parallel to SP-Y in plan will go to the vanishing point located by that construction line and the vertical from Y to the horizon.

STEP I AUXILIARY DRAWINGS MADE

STEP I AUXILIARY DRAWINGS MADE

STEP II VANISHING POINTS LOCATED

STEP II VANISHING POINTS LOCATED

STEP III PERSPECTIVE DRAWN

STEP III PERSPECTIVE DRAWN

EXTERIOR PERSPECTIVE

INTERIOR PERSPECTIVE

FIG. 97 ELEMENTARY TWO-POINT PERSPECTIVE

PICTURE PLANE

(A) PICTURE PLANE THROUGH NEAREST VISIBLE CORNER

PICTURE PLANE

(B) PICTURE PLANE THROUGH FARTHEST VISIBLE CORNER

FIG. 98 HEIGHTS IN EXTERIOR TWO-POINT PERSPECTIVE

The Determination of Heights. One of the most difficult phases of perspective drawing is the correct construction of heights. All scale height measurements must be laid out on a vertical line in the picture plane from which they can be traced to a vanishing point of the perspective which will take them to their correct perspective positions. Any vertical line in the picture plane which fulfills these requirements can be used as a vertical measuring line for a perspective drawing. More than one vertical measuring line may be necessary or convenient for the construction of a perspective.

These two and the four following pages are used to give simple drawings and text to explain the construction of heights on perspective drawings. The left pages have been used for illustrations of exteriors and the right pages for interiors. The sequence of five different relations of picture plane and object are in general from the most widely used to the less common arrangements.

The position of the picture plane through the nearest visible vertical corner of the object is the one most commonly used for exterior perspective. Since this corner is at scale height the T-square is used to trace the heights of the object horizontally to it. From the height positions estab-

—PICTURE PLANE

(C) PICTURE PLANE THROUGH NEAREST VISIBLE CORNER

—PICTURE PLANE

(D) PICTURE PLANE THROUGH FARTHEST VISIBLE CORNER

FIG. 99 HEIGHTS IN INTERIOR TWO-POINT PERSPECTIVE

lished on this corner lines are traced along the wall surfaces of the object by drawing to the correct vanishing points. This is a convenient position for the height line of the exterior of an object because it is in both wall planes, Fig. 98 A.

This is also a popular position for the height line for an interior perspective, Fig. 99 C. The heights are traced along the wall in which the height line lies by drawing directly to the VP. Heights for the other side must first be traced from the vertical measuring line to the vertical corner where the two walls meet by drawing to the VP of horizontal lines in that wall and then away from the other vanishing point along the second wall surface. This requires two steps to bring the heights into position on the wall farthest from the vertical measuring line.

The picture plane through the farthest visible vertical corner of an object is very convenient for interior perspectives. It provides height measurements in a position from which they can be traced along both wall surfaces with lines from the correct vanishing points, Fig. 99 D. The exterior requires tracing lines away from one VP to meet the nearest wall corner and then toward the other VP to locate heights on the wall which the height lines do not touch, Fig. 98 B.

108

PICTURE PLANE

SP

A C

VL VR HORIZON

B D

(A) PICTURE PLANE THROUGH THE OBJECT

PICTURE PLANE

SP

E G

VL HORIZON VR

F H

(B) OBJECT IN FRONT OF PICTURE PLANE

FIG. 100 HEIGHTS IN EXTERIOR TWO-POINT PERSPECTIVE

The picture plane cutting through wall surfaces between corners gives two vertical intersections with a simple box shape and therefore provides two vertical measuring lines, *A-B* and *C-D*, as shown in Figs. 100 A and 101 C. This position of the picture plane is equally convenient for both exterior and interior perspectives. Each of these vertical measuring lines provides points at scale heights within the length of the wall for lines to a VP. Heights are therefore traced both toward and away from the VPs along the walls from their established positions on the two height lines.

The object in front of the picture plane does not provide any contact for a vertical measuring line. In such a setup either of the two visible wall surfaces can be extended in plan to meet the

PICTURE PLANE

HORIZON

Ⓒ PICTURE PLANE THROUGH THE OBJECT

PICTURE PLANE

HORIZON

Ⓓ OBJECT IN FRONT OF PICTURE PLANE

FIG. 101 HEIGHTS IN INTERIOR TWO-POINT PERSPECTIVE

picture plane in an imaginary intersection which will provide a vertical measuring line in the perspective drawing for the perspective construction. Both of these imaginary intersection lines *E-F* and *G-H* are shown in the perspectives of Figs. 100 B and 101 D. Lines are traced from the VP through the height line points to their perspective positions. This procedure enlarges the measurements. The interior may have the imaginary extension of one wall surface completely or partly hidden behind the other visible wall. In exterior perspective the extended wall is usually visible to one side of the perspective. Both walls can be extended and two height lines located for the simple box shape. More complex shapes can have a vertical measuring line for each wall surface.

110

A OBJECT BEHIND THE PICTURE PLANE

B INDIRECT METHOD OF HEIGHT CONSTRUCTION

FIG. 102 HEIGHTS IN EXTERIOR TWO-POINT PERSPECTIVE

When the object is behind the picture plane one of the walls can be extended in the drawings to provide an imaginary intersection *X* with the picture plane, Figs. 102 A and 103 C. This imaginary intersection is a vertical measuring line *X-X* in the perspective drawing from which heights can be traced directly to the wall surface which was extended by drawing to the VP of horizontal lines in that wall. This procedure reduces the size of the measurements. Any wall surface can be extended to provide a vertical measuring line for that wall at its intersection with the picture plane.

The alternate method of determining heights in perspective is illustrated in the exterior of Fig. 102 B and the interior of Fig. 103 D. In this method a single height line is used in the perspective

FIG. 103 HEIGHTS IN INTERIOR TWO-POINT PERSPECTIVE

drawing. This often requires the tracing of heights around corners of the object or around imaginary corners to get them into correct perspective position from the height line. In Fig. 102 B the right vertical corner of the object is used for scale heights since it lies in the picture plane. The height of the top block is carried from VR along the right edge of the object to line E-F and thence from E and F toward VL to locate the heights of the top block. The lines which are used to trace a height to position must be (1) lines to vanishing points, (2) must intersect at a corner in plan, and (3) must lead to the line where the height is located. The construction can go around any number of corners of the plan or imaginary corners for construction if the tracing lines follow these requirements.

Ⓐ EACH DRAWING SEPARATE

Ⓑ DRAWINGS OVERLAP

Ⓒ EXAMPLE OF
COMPRESSED
CONSTRUCTION

FIG. 104 SPACE SAVING IN EXTERIOR PERSPECTIVE

The preceding explanations of two-point exterior and interior perspective have used illustrations in which the plan, elevation, and perspective drawings have been separated to make the construction of the perspective drawings as clear as possible. Experienced draftsmen frequently overlap the auxiliary and perspective drawings for perspective construction. Figs. 104 and 105 show this procedure. The perspectives are made close to the plans of the object with the plan positions of the station points falling within the perspective drawings. The elevations are placed near the perspectives with one VP in or beyond the elevation to save space horizontally. Perspective drawings usually take a lot of space and the compressing of construction is often necessary to keep the drawings on the board.

(D) EACH DRAWING SEPARATE

(E) DRAWINGS OVERLAP

PICTURE PLANE

(F) COMPRESSED CONSTRUCTION

FIG. 105 SPACE SAVING FOR INTERIOR PERSPECTIVE

An elevation has been included as an auxiliary drawing in each explanation of perspective construction given in this text. It makes the height construction visually clear and helps to remove some of the uncertainties of the draftsman concerning heights. Furthermore it lessens the chances of error in height measurements. Any elevation or section view which gives the required heights can be used for this purpose. If the auxiliary drawing of the elevation clearly explains the design of the object, the construction from it is more easily understood.

Although it is helpful, an elevation is not an essential part of the construction of a perspective drawing. Heights can be laid out directly on the vertical measuring lines of the perspective. The ground line can be used as a base line from which the heights are measured.

CHAPTER 19

The Variables in Two-Point Perspective

How is it possible to obtain the perspective view of the object which the delineator wishes to have? That is one of the major problems of the person who is learning to use perspective drawing to represent his designs. There are only three things which can be varied in a perspective setup to change the pictorial effect. A change of any one, or two, or of all three of these variables will change the appearance of the perspective. It is necessary for the designer to learn how to use each of these variables singly or in combinations in order to obtain the most effective illustrations from his perspective drawings.

The Three Variables Which Control the Pictorial Effect. Place some object on a desk. The three things which can be done to change the view of that object are the three items which can be changed in a perspective setup to vary the pictorial effect. The observer can look at the object (1) from different angles, (2) from different heights, and (3) from different distances. These three variations are the only ones which can be made to change the view of the object. The three variables in perspective are the three ways that the location of the station point can be changed to view the object from different angles, different heights, and different distances.

In the examples of each of the three variables only one thing, the variable under consideration, has been changed in the perspective setup of the sequence of illustrations explaining the effect of that variable on the picture. Thus any variation in perspective effect in a single sequence of drawings is due to the one factor alone.

I. The angle of the object with the picture plane as shown in plan can be varied to change the proportions of the two visible sides of an object seen in a perspective drawing, Fig. 106 I. Usually one face of the object is more important than the other. The angle of view can be adjusted to give the required amount of emphasis on the important side. It is more satisfactory composition if the two major areas are not equal in the perspective. It should be observed that in each of these three illustrations the plan is at a different angle with the picture plane. The station point for each drawing has been kept on the line of the center of vision. This line is perpendicular to the picture plane and through the center of the plan of the object. The SP should never be moved to one side of the plan to change the perspective. This will change the angle of view in the easiest way. However, it causes a distorted perspective which does not represent the true proportions of the object.

II. The height of the horizon in a perspective drawing determines whether the object is seen from above, from below, or from somewhere within its height, Fig. 106 II. The horizon carries with it wherever it is moved the perspective positions of the vanishing points of all horizontal lines. When an elevation is used as an auxiliary drawing the horizon is drawn in the chosen relation to the object on this drawing. Thus the draftsman is able to see a graphical representation of the height of the observer in relation to the object before drawing the perspective.

III. The distance from the object to the station point determines whether the object is viewed from very close, from far away, or from a middle distance, Fig. 106 III. When the SP is very near to the object the vanishing points are close to the perspective drawing. Lines to the VPs slant sharply. Horizontal areas appear large. There is a great contrast in size between near and distant parts of the object. When the station point is far from the object the vanishing points are far from the perspective. Lines to the VPs become more nearly horizontal. There is little contrast in size of near and distant parts of the object. Horizontal surfaces which are visible become thin and small. The perspective drawing approaches the appearance of an elevation of two sides of the object.

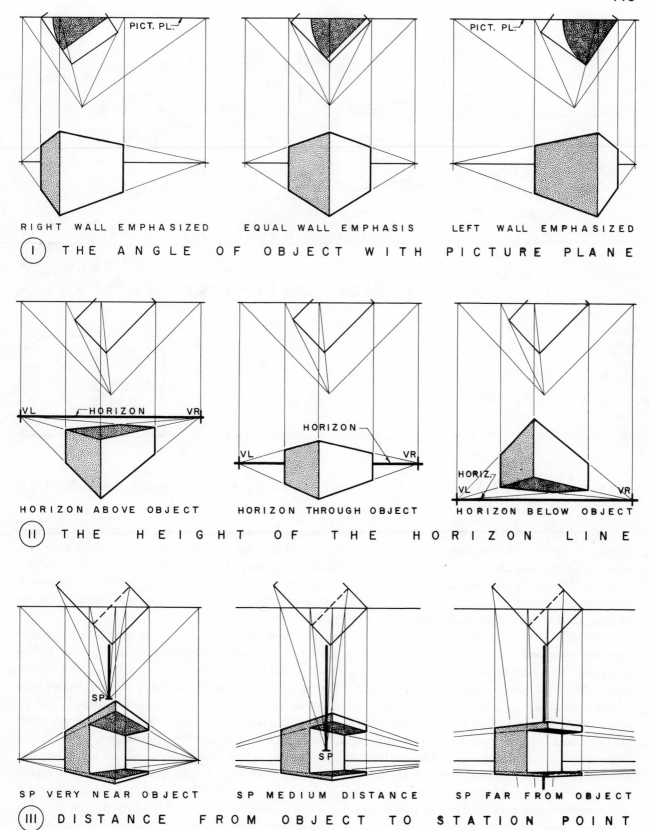

RIGHT WALL EMPHASIZED   EQUAL WALL EMPHASIS   LEFT WALL EMPHASIZED

(I) THE ANGLE OF OBJECT WITH PICTURE PLANE

HORIZON ABOVE OBJECT   HORIZON THROUGH OBJECT   HORIZON BELOW OBJECT

(II) THE HEIGHT OF THE HORIZON LINE

SP VERY NEAR OBJECT   SP MEDIUM DISTANCE   SP FAR FROM OBJECT

(III) DISTANCE FROM OBJECT TO STATION POINT

FIG. 106 THE THREE VARIABLES IN PERSPECTIVE

A PICTURE PLANE D A   D   L A R G E   P E R S P E C T I V E

A PICT. PL. C   A   C   M E D I U M   S I Z E   P E R S P.

A P. PL. B   A   B   S M A L L   P E R S P E C T I V E

SP

(A) D I S T A N C E   O F   P I C T U R E   P L A N E   F R O M   S P
C O N T R O L S   S I Z E   O F   P E R S P E C T I V E   D R A W I N G

(B) M E T H O D   O F   D E T E R M I N I N G
H E I G H T   O F   A   L A R G E R   O R
S M A L L E R   P E R S P E C T I V E
W H E N   W I D T H   I S   G I V E N

F I G. 1O7 C O N T R O L L I N G   T H E   S I Z E   O F   A   P E R S P E C T I V E

Controlling the Size of the Perspective Drawing. The obvious method of obtaining size variations in the perspective drawing of a given object is to change the scale of the auxiliary plan and elevation. This will produce a considerable variation of size and the perspective drawings will be exact duplicates if the setup is not changed in other ways. This method is simple. However it requires a completely new construction for each size variation, does not provide for small changes of size, and is limited by scale ratios to a few sizes.

Parallel positions of the picture plane can be used to control the size of the perspective drawing obtained from a given plan and elevation as suggested by the diagram of Fig. 107 A. The position of the picture plane can be varied by moving it either farther from or nearer to the station point. When the perspective setup is not changed in other ways, and all positions of the picture plane are parallel, the only change in the resulting perspective will be in size. This procedure allows small or large variations in size in the perspectives. The same auxiliary plan, elevation, and station point can be used for constructing perspectives of different sizes. New studies can be made on tracing paper over the first one. The width of the proposed perspective can be determined by extending the lines from the station point through the extreme left and right edges of the plan of the object and measuring the picture plane line between them as shown in Fig. 107 A. When both the height and width of one perspective are given and the widths of other sizes of the same perspective are assumed, their corresponding heights can be determined as shown in Fig. 107 B. This method is based on the fact that diagonals of rectangles having the same proportion are parallel when the corresponding sides of the rectangles are parallel. The method of controlling the size of the perspective precisely by the position of the picture plane is very useful and practical. Extreme enlargements produced by locating the picture plane far beyond the object will magnify inaccuracies.

Enlarging a perspective drawing is sometimes the simplest and best way to produce a larger perspective drawing. Two methods of enlarging a perspective are shown in Fig. 108. In the first method, which is shown in Fig. 108 I, a common point A and line A-B of the two perspectives are used as the beginning of the enlarged drawing which is superimposed on a copy of the small drawing. Any lines like A-C and A-D which meet at the selected pivot point A will be extended to make the enlarged drawing. Lines which do not coincide for a part of their lengths are parallel in the two drawings. A line drawn from the pivot point A through any corner X or other point on the small perspective will when extended pass through the same point on the large drawing. After the length of one line on the enlarged drawing is determined all other sizes are constructed by the use of radiating and parallel lines. With this method one size of enlargement is as easy as another. There is no advantage to simple fractional relations as there would be when using a scale to make an enlargement or reduction of size of a drawing.

The technique employed when using this method can be varied to suit the way the drawing is located and used. A simple method is to make the large drawing on tracing paper over the small one.

The second method of enlarging a perspective drawing is shown in Fig. 108 II. Its theory is simple. A rectangle is drawn tangent to the given small perspective. Lines of the perspective are extended to the edges of the rectangle. A larger rectangle of the same proportion is made the size selected for the large perspective. The points of intersection on the sides of the small rectangle are transferred to correct positions on the large rectangle. These points can be located by scale when the relative sizes permit. They can be located by methods of proportional enlarging regardless of size relation. The lines of the large perspective are drawn through the points on the tangent rectangle. It is more convenient and more accurate to use vanishing points when they are close enough.

(I) WITH RADIATING AND PARALLEL LINES

(II) WITH INTERSECTIONS ON THE BORDER LINES

FIG. 108 ENLARGING A PERSPECTIVE DRAWING

STEP ① $\overset{+}{S}P$ STEP ②   STEP ③

FIG. 109 THREE STEPS IN EVALUATING A PROPOSED SP

Ⓐ RIGHT WALLS ARE EMPHASIZED

SP-1

Ⓑ FRONT WALLS ARE EMPHASIZED

SP-2

Ⓒ BOTH WALLS EQUAL EMPHASIS

SP-3

FIG. 110 SELECTING AN SP

Selecting a Station Point. Since the position of the *SP* determines the characteristics of the perspective drawing obtained, its location is of greatest importance. The appearance of some of the important features of the perspectives from proposed station points can be judged without actually constructing the perspectives. This preliminary work will increase the probabilities of obtaining a satisfactory perspective drawing with the minimum amount of drafting. It may avoid repeated drawing of unsatisfactory perspectives.

The relative amounts of vertical shapes of the object appearing from a proposed *SP* can be determined from a plan of the object. In step I of Fig. 109 a trial *SP* is located in relation to the plan. In step II the tangents to the extreme edges of the plan are drawn from the *SP*. The center of vision line is drawn through *SP* bisecting the angle *A-SP-E* made by the tangents. In step III the picture plane is drawn perpendicular to the *CV* line. Important divisions are projected to the picture plane by drawing lines from their edges toward *SP*. The spacing along the picture plane of Fig. 109 III gives the total width of the perspective from that *SP* and the widths of the major divisions of the object. Fig. 110 gives a sequence of three studies of this type. Fig. 111 shows the chosen scheme Fig. 110 B turned until the picture plane is horizontal and the *CV* line vertical to construct the perspective. This procedure of testing the results of a proposed *SP* in plan requires only a small amount of time. It may save a great deal of time which is often spent making unsatisfactory perspective drawings.

PICTURE PLANE

CV LINE

SP-2

VR   HORIZON

A   B   C   DE

FIG. III PERSPECTIVE DRAWING FROM DIAGRAM 110 B

FIG. 112 PROPOSED HEIGHTS FOR THE HORIZON AS SHOWN ON ELEVATION

The effects of different heights of the horizon can be partly determined from an elevation drawing. Several possible horizon positions have been drawn at the side of the elevation of Fig. 112 and labeled *A, B, C, D, X,* and *Y.* The positions at *X* and *Y* would be unsatisfactory because they are at the height of important horizontal planes of the object. These planes would appear as horizontal lines in the perspectives. The top plane would be a continuous horizontal line from height *X* and the intermediate plane from *Y.* It is also usually unsatisfactory to have the horizon very near the height of an important horizontal plane so that it appears almost as a continuous straight line in the perspective. Position *D* is satisfactory for some purposes as shown in the perspective of Fig. 113 D. It simplifies shadows and foreground for rendering and provides emphasis of top silhouette. The positions at *A, B,* and *C* are usually the most satisfactory ones. Figs. 113 A, B, and C show perspectives from these positions.

The effects of varying distances from SP to object are difficult to visualize from most auxiliary drawings. Experience will help the delineator to judge the effects of this. The elevation parallel to the picture plane of the direct projection method of perspective drawing is useful for this purpose.

Block studies of the simple masses of an object can be drawn quickly in perspective when little detail is shown. They are useful for verifying conclusions from the above procedures and testing the distance from SP to object. They are often helpful in selecting a station point for a large perspective. The sequence for heights in Fig. 113 is a simple group of such studies.

(A) HORIZON ABOVE OBJECT

(B) HORIZON AT LINE B

(C) HORIZON AT LINE C

(D) HORIZON AT GROUND

FIG. 113 SELECTING HORIZON FROM AN ELEVATION

The estimated angle of clear vision of the human eyes has often been used to provide a minimum distance of SP from the object in making a perspective drawing. Such an arbitrary rule is likely to limit the imagination of the designer delineator, thus producing standardized and mediocre results. Furthermore it may eliminate consideration of special conditions which make a very large or very small angle of view appropriate and advantageous. The angle of vision of the human eyes is a rather speculative matter. We see most clearly a tiny area on which the eyes concentrate. Persons with two good eyes are able to see through a horizontal angle of 180°, a complete half circle. The center of this band is seen with both eyes, the edges with one eye only. The extreme edges of this area appear hazy and a person is seldom very conscious of the objects there. In between the center and the edges of vision are diminishing degrees of clearness of sight with no decided breaks in sharpness.

How can the designer determine the distance away from the object for his station point? There is no one answer which will be best for all objects and under all conditions. The perspective should look right for the object which is depicted. It should also give the effect which will best satisfy the requirements of its use and purpose.

There are conditions under which the observer is within the object, or group of objects, which is to be represented in perspective. The object extends all around him. This may be true in a landscape, in a group of buildings, and within an interior. Under such conditions, and when near a very large object, the delineator may wish to use a very wide angle of view for his perspective. In recognition of the variations of acuteness of vision he may choose to emphasize the center of his perspective area in presentation and subordinate the edges.

When an object is extremely small it would almost touch the eye of the observer to appear as objects are shown in closeup perspective. When it is drawn in this way it may appear unnatural and perhaps even ridiculous. Close up perspectives of ladies' compacts may appear very unreal because they are never viewed from very close by a person with normal vision. The same logic is even more emphatic for watches, jewelry, and other tiny objects.

Circular forms become quite warped in perspectives which are made from close station points. This is especially true of circles in or near the corners of the drawings. Interiors may not give a good effect from a close station point particularly when furniture, lighting fixtures, or other objects of distinctive forms appear in corners or along edges of the perspective drawing.

It is perhaps unfortunate that no satisfactory rule for the best distance from object to station point can be given here. However, the making of a good perspective requires judgment and artistic imagination. A perspective can be dull, distorted, restful and pleasing, or even exciting. It is a part of the designer's training to learn thoroughly the mechanics of perspective so that he can obtain the most satisfactory results possible for each object depicted.

Many interior decorators believe that interior perspectives should always be made from station points which could be used in the building to see the scene as it is depicted. This limits the amount which can be shown from within a room in a single perspective to a small proportion of the entire room. It does not allow a visual impression of the complete room. In some types of work it is permissible to assume that a part of the walls of the room are removed. The SP is then taken at a sufficient distance so that the entire room can be shown in a single perspective. When this is done the actual limits of the room should not be exceeded in the perspective drawing. These limits may actually be shown or the lines of the drawing may stop short of the volume of the room.

The purpose of a perspective drawing should influence the selection of a SP. If the purpose is to show the object as it would actually be seen, the choice of a SP is often very limited. If the objective is to explain the forms of the object as clearly as possible, the selection of a SP has no limits. Perspectives have disadvantages over observation of the actual object. A person looking at an object has two eyes with binocular vision and depth perception. He also has the advantage of moving his eyes and head to see through a greater angle and of moving to change his position. The perspective has a fixed picture with one eye from one position.

122

PICTURE PLANE

HORIZON

VL

STP

VR

Ⓐ HORIZON THRU OBJECT

Ⓑ HORIZON ABOVE OBJECT

Ⓒ TRANSPARENT FRONT

Ⓓ OPEN ARRANGEMENT
GIVING LINES TO THE VR

FIG. 114 ONE VP WITHIN THE PERSPECTIVE DRAWING IN TWO-POINT PERSPECTIVE

The location of one vanishing point within the drawing of a two-point perspective gives an effect approaching one-point perspective. The object is turned so that one side makes a very small angle with the picture plane and the other a very large angle as shown in the plan of Fig. 114 A. One vanishing point is very far away and the other falls within the edge of the perspective drawing. This special arrangement is effective under certain conditions where lines to the near vanishing point are visible in the perspective. When there are no visible lines to this VP as shown in the opaque box of Fig. 114 A the effect will be puzzling and unsatisfactory. However a view from above, as shown in B, or below improves the effect by showing lines to VR. A transparent or open object in exactly the same position as A may give a very good effect because there are visible lines of the object which converge to the VP within the drawing as shown in C. An open grouping of objects which gives lines to the VP within the drawing as shown in D may also be satisfactory. This special arrangement of the vanishing points allows extreme emphasis on the planes which are almost parallel to the picture planes. It avoids the stiff effect of one-point perspective. Its principal disadvantage is the somewhat minor difficulty encountered in locating and using the distant vanishing point.

FRONT ELEVATION

SIDE VIEW OF OBJECT, SP, CV, AND PICTURE PLANE

PERSPECTIVE DRAWING

FIG. 115 VERTICALS TO VP IN TWO-POINT PERSPECTIVE

Vertical lines to a VP in two-point perspective give an effect similar to three-point perspective. However one set of horizontal lines must be parallel to the picture plane and the other set of horizontal lines and the vertical lines converge to their respective vanishing points. The horizon of the perspective is vertical. It is the end wall horizon since the lines to the two vanishing points are all in end wall planes. The end wall horizon should be drawn through or near the horizontal center of the elevation. If the horizon is too far off center the perspective will seem to be leaning to one side.

As shown in Fig. 115 the side elevation for this type of perspective drawing serves the same purpose as the plan in normal two-point perspective. The picture plane is shown as a vertical line in side view and the side elevation of the object is drawn at an angle to the picture plane. The side view of the horizontal CV is then drawn through the vertical center of the side elevation of the object. The SP is located on the CV line and the VPs located as shown in the drawing. The lengths of the object are carried vertically to the horizontal measuring line from the front elevation and thence into perspective position. When Fig. 115 is seen from the right side its relation to common two-point perspective construction will be more apparent.

CHAPTER 20

One-Point Perspective

In one-point perspective the picture plane is parallel to one set of planes of the object. The two sets of parallel lines which form the boundaries of these planes are parallel to the picture plane.

The third set of lines of the object is perpendicular to the picture plane. These lines vanish to a VP within the width of the drawing.

A simple box shape shown in one-point perspective with a CV inside of its outline will be merely a rectangular shape like an elevation, Fig. 116 A. When a sunken area is added to the box shape the setback is visible in the perspective drawing and the effect is improved, Fig. B. A perforation completely through the object as shown in C or an extension far in front as in D give long lines to the VP and a more effective perspective. A transparent front to the box shape reveals interior areas and lines to the VP, Fig. E. This explains the object and adds interest to the drawing. If the simple box shape is kept and the horizon raised above the object as shown in F, or dropped below it, lines to the VP appear in the drawing and the pictorial effect is better. The shape of an object determines how effectively it can be represented in one-point perspective. When the design of the object provides long lines to the VP the perspective is most satisfactory. An object with no lines to the VP is unsatisfactory and when short lines only go to the VP the effect will be rather flat and lacking in emphasis. Some objects are naturally adapted to one-point perspective. A long corridor or room entered from the end, ond a street scene as the observer drives along the street appear very emphatic and natural in one-point perspective. A view into a deep display window may give a good effect also. Some unusual plan shapes are explained more clearly by a one-point than by a two-point perspective. These may be either simple geometric shapes other than squares, rectangles, or circles, or they may be irregular shapes. One-point perspective is the only type of drawing which shows three sets of wall planes in the same drawing.

The construction of a one-point perspective by the common method begins with the auxiliary drawings. In step I of Fig. 116 the plan of the object, picture plane, station point, and center of vision are drawn. One set of wall surfaces is parallel to the picture plane in the plan of the object. The elevation is drawn to one side of the plan and below the SP so these drawings will not overlap the perspective area.

In step II the horizon is drawn at the chosen height for the elevation. The VP is located directly by drawing a vertical line from SP to intersect the horizon. This short method gives the same result as drawing from SP parallel to the plan lines which are perpendicular to the picture plane to meet the picture plane at A and then drawing a vertical line from A to intersect the horizon and locate VP the one vanishing point of the perspective by the standard procedure for locating a VP. Since SP-A and A-SP merely go to the picture plane and then back to SP, the same result is obtained by drawing a vertical directly from SP to the horizon line. The part of the object which lies in the picture plane is now constructed by drawing verticals from plan and horizontals from elevation to locate points and lines. This part of the perspective drawing is a scale size part elevation of the object.

In step III projection lines are drawn from points in plan toward SP to meet the picture plane and then vertically into the perspective area. They locate the horizontal spacing of points and vertical lines in the perspective. Lines are drawn from corners B, C, D, and E of the scale drawing at the picture plane toward the VP to meet the verticals just drawn. The horizontals from these intersections complete this simple one-point perspective.

CV+VP

A PLAIN BLOCK SHAPE

B SUNKEN BLOCK SHAPES

C HOLE THROUGH BLOCK

D PROJECTIONS AT SIDES

E TRANSPARENT FRONT

F HORIZON ABOVE OBJECT

SUITABILITY OF OBJECTS
FOR ONE-POINT PERSP.

PICTURE PLANE

CV LINE

P L A N

+SP

ELEVATION

I AUXILIARY DRAWINGS LOCATED

SPACE

FOR THE

PERSPECTIVE

A

+SP

HORIZON

+VP

II SCALE LINES AND VP LOCATED

SP

B   C

VP

E   D

III THE PERSPECTIVE COMPLETED

STEPS IN ONE-POINT PERSPECTIVE

FIG. 116 ELEMENTARY ONE-POINT PERSPECTIVE

126

FIG. 117 WALL PLANE HEIGHT METHOD FOR EXTERIORS

The Determination of Heights. There are two general methods of determining heights in one-point perspective. They are (1) by carrying heights around wall planes into perspective position, and (2) by projecting from a scale silhouette in the picture plane with lines toward or from the V point.

The method of carrying heights around wall planes seems more obvious for interiors than for most exterior perspectives because the walls of the object are usually more nearly adequate to serve for height construction without using imaginary wall planes. The heights are carried from the scale size end wall area of the perspective along the side walls toward the *VP* in Fig. 117 and

PICTURE PLANE

SP

V

HORIZON

FIG. 118 WALL PLANE HEIGHT METHOD FOR INTERIORS

away from the *VP* in Fig. 118. The wall planes used for this construction may be planes of the object, imaginary planes, or a combination of the two. They must be vertical planes which are either parallel or perpendicular to the picture plane. The lines tracing heights on planes parallel to the picture plane are horizontal lines. Those on planes perpendicular to the picture plane are drawn either toward or away from the vanishing point *V* of the perspective drawing. These lines to or from *V* represent horizontal lines perpendicular to the picture plane in the perspective. The heights can be carried behind the picture plane as shown in Fig. 117 or in front of the picture plane as shown in Fig. 118.

PICTURE PLANE

FIG. 119 EXTERIOR HEIGHTS FROM SCALE SILHOUETTES

When using the scale silhouette method the elevation of the object is drawn on the picture plane of the perspective as a part of the construction. This elevation is a multi-view drawing of the side facing the station point. As shown by the shaded areas of Figs. 119 and 120 it furnishes silhouettes in the perspective of shapes of the object projected onto the picture plane. A line from V through any point on this silhouette will pass through the perspective of the point. The perspective of the point will be farther from V than the silhouette when the point is in front of the picture plane as shown by the construction lines with arrows close together for point A of Fig. 119 and point N of Fig. 120. It will be between the silhouette and V when the point is behind the picture plane as shown by point O of Fig. 120.

The perspective position of the point on the line from V is determined by drawing a line from the plan of the point toward or away from SP, as required by its location, to meet the picture plane.

F I G. I 2 O I N T E R I O R H E I G H T S F R O M S C A L E S I L H O U E T T E S

The vertical from this intersection meets the line from V in the required point. Projectors through the top and bottom points of vertical lines of the silhouette give their heights in the perspective.

This method of determining heights in a one-point perspective works very well for points which are far to one side of the station point. As construction nears a vertical line through the SP it becomes increasingly more difficult to locate accurately the intersections of the almost vertical lines from V and the verticals from plan. When the line from V is vertical there is no intersection with the vertical from plan and the point cannot be located by this method. In such cases where the direct construction is inaccurate or impossible an indirect method can be used as shown for point B of Fig. 119 and point P of Fig. 120 by the lines with small arrows spaced far apart. A line or plane of this part of the object is assumed to be moved horizontally to the right or left of the real object. Height construction is made for this new imaginary position and then carried across horizontally to the real position on the perspective.

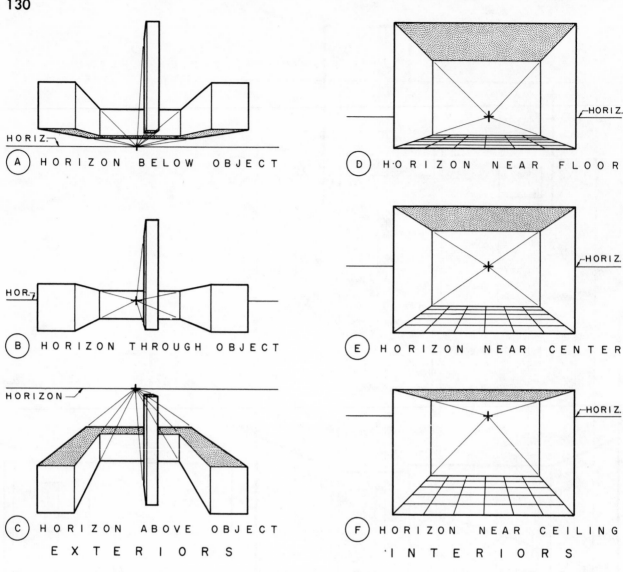

A HORIZON BELOW OBJECT

B HORIZON THROUGH OBJECT

C HORIZON ABOVE OBJECT

EXTERIORS

D HORIZON NEAR FLOOR

E HORIZON NEAR CENTER

F HORIZON NEAR CEILING

INTERIORS

FIG. 121 HORIZON HEIGHT IN ONE-POINT PERSPECTIVE

The Variables produce less extensive and less spectacular changes in the pictorial effects of one-point perspective than in two-point perspective. The angle of the object with the picture plane cannot be varied in one-point perspective. The variations of height are limited in interiors.

The variations of the height of the horizon in one-point perspective can produce in an exterior a view from below, a normal perspective, or a view from above as shown in Figs. 121 A, B, C. In interiors the horizon is almost always located between floor and ceiling, Figs. 121 D, E, F. The variations of height of the horizon are often further restricted by the necessity for showing tops of tables and other pieces of furniture. These are frequently shown from the height of a standing or seated person within the room. Stairways or differences of floor levels sometimes give variations of height of horizon different from those of actual view points within the interior of a single room.

The distance from SP to object does not change the position of the vanishing point since it is located by drawing a vertical from SP to the horizon. However it does change the angle of the projectors from SP to different points on the object. When the SP is close to the object, large areas of horizontal and vertical planes perpendicular to the picture plane appear in the perspective, Figs. 122 I, IV because of the widely diverging projectors in plan. As the distance from SP to object increases

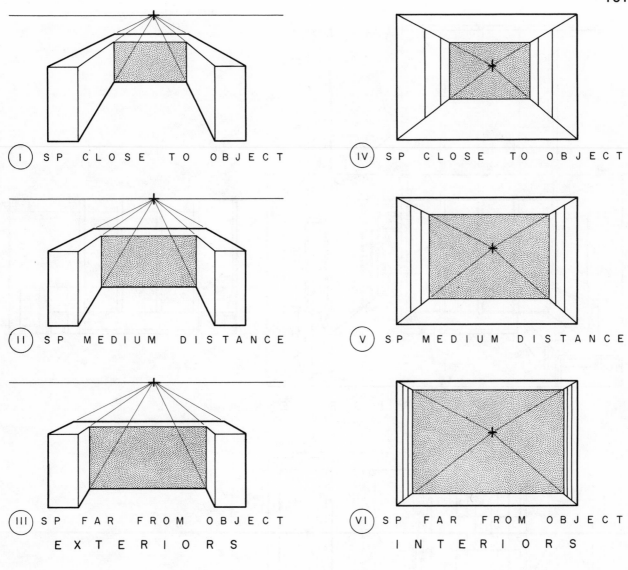

I	SP CLOSE TO OBJECT	IV	SP CLOSE TO OBJECT
II	SP MEDIUM DISTANCE	V	SP MEDIUM DISTANCE
III	SP FAR FROM OBJECT	VI	SP FAR FROM OBJECT
	EXTERIORS		INTERIORS

FIG. 122 DISTANCE FROM SP TO THE OBJECT

these areas become smaller. When the SP is near the object sizes of near and distant parts of the object vary a great deal, Figs. 122 I, IV. As the SP moves farther away the variation in size between the near and distant parts of the object decreases, Figs. 122 III, VI. A station point near the object gives a perspective with greater contrasts while one far away produces a flatter appearance which approaches the effect of an elevation.

The only variation in angle of view in one-point perspective is secured by moving the SP slightly to the right or left of the vertical center line of the plan. Whenever a satisfactory effect can be secured with the SP on center it is better to locate it there. If, however, the effect seems too stiff with a symmetrical object or unsatisfactory in other ways, the SP can be located a little to one side. When the off-center location coincides with the center of interest of the perspective the results are better in avoiding distortion. This is true because the observer will naturally look at the center of interest of the perspective which will be from the direction of the SP used. The SP should not be moved far off center of the plan. To do so will give a distorted effect. When one-point perspective will not give a satisfactory effect with the SP in the middle fifth of the width of the perspective, better results can probably be obtained with two-point perspective.

132

INTERIOR EXAMPLE

EXTERIOR EXAMPLE

FIG. 124 SPACE SAVING IN ONE-POINT PERSPECTIVE

GOOD PICTURE PLANE POSITIONS FOR EXTERIORS

GOOD PICTURE PLANE POSITIONS FOR INTERIORS

FIG. 123 SIZE CONTROL IN ONE–POINT PERSPECTIVE

The position of the picture plane determines the size of the perspective produced in one-point perspective as it does in two-point perspective. The closer the picture plane to the SP the smaller the perspective and the farther the picture plane from the SP the larger the perspective, Fig. 123. The picture plane is often located at either the farthest visible plane of the object or at the nearest plane. However, it can cut through the object at any selected position, be located beyond the object to produce a large perspective, or be placed in front of the object to give a small perspective. When other elements of the perspective setup are not changed, the different positions of the picture plane vary the size of the perspective but have no other effect on it, Fig. 123.

CHAPTER 21

Additional Perspective Methods

Perspective drawing is the process of locating on a plane surface the apparent positions of points of an object as seen from a selected point of view called the station point. The process requires the tracing of lines called projectors. These lines radiate from SP and extend through points on the object to determine their intersections with the picture plane. A drawing made in this manner shows the object as it would appear from the SP. When the eye of an observer of the drawing is at the exact position of its SP the pictorial effect will be precisely accurate. There are several methods of constructing a perspective drawing. The following paragraphs will give a brief description of two additional commonly used methods and discuss their advantages and disadvantages.

The Direct Projection Method. Two complete auxiliary setups are used in this method. Each shows the object, picture plane, and station point in their correct relation to each other. They must agree perfectly in distances, sizes, scale, shapes, etc. One of these auxiliary arrangements is a plan and the other an elevation looking parallel to the picture plane, Fig. 125.

The horizontal spacing of points and lines of the perspective is obtained from the plan setup. This is done most directly in Figs. 125 and 126 by tracing projectors from points on the object toward or away from SP to meet the picture plane and thence vertically into the perspective drawing.

The heights in perspective of points of the object are obtained from the elevation parallel to the picture plane. Projectors are drawn from points on the elevation of the object toward or away from the SP as required to meet the picture plane and determine these heights. The heights are carried across from their positions on the elevation of the picture plane by horizontal projectors to

FIG. 125 DIRECT PROJECTION METHOD OF PERSPECTIVE

134

their correct locations in the perspective. The vertical projectors from the plan of the picture plane meet the horizontal projectors from the elevation of the picture plane to locate points of the perspective. The construction from a point in plan meets the construction from the same point in elevation to locate the perspective position of that point.

The elevation parallel to the picture plane is an ordinary orthographic elevation or section in one-point perspective, Fig. 125. In two-point perspective this elevation is a view from a corner since the object is oblique to the picture plane, Fig. 126. It is a drawing which would never be made for other purposes and is therefore entirely a part of the perspective construction. When the object is simple, hidden parts of the elevation can be shown with dotted lines. If the object is complex, it may be necessary to use two complete elevations parallel to the picture plane, one on each side of the perspective. One elevation would show the view from the right and the other from the left. Each would include its SP and picture plane.

The theory of the direct projection method as given above is simple. The method does not require the use of vanishing points since the positions of the two ends of a line give its direction. Much of the process is visually apparent in both plan and elevation, allowing an accurate estimate of general perspective effect and also of details from auxiliary drawings. There are, however, several disadvantages. The elevation from a corner is more difficult to construct and understand than the common multi-view drawings. The method uses a lot of drafting space. It requires the drawing of many construction lines. Minor inaccuracies in construction will cause considerable error in directions of short lines when vanishing points are not used. The location and use of vanishing points makes the construction shorter and more accurate.

The Common Method. This method of perspective drawing has been used in preceding chapters on perspective. It is also called the office method and the mixed method. It uses the plan construction from the direct projection method and the height construction from the perspective plan method. It makes use of the common orthographic plan and elevation. When blueprints or tracing studies of these drawings are available they can be attached to the board and used for auxiliary drawings. The elevation is really not necessary but it does help to relate the heights and shapes of the elevation to the perspective. A height line can be used instead of an elevation to save space.

FIG. 126 TWO-POINT PERSPECTIVE BY DIRECT PROJECTION

Ⅰ THE PLAN DIAGRAM

Ⅰ THE PLAN DIAGRAM

Ⅱ PERSPECTIVE PLAN

Ⅱ PERSPECTIVE PLAN

Ⅲ THE PERSPECTIVE
TWO — POINT
PERSPECTIVE

Ⅲ THE PERSPECTIVE
ONE — POINT
PERSPECTIVE

FIG. 127 PERSPECTIVE PLAN METHOD FOR EXTERIORS

The Perspective Plan Method. The construction of a perspective by this method is divided into three steps in the following explanation.

I. The diagram is an orthographic plan drawing showing the outline plan shape of the object, the picture plane, and the SP. The vanishing points and measuring points are located as shown in step I of Fig. 127, and the intersection of the plan and picture plane is marked at X in the two-point and at Y in the one-point perspective. This drawing of the diagram provides the spacing of the vanishing points, measuring points, and a plan location point on the picture plane. These points are transferred to the horizon of the perspective plan. The diagram has no further use.

II. The perspective plan is constructed as shown in Fig. 127 step II. A horizon is drawn and the vanishing points, measuring points, and plan intersection with the picture plane transferred to it. Below the horizon a horizontal measuring line is drawn and the plan intersection with the picture plane is transferred vertically from the horizon to this line. In the two-point perspective this intersection point X is the corner of the plan. Lines are drawn from X to VL and VR. They are the left and right edges of the plan and are also base lines where measurement correction lines to the measuring points end. The measurements for the perspective plan are laid out on the horizontal measuring line. The measurements for the left side are laid out to the left of X and those for the right side to the right of X for the two-point perspective. For a measurement X-M extending in front of X-VR the distance is laid out to the right of X. It is a continuation of the left side measurements beyond X and overlaps the right side measurements. In this case the base line VL-X must be extended beyond X to receive the measurement correction line from MR. Lines to the vanishing points are drawn from the foreshortened measurements on the base lines to make the perspective plan, step II.

III. The perspective is constructed by drawing verticals from the perspective plan and tracing heights from a vertical measuring line. The verticals from perspective plan give the correct spacing of vertical lines in the perspective. The height or vertical measuring line must be a line in the picture plane. In step III it is the nearest corner of the large block shape of the object. Any of the methods of determination of heights which were explained for the common method can be used in the perspective plan method. They are applied through the perspective plan here and the orthographic plan in the common method. The method used in Fig. 127 employs a single true height line.

The perspective plan has been placed low enough in each of the examples of Figs. 127 and 128 to be clear of the perspective drawings. It could have been placed above the object or located on the ground plane and allowed to overlap and partially coincide with the perspective. Any convenient horizontal plane can be used for the perspective plan.

FIG. 128 COMPRESSED PERSPECTIVE PLAN METHOD

138

VL   ML   X   MR   PICT. PL.   VR

VL– SP = VL – ML   SP   SP – VR = ML – VR

Ⓐ   T H E   P L A N   D I A G R A M

VL   ML   HORIZON   MR   VR

BASE LINE FOR MR   BASE LINE FOR ML

A   C   D   X   E   F   G   HORIZ. MEAS. LINE

Ⓑ   P E R S P E C T I V E   P L A N

VL   HEIGHT LINE   HORIZ.   VR

Ⓒ   T H E   P E R S P E C T I V E

T W O – P O I N T

P E R S P E C T I V E

ML   PICT. PL.   H   V   I   J   Y   MR

CV LINE

K

L

M

SP – V = ML – V   SP   SP – V = MR – V

Ⓐ   T H E   P L A N   D I A G R A M

ML   HORIZON   V   MR

BASE LINE FOR ML

HORIZ. MEAS. LINE   H   I   J

M L K

Ⓑ   P E R S P E C T I V E   P L A N

HORIZ.   V   HEIGHT LINE

Ⓒ   T H E   P E R S P E C T I V E

O N E – P O I N T

P E R S P E C T I V E

Fɪɢ. 129 INTERIORS BY PERSPECTIVE PLAN METHOD

FIG. 130 COMPRESSED PERSPECTIVE PLAN METHOD

The interior two-point perspective of Fig. 129 has the farthest visible corner of the walls in the picture plane. This corner is the vertical measuring line from which heights are traced.

In the one-point interior perspective of Fig. 129, either wall line which is drawn to V in the perspective plan can be used for the base line. Either ML or MR can be used for the depth construction. When MR is used the measurements are to the right side of the base line and when ML is used they are to the left side, when the object extends in front of the picture plane as in this example. The measurements to MR are in the reverse order of those to ML.

The perspective plan method can be used to save space on the drafting board. It is preferred by some experienced draftsmen. It does require more theoretical knowledge than either the common method or direct projection method. The developing perspective cannot be analyzed from auxiliary drawings as easily as in either the common method or direct projection method. Variations of position of the picture plane to control the size of the perspective are more confusing in this method.

In the example, Fig. 130, the construction has been limited to the area of the perspective itself. The perspective plan has been drawn on the adequately large floor area. A point ½ ML which is one-half the distance from V to ML has been used for a measuring point for half scale depth measurements.

The Measuring Point Method. The construction is worked out more directly on the perspective drawing in this method than in any of the previously described methods. This method applies the perspective plan system of measuring points directly on the perspective drawing omitting the construction of a separate perspective plan. Whenever it is more convenient to do so, measuring points are used for wall planes instead of horizontal planes. The purpose of this method is to save space on the drafting board and work as directly as possible in constructing a perspective drawing. In order to use this method intelligently the draftsman must know a great deal about perspective. He must also have exceptional powers of visualization in three dimensions.

CHAPTER 22

Circles in Perspective

The perspective shape of a complete circle will be an ellipse, a straight line, or a circle. The perspective shape of the more distant part of a circle of which the near edge is too close to be visible, or is behind the observer, will be either a hyperbola or a parabola. These are the five possible shapes of perspectives of circles.

Ellipses as Perspectives of Circles. The ellipse is the most frequent and therefore the most important of the shapes which represent circles in perspective drawings. It occurs much more often than all the other possible forms together. Ellipses as perspectives of circles may vary in proportion from almost straight lines to nearly circular forms. The major axes of these ellipses may be horizontal or vertical under special conditions. They are usually inclined lines so that the ellipses are tilted.

Circles on horizontal planes are represented in the perspective of Fig. 131. It gives a comparison

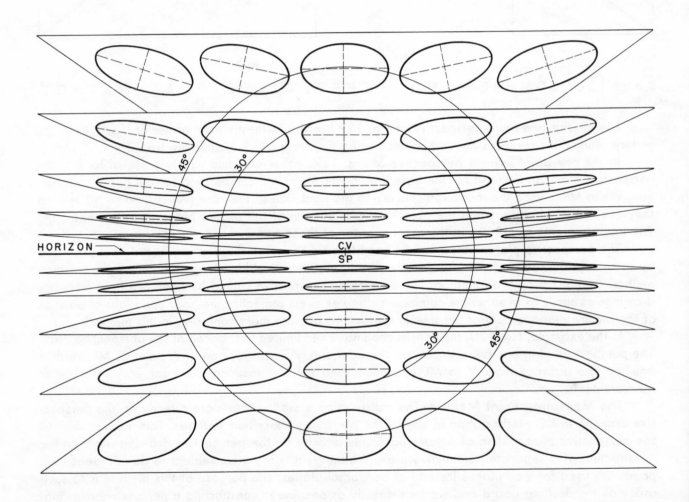

FIG. 131 HORIZONTAL CIRCLES AT DIFFERENT HEIGHTS

140

of the ellipses from circles of equal size which are the same distance from the picture plane but vary in their distances above and below the horizon. The plane through the horizon gives an edge view of the circles. They are represented by straight lines on this plane in the perspective. The vertical line through the *SP* and *CV* point of the perspective passes through the centers of a row of ellipses. All these ellipses are turned horizontally. Their major axes are horizontal lines and their minor axes vertical lines. The ellipses to either side of this vertical row have an inclined position. The farther they are located from the vertical line through *CV* and from the horizon the greater the angle of inclination of the ellipses. The ellipses in the four corners of this drawing are therefore tilted the greatest amount. Why should there be such a variety of shapes to represent the same form in perspective? Because these shapes on a plane surface must give the correct form when seen from the *SP* of the drawing. If a wide angle of vision is used the *SP* is close to the object and the drawing seems distorted unless it is viewed with one eye at this close position. When seen from the normal viewing distance the drawing appears distorted because it gives a decidedly different effect than from the close position. Fig. 131 shows how the shapes which are tilted the most are removed with a 45° cone of vision and even more of them with a 30° cone of vision. The cone of vision has its apex at the *SP* and its base at the picture plane. It is often more satisfactory to have the *SP* far from the objects when representing circles at the edges of a perspective drawing.

Figure 132 shows ellipses representing circles at different distances from the observer on two horizontal planes. One plane is above and the other below the eye level. As the ellipses get farther away from the observer they become closer to the horizon, smaller, and thinner in proportion.

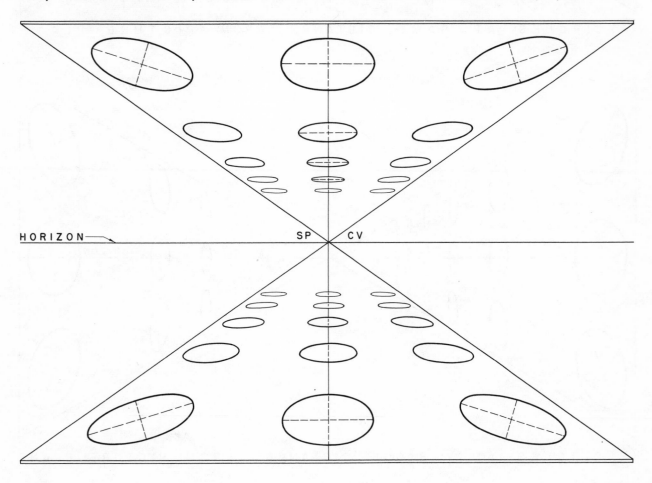

FIG. 132 HORIZONTAL CIRCLES AT DIFFERENT DISTANCES

142

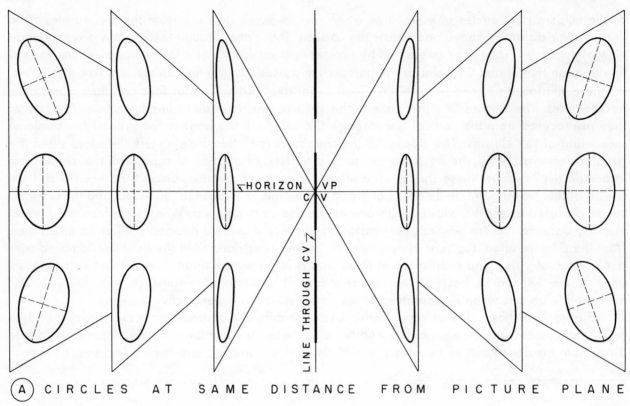

CIRCLES AT SAME DISTANCE FROM PICTURE PLANE

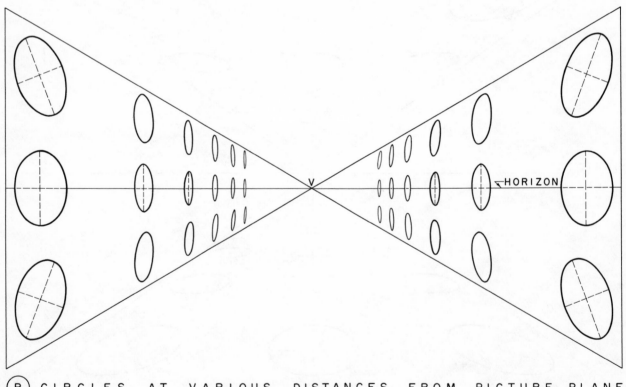

B CIRCLES AT VARIOUS DISTANCES FROM PICTURE PLANE

FIG. 133 VERTICAL CIRCLES NOT PARALLEL TO PICT. PL.

Circles on vertical planes which are either perpendicular or oblique to the picture are usually seen as ellipses. Fig. 133 A shows the perspective ellipses of several rows of circles on a number of of parallel vertical planes which are perpendicular to the picture plane. All of these ellipses are the same distance from the picture plane and are the same height in the perspective drawing. They vary in width. They are widest at the right and left edges of the drawing and decrease in width as they get closer to the vertical line through the CV point. At this line they are seen in edge view and are merely straight lines. The circles which center on the horizon have vertical major axes and horizontal minor axes for their perspective ellipses. All the other ellipses have inclined axes. The ellipses in the extreme corners of both Figs. 133 A and B are tilted the most. These ellipses follow the same general rules as horizontal ellipses. As the ellipses approach the vertical line through CV and the horizon their axes become more nearly horizontal and vertical. In Fig. 133 B there are two vertical planes which are perpendicular to the picture plane with circles at varying distances from the picture plane. These ellipses become smaller and less inclined as they become farther away.

Figs. 133 A and B are both drawn for one-point perspective with the ellipses on planes perpendicular to the picture plane. In two-point perspective the ellipses in the corners would tilt and ellipses centered on the horizon would have horizontal and vertical axes. However the circles on the vertical through the CV would be vertical ellipses and not straight lines.

Circles parallel to the picture plane are shown on a number of planes at varying distances in the perspective drawing, Fig. 134. The perspective form is always a circle for circles in this position. The observer may note that the circles which are far removed from his center of vision are seen at an angle and appear slightly elliptical on actual objects. When the eye is close to the perspective at the position of the SP the same effect will be obtained from the perspective drawing. Circles parallel to the picture plane usually occur in one-point perspectives.

FIG. 134   CIRCLES   PARALLEL   TO   PICTURE   PLANE

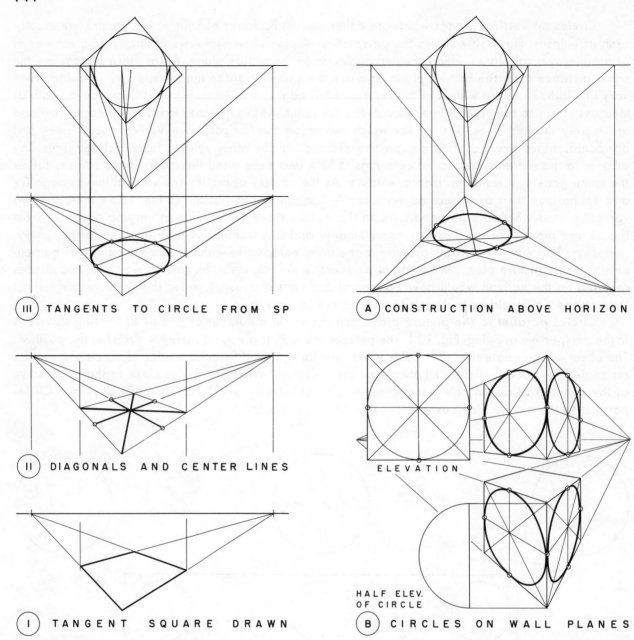

III TANGENTS TO CIRCLE FROM SP

A CONSTRUCTION ABOVE HORIZON

II DIAGONALS AND CENTER LINES

ELEVATION

HALF ELEV.
OF CIRCLE

I TANGENT SQUARE DRAWN

B CIRCLES ON WALL PLANES

FIG. 135 TANGENT SQUARE METHOD—CIRCLES IN PERSPECTIVE

Ellipse Construction in Perspective. Ellipses as the perspectives of circles can be constructed by three methods: (1) by tangent polygons, (2) by plotting the positions of a number of points, (3) by locating the axes or conjugate diameters of the ellipse, then plotting points by methods of constructing ellipses.

The tangent polygon method locates as construction the tangent points of the polygon and circle and also the tangent lines of the sides of the polygon, Figs. 135, 136. The tangent sides help to determine the direction of the curve of the ellipse. The square and octagon are easily drawn in perspective. One of the two is commonly used to provide the tangents for this construction. Four sides of the square or octagon follow the lines of the perspective. In two-point perspective these four sides vanish to the two vanishing points. In one-point perspective one pair of these parallel

FIG. 136 OCTAGON METHOD OF CIRCLES IN PERSPECTIVE

sides is drawn to V and the other pair is horizontal. The remaining four sides of the octagon parallel the diagonals of the square. They are miter 45° lines and vanish to miter points. Both the miter points are usually within reach in one-point perspective. In two-point perspective one is usually very far away. These M points are helpful as shown in Fig. 136 but are not essential for the construction. The tangent square is adequate for small circles, as shown in Fig. 135. The octagon with its greater number of tangent guiding lines and points of tangency is more accurate and better for larger circles, Fig. 136.

With the tangent square construction it is necessary to draw the lines toward SP from the edges of the circle in plan to intersect the picture plane and determine the exact length of the ellipse as shown in Fig. 135 III. It is also advisable to locate these points for the octagon construction.

TWO - POINT

PERSPECTIVE

FIG. 137 OCTAGON METHOD FOR VERTICAL CIRCLES

ONE - POINT

PERSPECTIVE

FIG. 138 TANGENT OCTAGON METHOD FOR CIRCLES

148

PICTURE PLANE

X

HEIGHT LINE FOR THE
CIRCLE ABOVE HORIZON

CIRCLE ABOVE

THE HORIZON

V   HORIZON

HORIZON

SP

HEIGHT LINE FOR THE
CIRCLE BELOW HORIZON

CIRCLE BELOW

THE HORIZON

FIG. 139 PARALLEL LINE METHOD FOR POINTS ON CIRCLES

The point method can be used to locate any number of points on ellipses of any size. However it is most useful for large ellipses for which the eight points of the octagon method seem inadequate for accuracy. The points can be plotted by any method of locating a point in perspective. This method eliminates the tangent polygon lines which may become confusing on some designs.

The parallel line method is a simple one for locating points on horizontal circles, Fig. 139. Any line A-A can be drawn in plan parallel to SP-X and intersecting the circle. Line A-A crosses the picture plane at Y in plan and in perspective it will cross the height line of the circle at its intersection Z with the vertical through Y. Line A-A and all lines parallel to it will be drawn to vanishing point V which is located where the vertical from X meets the horizon. The same line can be used to locate points on any number of circles which it intersects in plan. When the vanishing points already established are not conveniently located a new point V can be selected anywhere on the horizon for this construction. This may be advisable in one-point perspective. The parallel lines in the direction A-A in plan must always be drawn parallel to SP-X so that they will be lines to the vanishing point V for this construction.

The offset method has been used for the vertical circle of Fig. 140. It can also be used for horizontal circles.

With a given circle, picture plane, horizon, station point, and ground line, the construction on a one-point or two-point perspective arrangement will give identical ellipses. The draftsman can

FIG. 140 OFFSET METHOD FOR POINTS ON CIRCLES

choose the construction which is easiest for each problem. The point method can be used for irregular curves or other forms as well as for circles.

The method of constructing ellipses from their axes or conjugate diameters is seldom used. It requires new theory and construction methods. The axes can seldom be located and the method of plotting points from either axes or conjugate diameters is no easy road to perspective drawing. Theoretically it is the precise and workmanlike method. Practically it is too involved.

Part Circles in Perspective. It is rather rare to have a parabola or nyperbola as the perspective of a circular form. However it does occur occasionally and it usually disturbs the draftsman if he is not aware of the conditions causing the shape. When the SP is on a vertical line through the edge of a horizontal circle the perspective of the visible arc will be a parabola. When the SP is within the area of the circle in plan the visible arc will be a hyperbola in perspective. The perspectives of these shapes can be located by the point method which has been described for ellipses.

The drawing of ellipses or other irregular curves requires either skill at freehand drawing or infinite patience and care with irregular curves. Ellipses are of unlimited variety of sizes, proportions, and directions of axes. If the same shape and size repeat, it is sometimes helpful to make a template or pattern of transparent plastic or other material. This requires considerable time and work and is seldom practical for a single ellipse. When only a part of the ellipse is visible some or all of the hidden part should be drawn in order to secure greater accuracy in the shape of the visible part.

CHAPTER 23

The Division of Lines

The principal operation in perspective drawing is the foreshortening of measurements. This process causes the sizes of equal divisions on the object to decrease as they get farther from the station point. It produces the effect of realism in a perspective drawing by representing spaces as they would appear from the SP. It requires that equal measurements made on a measuring line which is parallel to the picture plane be corrected to become a diminishing sequence for perspective use.

The preceding chapters on perspective have shown methods of obtaining divisions in perspective drawing by using an auxiliary plan and elevation. These are the usual simple routine perspective construction methods. They are in general easy to understand and easy to use. They are the safest and best methods for the beginner and for the person who does only a little perspective drawing. The person who does a great deal of perspective drawing may eventually begin to wonder about two things: (1) "Isn't there some way that changes or additions can be made on this perspective without starting over with a plan and elevation? and (2) Is it necessary to construct all these repeating details by projecting from plan and elevation? Isn't there a shorter method?"

The purpose of this chapter on the division of lines is to give information which will help in the revising of an existing perspective drawing which is no longer set up with its auxiliary drawings. It will also help to shorten the process of constructing a perspective and aid in perspective sketching.

First some very simple procedures and then more complex ones.

To locate a vanishing point of a perspective drawing, extend two lines of the perspective, which were drawn to the same VP, until they meet. Their intersection is the required VP. Choose long lines which are as far apart as possible in order to obtain maximum accuracy, Fig. 141 A.

Vertical spacing of horizontal lines can be laid out for the vertical space between any two lines to a VP on any convenient vertical line between the two given lines or their extensions. The scale is kept in a vertical position and moved along horizontally until the required spacing fits between the two converging lines. This method can be used for equal or unequal spaces. Any convenient divisions on the scale which fit the space can be used for this purpose, as shown in Fig. 141 B. In this example Scale II is the most convenient one to use since it fits between the lines of the drawing. Scale I requires extension of the drawing to the left and Scale III to the right.

The center of the perspective of a rectangle A-B-C-D is found by drawing its diagonals A-C and D-B. This procedure can be repeated to divide the halves and fourths of the original rectangle, Fig. 141 C. Divisions are limited to two, four, eight, etc. divisions of the given rectangle. A given rectangle E-F-G-H of Fig. 141 D can be assumed to be a half rectangle and its half diagonal E-X extended to add an equal rectangle F-I-J-G to it. This process can be repeated indefinitely.

The method of triangles can be used to transfer measurements from a vertical measuring line to a line to a VP. Given line K-Y to VR which is to be divided, Figs. 141 E and F. From the point K draw a vertical line of indefinite length. Lay out from K the required divisions at any convenient scale on this vertical line. From the last measurement N draw a line to Y. Lines from the measurements toward VR intersect the diagonal (or hypotenuse of the triangle) N-Y at the required distances. Verticals from these points locate the divisions on line K-Y. The order of the divisions can be reversed from the same sequence of measurements by completing the rectangle and using the other diagonal K-Z as shown in Fig. 141 G. The sequence of measurements on K-Y can also be reversed by reversing them on the vertical measuring line for the construction as shown in Fig. 141 H.

A. LOCATING VANISHING POINTS BY EXTENDING LINES TO MEET

B. VERTICAL DIVISIONS USED WHEREVER A SCALE FITS

C. EQUAL DIVISIONS WITH DIAGONALS OF RECTANGLES

D. EQUAL ADDITION BY USING DIAGONAL OF HALF RECTANGLE

E. SMALL SCALE ON VERTICAL DIVIDES GIVEN LINE TO VP

F. LARGER SCALE ON VERTICAL GIVES SAME DIVISIONS AS E

G. USE OF OTHER DIAGONAL REVERSES ORDER OF DIVISIONS

H. REVERSING MEASUREMENTS ALSO REVERSES THE ORDER

FIG. 141 SIMPLE PERSPECTIVE LINE DIVISION METHODS

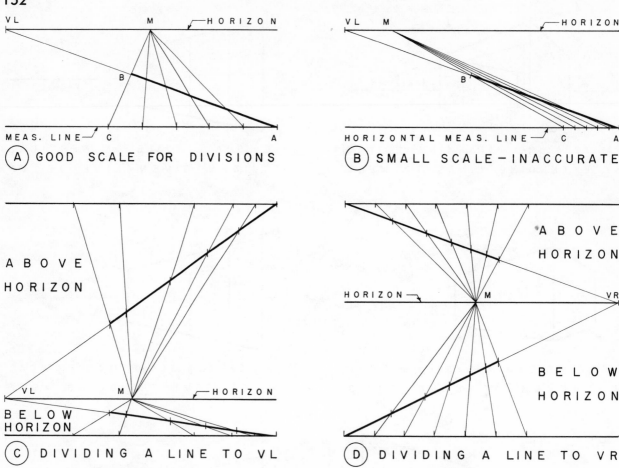

FIG. 142 MEASURING POINT METHOD OF LINE DIVISION

The measuring point method of dividing lines to vanishing points is illustrated in Figs. 142 and 143. In Fig. 142 A line A-B to VL is required to be divided. From A a horizontal line of indefinite length is drawn to the left. The measurements for the required divisions are laid out from A on this line. A line is drawn from the last division C through B and extended to meet the horizon at M, the required measuring point. All the measurements are transferred to line A-B by drawing lines from the points on the measuring line A-C toward M to intersect A-B.

The horizontal measuring line A-C is assumed to be parallel to the picture plane. Therefore it is at the same scale throughout its length and can be used as a measuring line. The two lines A-B and A-C lie in a horizontal plane which vanishes in the horizon. All lines in this plane are horizontal and vanish to points on the horizon. The extension of C-B locates M, the vanishing point of all lines parallel to C-B. Consequently the lines to point M in the perspective represent parallel lines in the direction of C-B whch is one side of the triangle A-B-C. These lines transfer proportional spacing from A-C to A-B in the perspective.

Any convenient scale can be used for the measurements. It will be most satisfactory to use a scale which gives reasonable line intersections which do not approach parallels and keeps all the construction in easy reach, Fig. 142 A, B. When it is possible to choose between several lines to the VP for the line to be divided select one which is far from the horizon. In Fig. 142 C the construction above the horizon is better than on the line below the horizon. The construction can be reversed and used on a line to VR on the right side instead of to VL, Fig. 142 D. It can also be used either above or below the horizon as shown in Figs. 142 C and D.

EITHER

ABOVE

HORIZON

OR BELOW

HORIZON

(I) USING A SUBSTITUTE LINE TO VP
WHEN LINE IS TOO CLOSE TO HORIZON

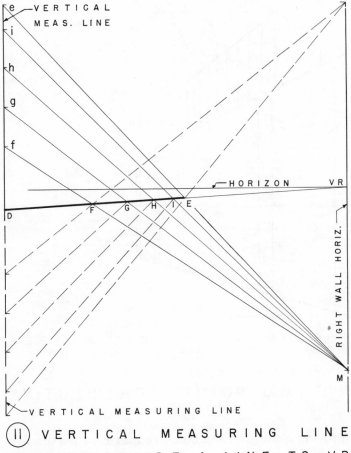

(II) VERTICAL MEASURING LINE
USED TO DIVIDE A LINE TO VP

FIG. 143 VARIATIONS IN THE
MEASURING POINT METHOD

When the line to be divided is too close to the horizon for accurate construction, either of two procedures can be followed:

I. A substitute line to the same VP as the line to be divided and either vertically below or above it can be used for the construction. The measurements are transferred with vertical lines from the substitute line to the line to be divided as shown in Fig. 143 I. In this example D-E is the given line to be divided and X-Y the substitute line on which the divisions are first worked out and then transferred vertically to required positions on D-E. The dotted lines show the same construction from above.

II. The second method uses a vertical measuring line D-e from D and a measuring point on the right wall horizon. The right wall horizon is the vertical line drawn through the vanishing point VR of line D-E, Fig. 143 II. After the measurements are laid out on the vertical measuring line D-e, a line is drawn from e through E to locate M, the required measuring point. The construction lines are then drawn from the measurements on D-e toward M to locate the required points on D-E. Choose a scale which will give reasonable construction. A large scale will cause M to be far from VR and a small scale will give a flat angle of lines to M with inaccurate intersections. The measuring line can be either above or below D. The construction is used to either VR or VL as required by the line to be divided.

This method may be more convenient to use in some instances even though the line to be divided permits the use of the horizontal measuring line and M on the horizon. In this method the construction is assumed to be in a right wall plane of which the triangle D-e-E is a part. D-e is a vertical line and is the same scale throughout its length since vertical lines are parallel to the picture plane.

Ⓐ DIVISIONS ON INTERIOR WALLS AND CEILING

Ⓑ DIVISIONS ON EXTERIOR OF BLOCK SHAPES

FIG. 144 LINE DIVISION IN TWO—POINT PERSPECTIVE

Line division methods are useful for supplying details on the block shapes of a perspective which is being constructed and for adding to or changing an existing completed perspective. In either of these cases the basic dimensions of the object must be known and the details fitted to conform to the known sizes. In the example of Fig. 144 A the distances A-B = 15 feet, B-E = 12 feet, and B-D = 8 feet are given. The wall B-E-D-F is divided by diagonals to represent four equal vertical wall panels each 3 feet wide. The 15 foot wall C-D is divided to represent 3 ft. wall panels at each end. The center 9 feet is divided with 1 ½ ft. at each edge and 6 ft. in the center. The ceil-

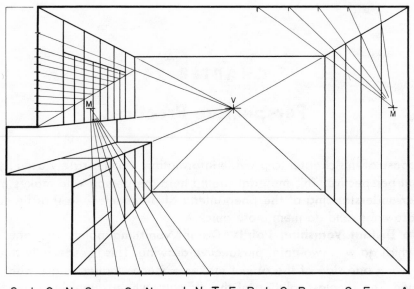

(I) DIVISIONS ON INTERIOR OF A ROOM

(II) DIVISIONS ON EXTERIOR OF BLOCK SHAPES

FIG. 145 LINE DIVISION IN ONE—POINT PERSPECTIVE

ing has the correct number of divisions for 1½ ft. squares. These measurements are laid out on line A-G and transferred to A-B. The dotted diagonal line E-G intersects lines from A-B to give the second set of ceiling lines.

Line division in perspective must be made to conform to the dimensions and design of the object represented. However, the objective is to make proportionate divisions which are correct for the perspective. Any convenient scale can be used for each construction. Several different scales may then be used for measurements for different line division constructions on the same drawing.

CHAPTER 24

Perspective Practices

It is the purpose of this chapter to provide information which is rarely used by those who learn only a little about perspective. This material should help the person who makes many perspectives to have a clearer understanding of the phenomena of perspective so that he can do better and more complete drawings, and do them more quickly.

Drawing to Distant Vanishing Points. Distant vanishing points are one of the necessary inconveniences which go with two-point perspective drawing. This is especially true when the drawing is large, or when one side of the object makes a much smaller angle with the picture plane than the other side. The simplest solution of the difficulty when a vanishing point falls beyond the area of the drawing board is to get a larger board. Another solution is to extend the surface of the board by attaching a second board to it with heavy paper across the joint and thumb tacks through the paper into each board. Heavy cardboard can be attached to the board and used to extend the drawing surface to include the VP. It may be necessary to block up under this flexible material to maintain the VP at its position. When the VP is so far away that the above described procedures are unsatisfactory, other methods can be used. The one described below requires no special equipment. It is easy to use and sufficiently accurate for a careful draftsman.

The scale method of drawing to a distant vanishing point uses the horizon line as the zero point for two vertical scales, Fig. 146. The scales extend above and below the horizon as far as is necessary for drawing the lines of the perspective. The horizontal distance between the scales and their spacing from the VP are selected to fit the perspective drawing being constructed. Fig. 146 A shows a perspective drawing with *VR* very far away. A position is chosen for the scale on the left which is the farthest one from *VR*. In the example this scale is located beyond the left edge of the perspective so it will be out of the way of the perspective construction. The space from *VR* to this scale is divided into three equal divisions. These divisions are ⅓, ⅔, and ⅗ of the distance from *VR*. By using scales which are in this proportion on the three vertical lines, a line to *VR* cutting the scale lines will pass through the same position on each scale. Since only two scales are needed the two which are farthest from *VR* are used. They are most conveniently located. The numerical scales used on these two lines must provide divisions on the right which are two thirds of those on the left since the right measuring line is ⅔ as far from *VR* as the left measuring line. Any convenient scales can be used as long as they are in the correct size relation to each other. On the architects scale 1½-1, ¾-½, ⅜-¼, ³⁄₁₆-⅛, ³⁄₃₂-¹⁄₁₆ all give this ratio. When the lines of the object do not go exactly through the marked divisions on the scale, it is necessary to estimate by eye the same relative positions on the scales used. This is illustrated in the more detailed drawing, Fig. 146 c.

The scales can be located at any convenient positions where their distances to the VP can be fitted with correct relative scales. The interior example of Fig. 146 B uses ¼ scale at the left side of the drawing and at ¾ this distance from *VR* uses three-fourths of ¼ scale which is ³⁄₁₆ scale. Results are more accurate when small scale divisions are used and when the scales are relatively far apart. One or both scales can fall on the edges of the drawing. However, it is usually more satisfactory to keep them out of the drawing area when this can be done. If the drawing extends appreciably beyond the scales, the lines located by the scales will not be as accurate in direction since inaccuracies of position are magnified when the scales are close together. In general this method is sufficiently accurate, easy to use, and entirely satisfactory.

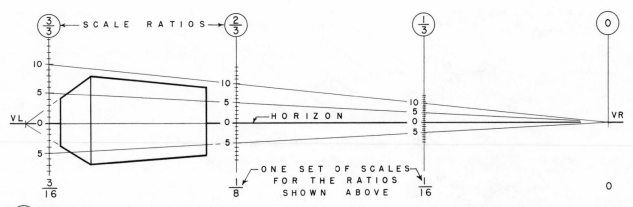

(A) EXTERIOR DIAGRAM OF SCALE METHOD OF LINES TO A VP

(B) INTERIOR DIAGRAM OF SCALE METHOD OF LINES TO A VP

(C) USING VP SCALES ON A PERSPECTIVE DRAWING

FIG. 146 SCALE METHOD OF DRAWING TO DISTANT VP

158

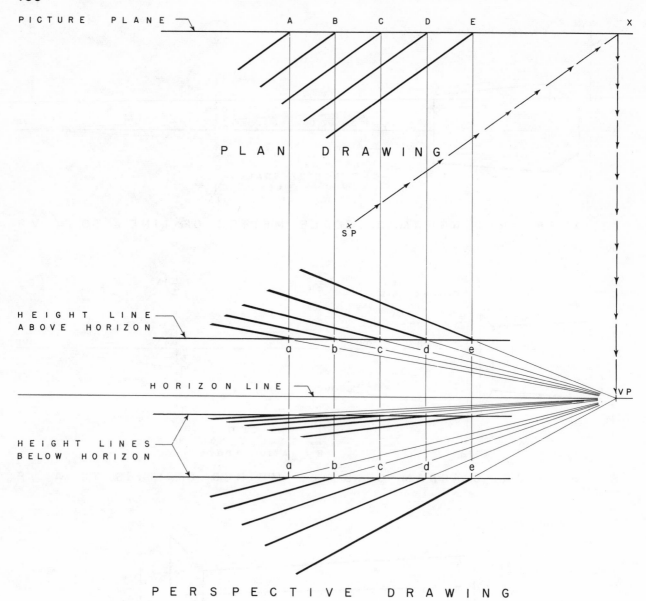

PICTURE PLANE

A B C D E X

PLAN DRAWING

SP

HEIGHT LINE
ABOVE HORIZON

a b c d e

HORIZON LINE

VP

HEIGHT LINES
BELOW HORIZON

a b c d e

PERSPECTIVE DRAWING

FIG. 147 SIMPLE THEORY OF A VANISHING POINT

The Location of Vanishing Points. Vanishing points for perspective drawings are a great mystery to many draftsmen and designers. The theory of the location of vanishing points is quite simple. A line in any direction which goes through the center of sight of the observer is seen as a point. All lines which are parallel to this line vanish at the point position of the line.

The mechanical process of locating vanishing points for a perspective drawing is not difficult for a good draftsman. The vanishing point of any set of parallel lines is located where the line through the station point and parallel to the set intersects the picture plane. *The location of the vanishing point of any line in a perspective drawing is the drafting problem of locating the intersection with the picture plane of a line through the station point and parallel to the given line.*

Horizontal lines always have their vanishing points on the horizon. The following procedure is used to locate the vanishing point of any given set of horizontal lines, Fig. 147. In plan draw a

P L A N

D R A W I N G

SP

← H O R I Z O N   L I N E →

P E R S P E C T I V E   D R A W I N G

FIG. 148 VANISHING POINTS OF HORIZONTAL LINES

line parallel to the set and through *SP* to meet the picture plane at *X*, the plan position of the required *VP*. A vertical line from *X* intersects the horizon in the location of the perspective position of the required *VP*. This method has been used to locate the standard vanishing points of two-point and one-point perspectives in preceding pages. It is used to find the vanishing points of all horizontal lines which are not parallel to the picture plane.

In Fig. 148 there are horizontal lines in several directions. Each horizontal line has its vanishing point on the horizon. Some of these vanishing points are beyond the limits of the drawing while others are conveniently near. It is often helpful to use vanishing points other than the standard one for one-point perspective and the two for two-point perspective.

"To which VP does this line of the object go?" is a common puzzle in perspective drawing. It goes to the VP which was located by drawing parallel to it through the SP in plan.

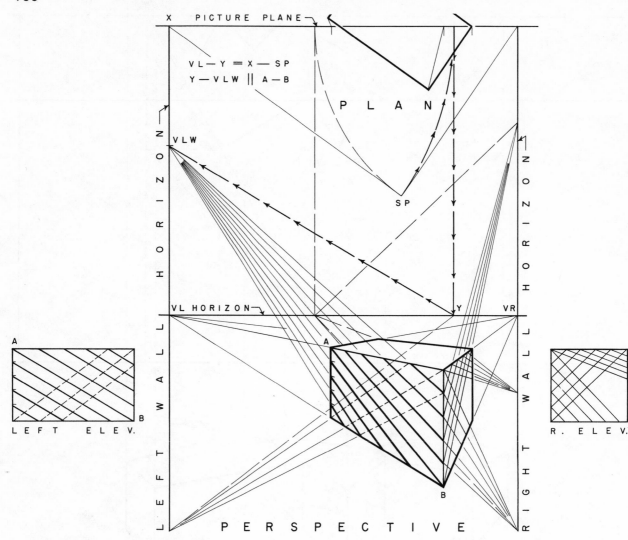

FIG. 149 VANISHING POINTS OF INCLINED LINES

Inclined lines in or parallel to wall planes have their vanishing points either above or below the horizon on the vertical line through the vanishing point of horizontal lines in the same planes. Thus in Fig. 149 all inclined lines in or parallel to the left wall plane will have their vanishing points on the vertical through *VL*. All inclined lines in the right wall plane direction will have their vanishing points on the vertical line through *VR*. This line through *VR* is called the right wall horizon and the vertical through *VL* is called the left wall horizon. These two wall horizon lines are the vanishing lines of all wall planes in these two directions and the loci of vanishing points of lines in all possible directions oblique to the picture plane in the wall planes. They compare with the horizon which is the vanishing line of all horizontal planes and the locus of vanishing points of horizontal lines oblique to the picture plane in all possible directions.

In order to locate the vanishing point of line *A-B* of Fig. 149 and all lines parallel to *A-B* the following construction is used. The distance *X-SP* is laid out to the right of *VL* on the horizon to locate point *Y*. A line drawn from *Y* parallel to the left elevation of *A-B* intersects the left wall horizon at *VLW* the perspective vanishing point of *A-B* and of all lines parallel to *A-B*.

The above construction is a partial left elevation of the perspective setup. The left wall hori-

FIG. 150 VANISHING POINTS OF INCLINED LINES

zon, the horizon, the *Y-VLW* are parts of this elevation. *VL-Y* of the part elevation is the same line as *X-SP* in plan. The plan line *X-SP* also represents the plan of *VLW-Y*. The lighter lines on the right side of the object show the location and use of a number of vanishing points of inclined lines in right wall planes.

Inclined lines in wall planes of one-point perspective are shown in Fig. 150. The construction locating vanishing point *VW* of line *C-D* and all lines parallel to *C-D* is shown with heavy lines and arrows. The distance *SP-O* from plan is laid out to the right of *V* on the horizon to locate point *N*. A line from *N* parallel to the right elevation of *C-D* intersects the vertical through *V* in *VW* the perspective vanishing point of *C-D* and all lines parallel to *C-D*. It should be observed that parallel inclined lines on the left and right elevations would go to the same vanishing point. This vanishing point could be located with construction from either side of *Y*.

Inclined lines not in or parallel to the wall planes of the object have their vanishing points located by using auxiliary wall planes through these lines in plan. For each new plan direction a new VP on the horizon and a new wall horizon is established. The construction is identical in other respects with that of Fig. 149 in locating the required VP of the inclined lines.

(A) MPS FOR HORIZONTAL PLANES

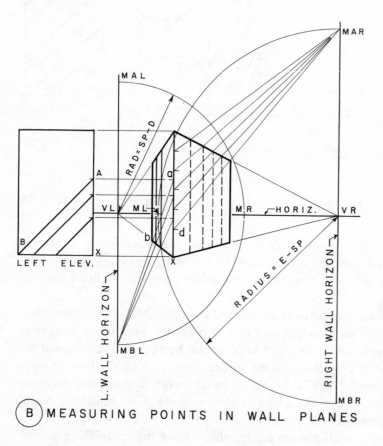

(B) MEASURING POINTS IN WALL PLANES

FIG. 151 MEASURING POINTS FOR TWO-POINT PERSPECTIVE

Measuring Points for Perspective Construction. A measuring point is used in perspective to transfer scale measurements laid out on a line in the picture plane to a line which is drawn to a vanishing point. The measuring point is a vanishing point of a set of parallel lines which transfer these measurements. Measuring points are used in some perspective methods to eliminate the use of an auxiliary orthographic plan. In order for a measuring point to transfer equal sizes, the measuring line A-X, Figs. 151 A and 152 I, and the line to which measurements are transferred, B-X, must represent the two equal sides of an isosceles triangle. The set of parallel lines transferring the measurements must be parallel to the base A-B of this triangle.

For two-point perspective the top of Fig. 151 A illustrates this procedure in an orthographic plan. In the bottom of the figure this same diagram is converted into perspective. Line SP-C is drawn in plan parallel to A-B to locate the plan position of the measuring point MR at C. The vertical line from C locates MR on the horizon of the perspective. MR is the vanishing point of line A-B and all lines parallel to A-B in perspective.

Since triangles A-B-X and D-C-SP have all three of their sides parallel they are similar triangles. Therefore D-C and D-SP are equal distances since they parallel the two equal sides A-X and B-X of the triangle A-B-X. A variation of the method of locating MR is to lay out a distance D-SP from D on the picture plane line of the plan to locate C and draw vertically to the horizon to find MR. To locate ML lay out distance E-SP horizontally to left of E to obtain point F from which a vertical to the horizon locates ML. These distances D-SP and E-SP can be laid out directly on the horizon from VL and VR respectively to locate MR and ML.

In one-point perspective, Fig.

152 ɪ, the line from *SP* parallel to *A-B* locates the point O from which a vertical is drawn to the horizon to locate *ML*. Measuring point *ML* transfers dimensions from *x-a* to *x-b* of the perspective. This construction can be worked out on the ceiling or any other horizontal plane of the one-point perspective. The distance *V-ML* is equal to *SP-P*, the perpendicular distance from *SP* to the picture plane. This distance *SP-P* can be laid out on the horizon to the left of *V* to locate *ML* and to the right of *V* to locate *MR* in any one-point perspective.

Either ML or MR can be used to work out the depth construction in a one-point perspective. Sometimes it may be more convenient to use one than the other because of the available room on the drafting board. When the construction lines become numerous it may be convenient to use both of the measuring points.

Measuring points for wall planes are located on the verticals through the vanishing points of the perspective. These verticals are the wall horizons, Figs. 151 ʙ and 152 ɪɪ. An inclined line in the direction of a wall plane in plan and at 45° to a horizontal plane passes through *SP* and locates a wall measuring point where it intersects the picture plane. Since this duplicates vertically the distance *SP-D*, Fig. 151 ᴀ, this distance can be laid out vertically above and below *VL* to locate the two measuring points *MAL* and *MBL* on this wall horizon of Fig. 151 ʙ. The distance *E-SP* can be laid out above and below *VR* to locate the two measuring points *MAR* and *MBR* on the right wall horizon. Since these distances equal *VR-ML*, a radius *E-SP* can be used with a center at *VR* to locate with an arc *ML* and the measuring points *MAR* above and *MBR* below *VR* on the right wall horizon. The radius *SP-P* can be used in one-point perspective, Fig. 152 ɪɪ, with a center at *V* to locate four measuring points. Two are on the horizon and two on the wall horizon.

Ⓘ M P S   F O R   H O R I Z O N T A L   P L A N E S

Ⓘⓘ MEASURING POINTS IN WALL PLANES

FɪG. 152   M E A S U R I N G   P O I N T S
F O R   O N E — P O I N T   P E R S P E C T I V E

164

Distortion in Perspective Drawings. Any correctly constructed perspective drawing provides a true picture of the object when the drawing is seen from its station point. When a person cannot look at the drawing in a normal way and see it approximately as it would appear from the station point, the drawing gives a distorted representation of the object. There are two general causes of distortion.

1. The station point located too close to the object causes a disturbing difference between the appearance of the drawing as seen from the SP very near the drawing and from a comfortable viewing distance farther away, Fig. 153 A, B. Objectionable distortion from this cause occurs particularly in corners and edges of perspectives. Circular objects and furniture in these positions are likely to be most distorted. Interiors frequently have important shapes in corners and at the edges. Therefore a wide angle of view is more likely to cause objectionable distortion in an interior than in an exterior perspective.

2. When the station point is located to one side of the plan and not directly below its center, as it should be, the proportions of the object will be distorted. The drawing made from an SP off center when seen from the side at the distance and angle of the SP will give a true picture of the object. When this same drawing is viewed from the natural center observation position the proportions will be changed and the object appear distorted. The proportions seen in plan will not be repeated in the perspective. A square shape in plan may appear to be a long rectangle in perspective and a square plan shape may appear

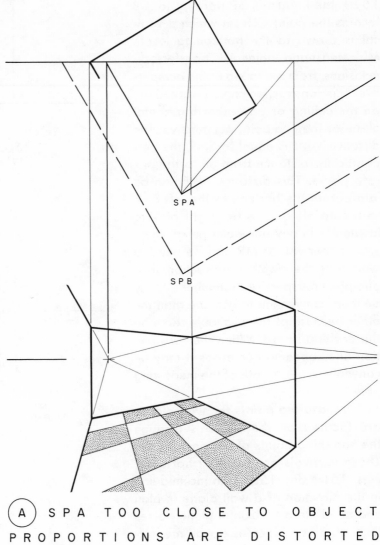

(A) SPA TOO CLOSE TO OBJECT PROPORTIONS ARE DISTORTED

(B) SPB IS FARTHER AWAY AND GIVES MORE NORMAL PERSPECTIVE WITH MORE PLEASING SHAPES

FIG. 153 DISTORTION FROM SP TOO CLOSE

rectangular, Fig. 154 I.

Some very correct perspectives seem distorted while some distorted perspectives are accepted as correct. There seems to be a mental block to the acceptance of correct but extreme three-point perspectives. They give the observer a decided shock with the feeling of being unreal. Most of us just do not consciously observe and accept such phenomena in our daily lives. It seems we feel that the objects "just are not like that," and that they should not be shown from such extreme and unnatural points of view. Few of us ever get above a tall building and looking down on it realize the forms which are visible.

There is a mental acceptance of vertical lines on aerial and "worm's eye" views. Perhaps this is because the height of the observer is obvious from the drawings. Furthermore we know that the vertical lines are vertical and we like to see them drawn that way. A horizontal displacement of the SP is not indicated by anything in a two-point perspective. In one-point perspective the vanishing point explains the way the object is seen and a position moderately to one side of center is accepted by eye and mind. We often see things that way when walking down one side of a street or corridor. When the SP is obviously off center, the mind and eye adjust to its position in the perspective drawing. There may be nothing to mark positively the exact position of the SP of a one-point perspective drawing. However the converging lines and areas of the perspective point to it and suggest its position even though the conscious mind of the observer may not be aware of its location.

THIS SP II IS CORRECT SP POSITION

THIS SP I TO ONE SIDE OF PLAN CAUSES DISTORTION

(I) SP I GIVES DISTORTED SHAPES COMPARE TOP AREAS WITH PLAN

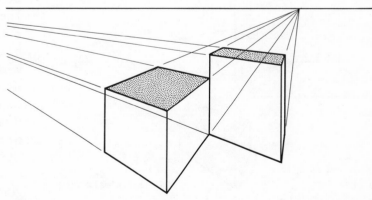

(II) SP II CENTERED BELOW THE PLAN GIVES CORRECT PROPORTIONS COMPARE TOP AREAS WITH PLAN

FIG. 154 DISTORTION FROM SP TO SIDE

PICTURE PLANE

HORIZ.

SP

A   D
B   E
    F
C

A - B = B - C
D - E = E - F

(A) OBJECT TOUCHING MIRROR

PICTURE PL.

SP

HORIZ.

G   J
    M
H   K
  N
I   L

G - H = H - I
J - K = K - L

H - M - K - N IS
VERTICAL
PROJECTION
ONTO MIRROR

(B) OBJECT ABOVE MIRROR

FIG. 155 EQUAL HEIGHTS
USED FOR REFLECTIONS
ON HORIZONTAL MIRRORS

Reflections in Perspective. Reflections are an important part of the design and presentation of three-dimensional objects. We usually think of reflections as belonging to mirrors or still bodies of water. Any shiny surface such as a table top, floor, wet pavement, display window, piece of polished metal, or painted area can provide reflections of lights, shapes, and colors from other objects. The sharpness and clarity of a reflection depends on the perfection of the reflecting surface and lighting conditions. Mirrors, smooth water, and polished metal often give reflections which are very nearly perfect. Some surfaces such as table tops or shiny paint may give only a suggestion of the reflected object. The reflection is never an exact duplicate of the object because it is never seen from the same angle as the object. The reflection is most nearly like the object when the observer views the two from almost the same angle. This condition occurs when the line of sight is almost parallel to the reflecting surface. When the reflection is seen from a much higher, lower, or otherwise greatly varying angle of view than the object, the two differ decidedly. Reflections may add to the effect of a presentation by showing details of the opposite side of the object. The bottom of a spoon may be reflected on a polished horizontal surface. The back of a vase or other object may be seen in a vertical mirror. Thus a reflection may make one drawing give two views of the same object in a perspective. Reflections can be undesirable or even disturbing. The reflection from the polished surface behind a bar or counter may reveal stored material which is not attractive. Reflections of horizontal walks and floor patterns on slanting glass or other polished wall surfaces will seem to be inclined. They may be disturbing and dangerous to pedestrians. The designer draftsman should be able to represent reflections correctly and accurately. They are a part of his designs and a part of their accurate presentation in order to give a correct visual effect.

Horizontal mirror surfaces occur often in design, and produce reflections which can be constructed easily for simple shapes. In Fig. 155 A the simple block shape with a slanting top rests on a horizontal mirror surface. The perspective of the object is drawn first. The vertical lines of the object are continued in the reflection. Their lengths in the reflection are the same as in the object. This reflection can then be laid out by the drawing of equal verticals and connecting lines.

This method of vertical measurements is most easily used when the object rests on the mirror. The vertical lines of the object touch the reflecting surface where the reflection begins. When the object does not touch the mirror it is necessary to draw its projection on the plane of the mirror. The verticals must be measured to the plane of the mirror. In Fig. 155 B the object is suspended above the mirror. The verticals include the extension to the mirror in measuring for this reflection. When the visible mirror does not extend under the vertical plane of the object, the projection onto the plane of the mirror can be drawn to establish the vertical distances from the object to the mirror. These distances can then be duplicated below for the reflection.

Since the reflection is an inverted duplicate of the object, the inverted elevation can be used in constructing the reflection, Figs. 156 I and II. The heights of the reflection are constructed from this inverted elevation in the same way that the heights of the object are constructed from the standard elevation. Some parts of an object may be partly or completely concealed in the reflection. This is more often true when the mirror does not extend under the object, Fig. 156 II. However, it may be caused by the shapes of the object as in Figs. 155 A and 156 I where the top surface is concealed in the reflection by the reflected block shape above it. Fig. 156 II shows how more distant objects may show only a little in the reflection or even be entirely hidden.

Ⓘ MIRROR IN FRONT OF OBJECT

Ⓘ️Ⓘ AMOUNT REFLECTED VARIES

FIG. 156 INVERTED ELEVATIONS USED FOR REFLECTIONS ON HORIZONTAL MIRRORS

Ⓐ SIDE WALL REFLECTION   Ⓑ END WALL REFLECTION

ONE POINT PERSPECTIVES OF WALL REFLECTIONS

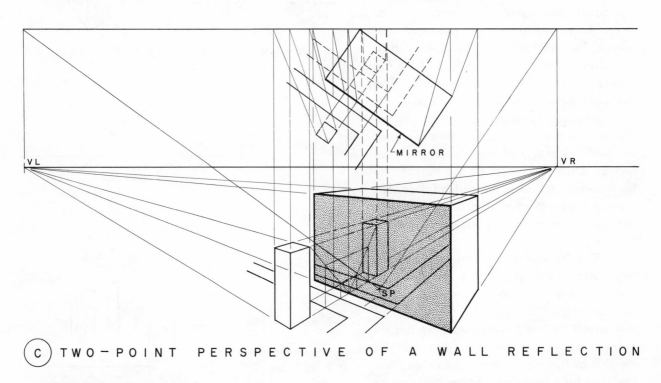

Ⓒ TWO-POINT PERSPECTIVE OF A WALL REFLECTION

FIG. 157 SIMPLE REFLECTIONS ON WALL SURFACES

Vertical mirrors on planes perpendicular to the picture plane provide duplicate horizontal measurements which are reversed from left to right. This is illustrated in the one-point perspective of Fig. 157 A. This reflection can be constructed by duplicating the plan of the object in the reversed position beyond the mirror as shown. In the one-point perspective of Fig. 157 B the mirror is on the end wall and parallel to the picture plane. The reflection is farther away and is smaller than the object. When the mirror is on a side wall as in Fig. 157 A the proportions are changed but the size remains the same in object and reflection.

EQUAL ANGLES

PLAN OF REFLECTION

MIRROR

PLAN OF OBJECT

ELEV. OF OBJECT

VL   VM   SP   V   VR

Ⓘ VERTICAL REFLECTING WALL AT OBLIQUE ANGLE

B

A

VL   VR

A

B

EQUAL ANGLES

C

SP

C

RIGHT ELEVATION

ⒾⒾ REFLECTIONS ON TILTED WALL MIRROR

FIG. 158 REFLECTIONS ON INCLINED WALL MIRRORS

Vertical mirrors in two-point perspective are illustrated in Fig. 157 c. The plans of parts reflected are duplicated in reverse beyond the mirror for the construction of the reflection.

Inclined mirror planes duplicate the object beyond the plane of the mirror as is the case with all reflecting planes. However the lines of the object are neither parallel nor perpendicular to the mirror. Their directions are therefore changed in the reflection and it is necessary to establish new vanishing points for them, Figs. 158 I and II, or locate points on the reflection and connect them without use of special vanishing points.

PART FIVE

Shadows on Drawings

CHAPTER 25

Shadows in Design

Shadows are an inevitable part of our every day lives. Wherever we go, either indoors or outside, if there is directional light there are shadows. These shadows provide tones, masses, contrasts, and explanation of forms. They are an integral part of any design. Objects and drawings without shadows usually appear flat and uninteresting. Their details are obscured so that they are difficult to understand. Shadows are an important part of seeing. They reveal shapes, distances, and directions of elements, Figs. 159, 160.

Fig. 159 A shows an object with no distinct shadows. In Fig. 159 B a strong light from one direction produces a shadow on object and background. Fig. 160 compares the effect of small weak shadows and larger strong ones on three examples. Shadows are important design elements.

A CERAMIC DESIGN BY HAROLD S. NASH

(A) WITH SLIGHT SHADING   (B) WITH DEFINITE SHADOWS

FIG. 159 SHADOWS ADD TO AN OBJECT OR DRAWING

(I) CONTOUR MODEL BY STUDENT DON MCCARTY

(II) CAST OF A DESIGN BY HAROLD S. NASH

(III) WOOD CARVINGS BY FRESHMAN STUDENTS

MINIMUM SHADOWS   LARGER SHADOWS

FIG. 160 SHADOWS EXPLAIN THE OBJECTS

172

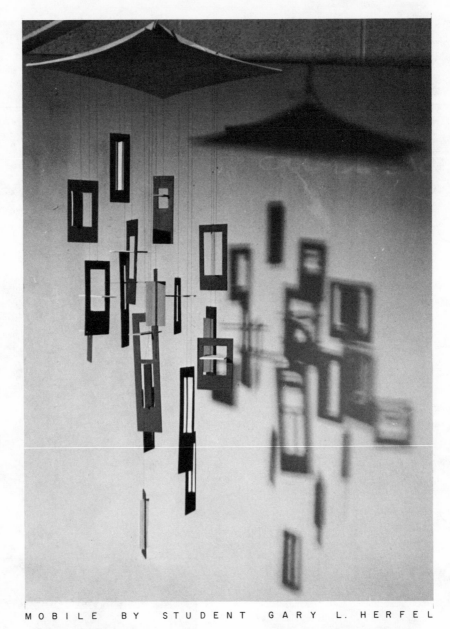

MOBILE   BY   STUDENT   GARY   L.   HERFEL
REPEATING   VARIATIONS   IN   OBJECT   AND   SHADOW

Fig. 161 SHADOWS PROVIDE DESIGN ELEMENTS

Shadows can produce an atmosphere of clarity, brilliance, excitement, mystery, etc., Fig. 162. They are powerful elements in the presentation of objects and of drawings of designs. The shadows on the object itself help to explain the object. The shadow of the object may add an interesting design form on another plane, Fig. 161. When the object moves, the shadow provides an interesting repeating variation of the shapes and movements of the object.

As a part of a study of shadows on drawings the student should observe the shadows of objects in different types of light. Small objects can be used as models either in sunlight or with artificial lighting in addition to observation of actual full size objects.

WOOD CARVINGS BY FRESHMAN STUDENTS

EXCITEMENT FROM CURVING AND DIAGONAL SHADOWS

MODEL BY STUDENT GEORGE J. KELSO JR.

RESTFUL EFFECT FROM LARGE SHADOW SHAPES

FIG. 162 SHADOWS HELP PRODUCE ATMOSPHERE

In shadow casting and rendering, the distinction between shade and shadow is more of a technicality than a reality. Both terms refer to the exclusion of light from an area or areas. Since both result in the absence of direct light on surfaces, the effects are often identical. There is no consistent variation of darkness or other optical difference between shades and shadows.

In shadow casting, a shade is caused by the exclusion of light from a surface by the shape of the object itself. A shadow goes through the air from one object to another or from one part of an object to another part of the same object. Since an attempt to distinguish between these two terms is often more confusing than helpful, both will usually be called shadows in this text.

CHAPTER 26

Multi-View Shadows

A standard or conventional direction of light is almost always used for shadows on multi-view drawings. The light is assumed to be from the sun or from some other source which provides parallel rays. The direction is the diagonal of a cube from the top, left, front corner to the lower, right, rear corner, Fig. 163 A. In each of the six standard views the direction of light will appear to be the diagonal of a square, Fig. 163 B. The direction of a ray of light can be traced on any of these views with a 45° triangle.

The true angle of light with a horizontal plane can be determined by drawing an auxiliary view of a cube on a vertical plane which is parallel to the plan direction of light, Fig. 163 C. The same result is obtained by constructing a rectangle with the short side the side of a square and the long side the diagonal of the same square, Fig. 164 D. This angle is used in some shadow constructions on circular objects. It is of minor importance.

The advantages of the conventional direction of light are, (1) simplicity of shadow construction, and (2) precise information from the shadows. In Fig. 164 I the wall plane and surface of the block projecting from it are parallel to the front view plane. The shadow widths of the vertical and horizontal edges of the block are equal to its projection from the wall surface. This is true because light travels back, down, and to the right equally, telling exactly how far the block projects.

FIG. 163 THE CONVENTIONAL DIRECTION OF LIGHT

I SHADOW CONSTRUCTION USING 45° PROJECTION

II SHADOWS LOCATED WITH MEASUREMENTS

SHADOWS OF PROJECTING BLOCKS ON WALLS

III LOCATING SHADOWS ON THE FRONT VIEW

IV LOCATING SHADOW ON A TOP VIEW

SHADOWS OF SUNKEN BLOCK SHAPES ON WALL AND FLOOR

FIG. 164 SHADOWS OF SIMPLE BLOCK SHAPES

Block Forms on Wall Surfaces. Some of the simple shadows occur very frequently on drawings. Block forms turned in different directions, and of different shapes are used in the following paragraphs to illustrate and explain some of these shadows.

Simple block shapes with horizontal and vertical edges cast shadows which are equal in width to the projection of the block from the vertical wall. The shadow widths can be worked out from top view or from either side view by 45° projection as shown in Fig. 164 I. They can also be worked out directly on the front view from measurements when the projection "A" is known, Fig. 164 II. The slanting shadow lines at the top right and bottom left corners of the projection are parallel to the front view direction of light. These corner points represent the front views of the lines perpendicular to the wall plane. Since one point represents each line in front view, every part of each line casts its shadow at 45° from that point making a 45° shadow.

Areas which sink into the wall surface have the horizontal shadow at the top and the vertical shadow at the left, Fig. 164 III. This is the reverse of the shadow positions of the projecting block.

In a top view the shadows of these same simple forms are similar to those in an elevation. Although the direction of light is different, the shadows on the horizontal plan plane are constructed by the same procedure and have similar characteristics to those in elevation, Fig. 164 IV.

E L E V A T I O N

S E C T I O N

P L A N

(A) SHADOWS ON BLOCK SHAPES OF AN INTERIOR

E L E V A T I O N

S E C T I O N

(B) SHADOWS ON A SPACE DIVIDER CABINET

FIG. 165 EXAMPLES OF SIMPLE SHADOWS

① PRINCIPAL SHADOWS ON A SMALL BUILDING

Ⅱ SHADOWS ON DOOR AND WINDOW SHAPES

FIG. 166 EXAMPLES OF SIMPLE SHADOWS

(A) BEVELS MORE THAN 45°

(B) BEVELS AT 45° ANGLE

SHADOWS OF PROJECTING BEVELED AREAS

(C) BEVELS MORE THAN 45°

(D) BEVELS AT 45° ANGLE

SHADOWS OF SUNKEN BEVELED SURFACES

FIG. 167 SHADOWS OF OBLIQUE LINES AND PLANES

Shadows of oblique lines and planes are provided by the beveled blocks of Figs. 167 and 168. These blocks have beveled surfaces which are oblique to the wall planes and connect the blocks to the walls. The corners where beveled surfaces meet provide four lines oblique to the wall planes on each block. If the projecting face of the block is smaller than the face touching the wall, the side surfaces are visible in front view, Fig. 167 A, B. The total width of the shadow at the right of and below the block is still equal to the projection of the block. However, the corners going back to the wall are now visible as lines in front view. The shadow of the near end of such a line is found by 45° projection as shown for point L of Fig. 167 A. The other end of the line touches the wall at point M. The shadow of line L-M is the line connecting the front view of M to the shadow of L. The shadow at the top corner is more nearly vertical and the one at the lower left corner more nearly horizontal than a 45° line. When the side surfaces are at more than 45° to the wall as shown in side view (or plan) the shadow will have the characteristics shown in Fig. 167 A. When the side

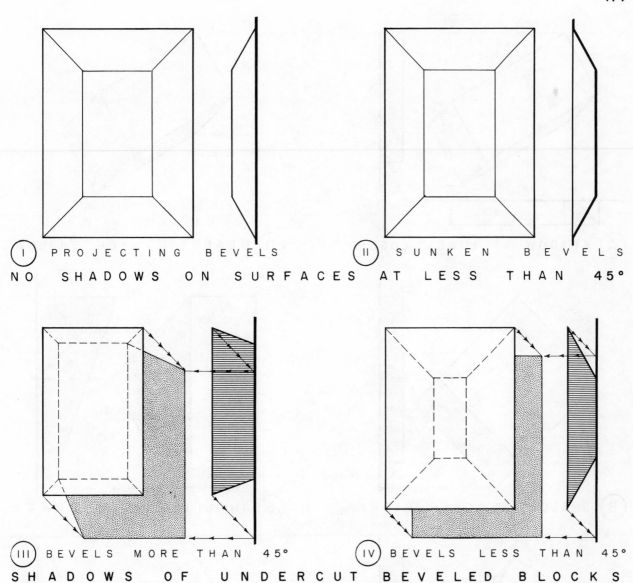

Ⅰ PROJECTING BEVELS Ⅱ SUNKEN BEVELS

NO SHADOWS ON SURFACES AT LESS THAN 45°

Ⅲ BEVELS MORE THAN 45° Ⅳ BEVELS LESS THAN 45°

SHADOWS OF UNDERCUT BEVELED BLOCKS

FIG. 168 SHADOWS OF OBLIQUE LINES AND PLANES

surfaces are at 45° they will be in shadow but there will be no shadow bands below and to the right of them, Fig. 167 B. When the angle between the side surfaces and wall is less than 45° there will be no shadow on or from the block, Fig. 168 I. There will, however, be a variation of intensity of light on the flat and beveled surfaces. This is a part of rendering and not of shadow casting. When the bevels sink back into the wall plane the same general rules apply. When the bevel is at more than 45° with the wall plane it will be in shadow at the top and left and its near edges will cast a shadow onto the sunken wall on these two sides, Fig. 167 C. When the bevel is at 45° there will be shadow on the top and left slanting surfaces but no shadow on the wall plane, Fig. 167 D. When the bevel is less than 45° with the wall plane there will be no shadow areas, Fig. 168 II.

When the projecting surface of the block is larger than the surface touching the wall the corner lines make shadows when the angle between side surfaces and wall is greater than 45°, Fig. 168 III. The shadow is entirely from the face of the block when this angle is 45° or less, Fig. 168 IV.

180

Ⓐ SHADOW AT LOWER EDGES

Ⓓ MEASURING FOR SHADOW

P = PROJECTION OF BLOCK FROM WALL

Ⓑ SHADOW AT LOWER RIGHT

Ⓔ INCLINED BLOCK FACE

Ⓒ SHADOW AT RIGHT EDGES

Ⓕ DIAGONAL INCLINED BLOCK

THREE POSSIBLE POSITIONS
OF DIAGONAL BLOCKS

VARIATIONS IN CONSTRUCTION
AND IN BLOCK SHAPES

Fɪɢ. 169 SHADOWS OF DIAGONAL LINES AND PLANES

SECTION   ELEVATION   SECTION

FIG. 170 BEVEL AND BLOCK SHADOW EXAMPLES

Diagonal projecting blocks cause various shadow effects which depend on the angles at which the blocks are turned. When the block is not at 45° the shadows of the two shade line corners can be located by 45° projection from side view (or plan), Fig. 169 A. The shadow lines can then be drawn parallel to the front view of the lines casting the shadow. One shadow band will be greater than the projection of the block from the wall and the other less than the projection. The shadow of a corner can also be located by measuring the amount of the projection vertically and horizontally in an L shape, Fig. 169 D. The remainder of the shadow can then be located by using 45° projection lines and parallels. It should be observed that lines perpendicular to the wall always make 45° shadow lines. When the block is turned at 45° there will be only one shadow band. It is located at the lower right of the projecting block, Fig. 169 B.

When the surface of the block is not parallel to the wall the shadow of each corner of the block is located. The shadows of the corners are then connected, Figs. 169 E, F.

Shadows of Plane Figures. Any plane figure parallel to the plane on which the shadow falls has a shadow duplicating the figure as shown by a rectangle A-B-C-D of Fig. 169 C. One point on the shadow can be determined by 45° projection or measuring and the shadow drawn in the simplest manner possible. This rule applies to any shape of plane figure. Plane figure sections cut through a solid object are often useful in locating shadows of critical points or a sequence of areas around which the shadow can be drawn.

PICTORIAL VIEW

OF THE THREE

MOST COMMON

LINES AND THEIR

SHADOW SHAPES

FRONT ELEVATION   R. ELEV.

PLAN LOOKING UP

MULTI-VIEW SHADOWS OF THE LINES

FIG. 171 THE THREE MOST COMMON LINES

Shadows of the Three Most Common Lines. These lines are: (1) lines perpendicular to the picture plane and consequently seen in end view, (2) horizontal lines parallel to the wall planes and to the picture plane of the view, (3) vertical lines. These three types of lines cast a large proportion of all multi-view shadows. They are the three line directions of any simple box shape and are the most common lines of multi-view drawings. The student should understand the construction and shapes of their shadows so he can locate them quickly and accurately. In Fig. 171 the three common line types and their shadows are shown on a single object. They are explained in detail in the following pages. Each of these line types has definite shadow characteristics. The last two have shadow outline forms which are similar in shapes and distances to the forms shown in other multi-view drawings of the object as shown in Fig. 171. While the shadows of all three can be plotted over irregular surfaces it is much quicker and more satisfactory to know the shapes produced in the shadows and draw them in the most efficient and easiest way.

1. Lines seen in end view make shadows which appear to be straight lines in any type of drawing and over any surface. This is true whether the surface be flat, curved, warped, or made of several different forms. In many cases the shadow is not actually straight. However, it always appears to be straight as it is seen in the drawing because the observer is looking at the end of the line making the shadow, Fig. 172 A front elevation and 172 B plan. Any straight line which is not parallel to the rays of light casts a plane of shadow. When a person looks at the end of such a line he looks parallel to its shadow plane which is seen as a straight line. Then any line form in the plane appears to be a straight line.

If the shadows of a number of points on a line in the view where the line is seen as a point are constructed, every shadow point will fall on the same straight line. In Fig. 172 A the line C-D is seen as a point in front view. The construction for the shadow of every point on this line is drawn at 45° from its point front view. The result is then a 45° straight line shadow. If this shadow is broken by shadow bands, the segments of the shadow of the line seen in end view are parts of one continuous straight line. Vertical line E-F is seen in end view in the plan of Fig. 172 B.

PICTORIAL VIEW

C-D
IN END
VIEW

SHADOW LINE
FROM C-D

FRONT ELEVATION

D   C

RIGHT ELEVATION

(A) SHADOW OF HORIZONTAL LINE SEEN IN END VIEW

END VIEW
OF E-F

SHADOW
OF E-F

PLAN

E

SHADOW OF
THE LINE E-F

PICTORIAL VIEW

F

RIGHT ELEVATION

(B) SHADOW OF VERTICAL LINE SEEN IN END VIEW

FIG. 172 SHADOWS OF LINES SEEN IN END VIEW

(A) MULTI—VIEW DRAWINGS

(B) PICTORIAL DRAWING OF A

(C) VERTICAL BANDS MAY INTERRUPT THESE SHADOWS

(D) METHOD OF PROJECTING FROM SELECTED POINTS

FIG. 173 SHADOWS OF HORIZONTAL LINES PARALLEL TO WALL

2. Horizontal lines parallel to wall planes cast shadows which duplicate the shapes of the plan looking up and are the reverse of the shapes of the plan looking down, Fig. 173 A. These horizontal lines are commonly found in furniture tops, mantels or fireplaces, and overhangs above window and door openings. An understanding of the shapes produced by the shadows of these horizontal lines will greatly simplify the shadow construction. Any method of reproducing the required shapes may be used. These methods include trace and transfer, measuring with dividers, and 45° projection from plan or side view for necessary points. Dividers can be used on any continuous vertical line through the top or bottom, and front views as shown in Fig. 173 A. Here distance A-B in bottom view and B-A in top view are equal to D-B in the front elevation. In Fig. 173 D a 45° line is drawn from E to locate G in top view. A vertical line from G in top view locates the same point G in front view, and a 45° line from G in front view intersects the vertical from E in the shadow of G.

3. Vertical lines in front views cast shadows which duplicate the distances from these lines in side views, Fig. 174 I distance R-S. The shapes of the shadow edges are identical with those of the right side views and the reverse from left to right of those shown in left side views, Fig. 174 I. These vertical lines cast 45° planes of shadow back, down, and to the right. These planes of shadow go back and to the right equally. The distances to the right can be constructed from either the plan or the side view, both of which show the distances back from the line, Fig. 174 III.

IDENTICAL DISTANCES

REVERSED SHAPES

IDENTICAL SHAPES

LEFT SIDE

FRONT

RIGHT SIDE

(I) SIDE VIEWS COMPARED WITH SHADOW OF FRONT VIEW

(II) PICTORIAL DRAWING OF I

(III) HORIZONTAL BANDS MAY INTERRUPT THESE SHADOWS

FIG. 174 SHADOWS OF VERTICAL LINES IN FRONT VIEW

In the top view of Fig. 174 III a 45° construction line is drawn from the point representing line J-K. This 45° line intersects each of the projecting planes at points L, M, and O. From these points of intersection vertical lines are drawn to the correct areas of the front view to locate the shadow outline. In the same figure the construction is also made from the right side view. From any point Z on the side view a ray of light is traced back to locate point P on line J-K. Point P casts its shadow on the horizontal line drawn across from Z. After the front view of point P is located, a 45° construction line is drawn to locate the shadow of this point on the horizontal line from Z. As many points as necessary are located by this system to complete the shadow.

Since on any continuous horizontal line the distance back from the shadow-casting vertical line on the left in the right side view must be equal to the distance used from the front view of the same line on the left, the two shapes are identical. It is possible to transfer these equal distances with dividers or in any other convenient way to obtain the shadow outline. The shape can be traced and transferred. It is not immoral or illegal to use the easiest method to construct a shadow.

When the shadow made by the vertical line is interrupted by horizontal bands of shadow from projections, the parts of the shadow of the vertical line in front view will be identical with the right side profile, Fig. 174 III. It should be observed that circular, irregular, curved, and slanting shapes repeat in the shadow of front view the identical forms and angles of the right side view.

186

FRONT ELEVATION   SECTION

PLAN THROUGH FIREPLACE

(A) SHADOWS AROUND A FIREPLACE

FRONT ELEVATION   RIGHT ELEV.

(B) SHADOWS OF A CHEST OF DRAWERS

FIG.175 EXAMPLES OF SHADOW CONSTRUCTION

PLAN

FRONT ELEVATION

RIGHT ELEVATION

Ⓒ SHADOWS INTO A ROOM INTERIOR

FRONT ELEVATION

RIGHT ELEV.

PLAN

Ⓓ SHADOWS ON AN ENTRANCE TO A BUILDING

FIG. 176 EXAMPLES OF SHADOW CONSTRUCTION

A   BASIC OVERHANG SHAPE

B   MULTIPLE OVERHANG

C   ONLY THE LINES IN LIGHT CAST SHADOWS

D   PLOTTING A CURVE

E   FRONT OVERHANG

FIG. 177 SHADOWS OF COMMON OVERHANGS

Overhangs, or Extending bands, are Found on Many Objects. The common overhang with equal projections on front and sides is illustrated in Fig. 177 A. The shadow on the nearer wall surface should be found first, then the shadow cast onto the more distant wall surface around the projecting parts. This procedure helps prevent construction from lines in shadow which cannot cast shadows. The shadow can be constructed on the front view from either the plan or side view. The horizontal projection A of the shadow is greater than the overhang at the right side because of the equal extension in front. Its horizontal distance is the sum of the side and front projections. It should be observed that the part B-C of the right vertical edge is in shadow and consequently cannot make a shadow on the wall or anything else. Fig. 177 B shows a multiple overhang with each element partially in light. Each part in light makes a shadow on the wall at the side of the overhangs. A

I U N E Q U A L   O V E R H A N G S   A T   S I D E   A N D   F R O N T

II O V E R H A N G S   O B L I Q U E   T O   F R O N T   W A L L

III B E V E L E D   A N D   I N C L I N E D   O V E R H A N G S

F I G. 178 S H A D O W S   O F   I R R E G U L A R   O V E R H A N G S

similar treatment in Fig. 177 c has greater projections and all elements except the top one are completely in shadow. The general shadow shape on the wall is similar to that on Fig. 177 A. The parts in shadow have no effect on the shadow outline. In Fig. 177 D the molding shape is in light. Shadow points can be plotted from the elevation and either the plan or side elevation of the molding. Be sure to use the points which are on the same vertical line in plan and elevation or on the same horizontal line in elevation and side elevation in tracing construction to find a shadow point. These points represent the same point on the object and must be used together.

Unequal overhangs are illustrated in Fig. 178 I and oblique ones in Figs. 178 II and III. The two segments of the slanting shadows are parallel in each illustration of Fig. 178 II because they are shadows of the same line on parallel surfaces.

① HEIGHT GREATER ② HEIGHT = DEPTH ③ DEPTH GREATER

PRISMS   TOUCHING   BOTH   WALL   AND   FLOOR

④ DIVIDED SHADOW ⑤ SHADOW ON FLOOR ⑥ SHADOW ON WALL

SHADOW   VARIATIONS   FOR   FREE   STANDING   PRISMS

FIG. 179 SHADOWS OF RECTANGULAR PRISMS

Shadows of Plane Surface Solids. The shadows of plane surface solids may consist of shadows on the object itself and shadows from the object onto one or more background surfaces, Fig. 180. The object may not have any of its visible surfaces in shadow as shown in Fig. 179, however there may be visible shadows on the background surfaces of both wall and floor as shown in Figs. 179 1, 2, 3, and 4, on floor only as in 5, or on wall only as in 6.

Location of the shadow from a free object is sometimes a puzzle to a beginner in the casting of shadows. It may require study to learn to visualize the object and its shadow positions from multi-view drawings. The sequence of illustrations of rectangular blocks in Fig. 179 shows the effect on the shadow of different distances from the wall and floor planes. The following paragraphs are numbered to coincide with the numbers of the illustrations.

1. The box touches both wall and floor planes as though it were attached to them. This form is a projection from the two planes with its height greater than its depth in the first illustration. This gives a triangular shadow in plan and a vertical shadow with a 45° top in elevation.

2. In the second illustration the box has equal height and depth. The shadows are triangles.

3. When the box extends farther from the wall than from the floor as shown in the third illustration the wall shadow is a triangle and the floor shadow a rectangular area with a 45° point.

4. The box has been moved out from the wall. It still rests on the floor and is close to the wall. The shadow of the top of the box drops down at its top edge the distance A.

5. When the distance from the wall as shown in plan exceeds the height of the object above the floor the entire shadow falls on the floor.

6. When the object is suspended above the floor at a height greater than the distance back to the wall shown in plan the entire shadow falls on the wall.

The vertical prisms of Fig. 180 A illustrate the varied shadows of commonly used prism shapes on wall planes. When the entire shadow falls on the wall the complete shadows of the parallel top and bottom of a vertical prism will be identical as shown for the triangular prism of Fig. 180 A. Since only a part of top and bottom casts a shadow and each part is from an opposite side of the prism, the part shadows are never alike. The shadow of the complete end of the prism on the floor will always be identical with its plan view shape since the ends are parallel to the floor as shown in the illustration of the octagon.

The shadows of a simple pyramid are shown in Fig. 180 B. The first example shows the complete shadow falling on the floor and the second the complete shadow on the wall. The last two examples illustrate how the complete shadow can be outlined in plan or elevation to find the part shadows on the two drawings.

The shadow on and from a pyramid will vary with its shape. The illustrations are of pyramids having a sufficiently steep slope so that two sides are in shadow. When the slope is 45° there will not be a shadow in plan from the sides of the pyramid, although the two sides are still in shadow (shade). When the slope is less than 45° there will be no shadow on the sides of the pyramid. Then any shadow in either plan or elevation will come from the base only.

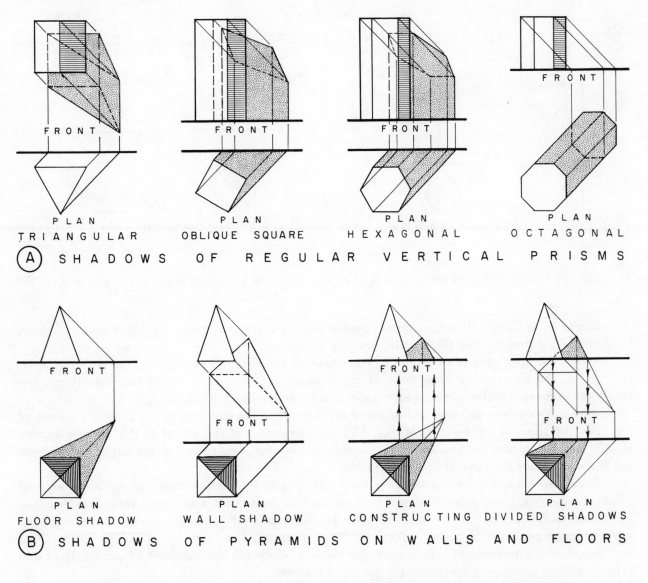

FRONT — PLAN
TRIANGULAR OBLIQUE SQUARE HEXAGONAL OCTAGONAL

(A) SHADOWS OF REGULAR VERTICAL PRISMS

FLOOR SHADOW WALL SHADOW CONSTRUCTING DIVIDED SHADOWS

(B) SHADOWS OF PYRAMIDS ON WALLS AND FLOORS

FIG. 180 SHADOWS OF PRISMS AND PYRAMIDS

FIG. 181 POSSIBLE SHAPES OF SHADOWS OF CIRCLES

Shadows of Circles. There are three possible shapes of the shadows of circles on plane surfaces. They are, (A) a straight line, (B) a circle, and (C) an ellipse.

When the light rays are parallel to the plane of the circle its shadow will be a straight line, Fig. 181 A. The illustrations show three of many possible positions of circles making straight line shadows. However, circles almost never appear in these positions on drawings.

When the circle is parallel to the plane receiving the shadow and to the projection plane of the view, the shadow will be a circle, Fig. 181 B. The shadow of the center of the circle is located by 45° projection and the shadow drawn in with a compass. The radius of the circle and shadow are the same since the rays of light are parallel.

Circles which are neither parallel to light rays nor to the picture plane of the view will cast elliptical shadows. Vertical and horizontal circles seen as lines in front view and vertical circles seen as vertical or horizontal lines in top view will cast elliptical shadows in those views. These are the most common positions of circles making elliptical shadows. They are shown in Fig. 181 C. There are two common methods of constructing the ellipses which are the shadows of circles. They are: (1) the method of tangent polygons, (2) the point method.

FRONT ELEV. ⎿ **R. ELEV.** ⎿

① FROM RIGHT ELEVATION

FRONT ELEV.

② WITH D ONLY

PLAN

③ FROM PLAN

CONSTRUCTION OF SHADOW OF TANGENT SQUARE

ELEVATION SHADOWS

SHADOWS IN PLAN

④ FOUR POSITIONS OF SHADOW SQUARE IN ELLIPSE CONSTRUCTION

⑤ TANGENT POINTS OF SQUARE AND CIRCLE

FIG. 182 TANGENT SQUARES FOR SHADOWS OF CIRCLES

   The tangent polygon is turned in the most convenient direction for easy construction. In Fig. 182 a tangent square is used. As shown in the right elevation view of Fig. 182 ɪ two sides of the square are parallel and two are perpendicular to the wall on which the shadow falls. The two sides which are parallel to the wall cast shadows which remain parallel to the front elevation of the circle. The two sides which are perpendicular to the wall cast 45° shadow lines. An inspection of the shadow of the square in Fig. 182 ɪɪ shows that two corners appear on the same construction line A-B which is horizontal for this position of the circle. Since the distance D is the same in front and side view the construction can be made without the side view or the plan when D, the distance from the circle to the wall receiving the shadow, is known. This construction for the tangent square is shown in the four commonly used positions in Fig. 182 ɪᴠ. The points of tangency of the four sides of the square with the circle can be located easily, Fig. 182 ᴠ. First draw the diagonals of the shadow of the square to locate its center C. Then through C draw lines L-M and N-O parallel to the sides of the shadow of the square. The intersections with the shadow of the square at L, M, N, and O are the required points of tangency of the square and circle. The ellipse can be drawn through these four points— It is difficult to draw a good ellipse with only four points and four tangents.

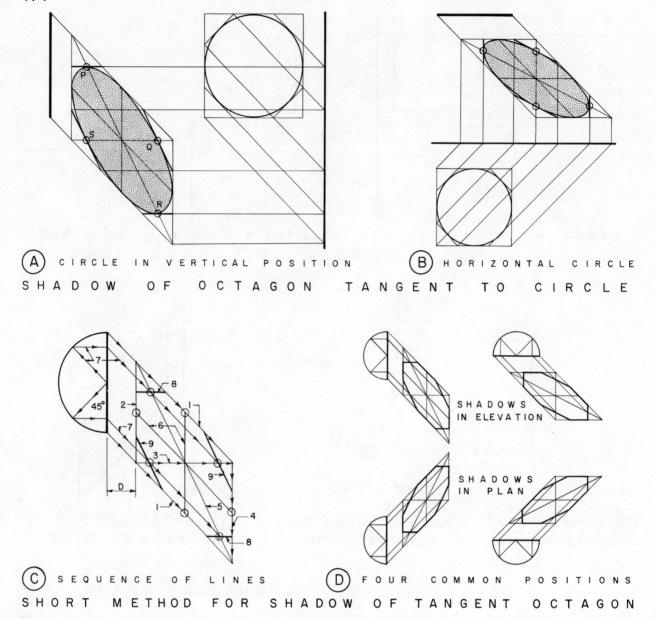

A CIRCLE IN VERTICAL POSITION   **B** HORIZONTAL CIRCLE

SHADOW OF OCTAGON TANGENT TO CIRCLE

C SEQUENCE OF LINES   **D** FOUR COMMON POSITIONS

SHORT METHOD FOR SHADOW OF TANGENT OCTAGON

SHADOWS IN ELEVATION

SHADOWS IN PLAN

FIG. 183 OCTAGON METHOD FOR SHADOWS OF CIRCLES

The tangent octagon can be used to provide four additional tangent lines and points when the tangent square does not give sufficient construction for the accuracy required. The octagon is drawn around the circle in the side view of Fig. 183 A and projected onto the shadow construction in the front view as shown. The shadows of the four added octagon sides cross the diagonals of the shadow of the square in the required points of tangency P, Q, R, S. Fig. 183 C shows a short cut in locating the octagon points of tangency and sides of the octagon when distance D is given. Two sides of the shadow of the octagon are parallel to each shadow of a diagonal of the square. The numbers give the order of drawing the lines and the arrows the directions they are drawn.

The point method of constructing the shadow of a circle locates the shadows of points only. It does not provide lines tangent to the curving shape of the shadow. It requires two views of the circle for the shadow construction. In Fig. 184 I the plan view of the circle is true shape. Points G

① FROM PLAN CIRCLE   ② FROM CIRCLE IN RIGHT ELEV.

THE POINT METHOD OF SHADOWS OF CIRCLES

③ VERTICAL CIRCLE   ④ HORIZONTAL CIRCLE

SHAPES OF SHADOWS OF PARTS OF CIRCLES

FIG. 184 CONSTRUCTION OF SHADOWS OF CIRCLES

and *H* are located on both views and their shadows *g* and *h* are located by 45° projection. When sufficient points have been located in this manner for the accuracy required, the curve is drawn through them.

When both given views of the circle are straight lines it is necessary to draw an additional view which will give the true shape of the circle for construction.

Shadows of parts of circles can be constructed by either the point or polygon method. It is more accurate to construct a greater amount of the circle than the small part required in order to get the ends of the curves precisely. A careful observation of the characteristics of shadows of half and quarter circles as shown in Figs. 184 III and IV will help in drawing these shapes correctly. Note particularly that the end directions of shadows of quarter and half circles are 45°, vertical, or horizontal for the shadows of circles in common positions.

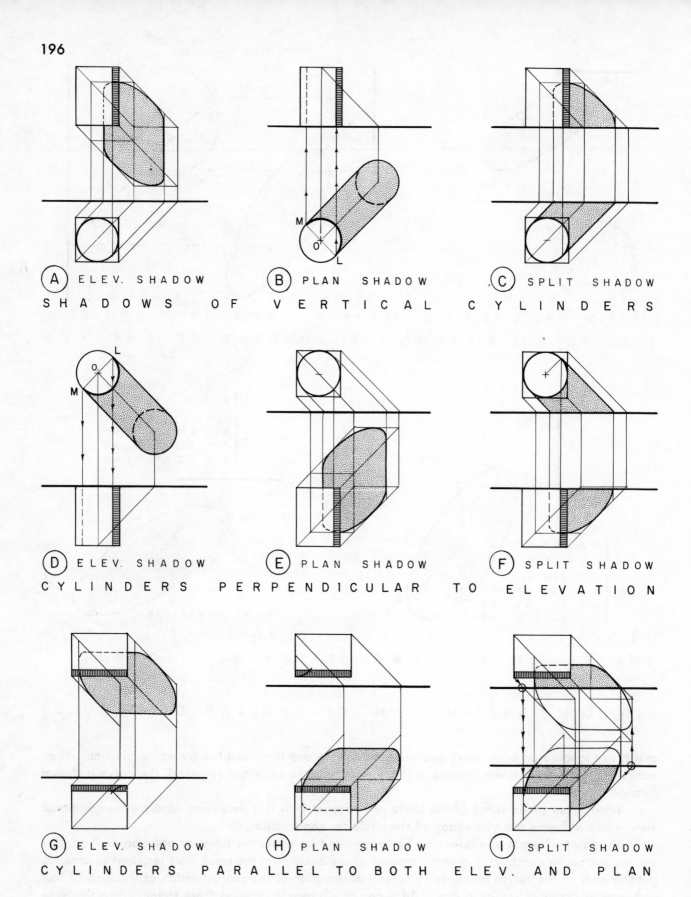

Ⓐ ELEV. SHADOW Ⓑ PLAN SHADOW Ⓒ SPLIT SHADOW

SHADOWS OF VERTICAL CYLINDERS

Ⓓ ELEV. SHADOW Ⓔ PLAN SHADOW Ⓕ SPLIT SHADOW

CYLINDERS PERPENDICULAR TO ELEVATION

Ⓖ ELEV. SHADOW Ⓗ PLAN SHADOW Ⓘ SPLIT SHADOW

CYLINDERS PARALLEL TO BOTH ELEV. AND PLAN

FIG. 185 SHADOWS AND SHADE LINES OF CYLINDERS

Ⓘ SHADOW FROM LINE SEEN IN END VIEW

Ⓘ HORIZONTAL LINE PARALLEL TO FRONT

Ⓘ SHADOW FROM A LARGER CYLINDER

FIG. 186 COMMON SHADOWS ON CYLINDERS

Shadows of Circular Solids. The simple geometric forms of cylinder, sphere, and cone are the simplest circular solids. Other less common circular geometric solids are the ellipsoid and the torus. Bowls, plates, urns, door knobs, and many other forms shaped by revolving on an axis are also circular solids. Most of these forms produce interesting shadows.

The shade line on a cylinder is located by finding the tangent point of light in the view where it is seen as a circle, Figs. 185 B and D. The point of tangency L is located accurately by drawing from the center O of the circle the line O-L perpendicular to the tangent. The shadow area on the surface of the cylinder extends from the visible shadow starting at L to a hidden shade line at M.

The shadow of a cylinder consists of the shadow of its bases and the straight line shadows made by its shade lines, Fig. 185 A. When the circular base is parallel to the floor or wall on which its shadow falls the shadow is a circle, Figs. 185 B, D. When the base is perpendicular to the wall or floor on which its shadow falls the shadow is an ellipse, Figs. 185 A, E, G, H. (Except when it is turned parallel to light rays.)

Shadows on cylinders from overhangs above them fall into three common classifications:

I. When the straight line making the shadow is seen in end view, the shadow is a 45° straight line, Fig. 186 I.

II. When a line perpendicular to the axis of a vertical or horizontal cylinder and parallel to the plane of the view casts a shadow on the cylinder, the shadow will be an arc of a circle in the view where the length of the cylinder is seen, Fig. 186 II. The radius of the arc will be the same as that of the cylinder. Sometimes a part of the shadow is type I and part type II.

III. When the shadow is from a larger circular form concentric with the cylinder the shadow will be elliptical in shape. It can be plotted by finding the shadows of a number of points. Be sure to use the same point in each view when plotting a shadow point, Fig. 186 III.

(A) SHADOWS BY PROJECTION

(B) SHADE LINES METHOD

CONSTRUCTION FOR UPRIGHT CONES

SHORT METHOD OF LOCATING SHADE LINES IN ELEVATION BY SUPERIMPOSING PLAN SHADOW OF A

(C) SHADOWS BY PROJECTION

(D) SHADE LINES METHOD

CONSTRUCTION FOR INVERTED CONES

SHORT METHOD OF LOCATING SHADE LINES IN ELEVATION BY SUPERIMPOSING PLAN SHADOW OF C

FIG. 187 SHADES AND PLAN SHADOWS OF CONES

I SLOPE OVER 45°   II SLOPE AT 45°   III 35°–16' SLOPE

FIG. 188 ELEVATION SHADOWS OF UPRIGHT CONES

The shade lines on a cone are located in an indirect manner. These shade lines cannot be located by tangent 45° lines as in the case of cylinders because the curving surface of the cone slopes instead of being perpendicular to the base of the cone. The shadow of a cone is outlined by the shadows of its base and two shade lines. The shade lines on the cone can be located from their shadows. In Fig. 187 A the shadow of the cone is constructed in plan view. The shadow A of the apex is located by 45° projection. It is connected to the shadow of the base by tangent lines A-B and A-C to complete the shadow outline. Since the base rests on the horizontal plane the shadow of the base coincides with the plan view of the base. O-B and O-C which are drawn from O perpendicular to the tangents A-B and A-C locate the points of tangency B and C. O-B and O-C are the shade lines of the cone. They are located in elevation by drawing vertical lines from their plan positions on the base of the cone to locate points D and E from which the shade lines are drawn to the elevation of the apex F. The entire construction can be duplicated more directly on the elevation, Fig. 187 B. From the apex G of the cone draw a horizontal line to the right. From the center O of the base draw a 45° line up to the right to meet the horizontal at X. Draw the circle plan of the base with O as a center. Draw tangents from X to the circle. Locate points of tangency H and I and then the ends of the shade lines on the base of the cone at J and K with verticals from H and I. This construction duplicates the shape of the plan shadow of Fig. 187 A.

The inverted cone of Fig. 187 C touches the floor plane at its apex. Its shadow is located in plan in this figure. The shade point can be traced back to the plan from the shadow and then from the plan to elevation. The entire construction for locating the shade lines can be duplicated on the elevation without use of plan as shown in Fig. 187 D.

The amount of shadow on a cone varies with the proportions and position of the cone. The shadow on an upright cone increases in width as the cone approaches the shape of a cylinder. Its maximum limit is the width of the shadow on a cylinder. When the slope of the cone is 45° there is no visible shadow in front view, Fig. 188 II. At the angle of light 35°–16' or less there is no visible or hidden shadow on the conical surface, Fig. 188 III.

The shadow on an inverted cone approaches the shadow width of a cylinder as its minimum. At 45° three-fourths of the cone is in shadow and at 35°–16' it is in complete shadow.

It should be observed that the hidden and visible shade lines are not at equal distances from the edges of a cone. The hidden shade line is farther from the edge on an upright cone, line F-D, Fig. 187 A. The visible shade line is farther on an inverted cone, Fig. 187 C. The shadow covers less than half the conical surface of an upright cone, more than half of an inverted cone surface.

FRONT VIEW
OF A SPHERE
① SHADE LINE

FRONT VIEW
OF SPHERE
② SHADOW ONTO A WALL

RIGHT SIDE
VIEW OF SPHERE

FIG. 189 SHADE LINE AND SHADOW OF A SPHERE

The shade line on a sphere is an ellipse as seen in any of the standard multi-view drawings. It is actually a great circle of the sphere which is seen obliquely in all multi-view drawings where it appears as an ellipse. In front view the visible shadow is a crescent shape at the lower right of the sphere. The hidden shadow extends from the edge of the visible shadow to an outline at the top left which exactly duplicates the visible shadow in reverse, Fig. 189 I. The entire shade line is a complete ellipse. Its major axis A-B is a 45° line extending from the lower left to the top right edges of the sphere and passing through its center. This line locates points A and B the tangent points of light at the lower left and upper right edges of the sphere. The minor axis is the 45° line C-D through the center of the sphere and perpendicular to the major axis. From point A or B lines at 30° to the A-B axis locate points C and D. A horizontal and vertical line are drawn from A and from B to meet the vertical and horizontal center lines of the sphere. These intersections E, F, G, and H give four additional points on the shade line. Points A and G are equidistant from the vertical 45° light plane through the center of the sphere. They are therefore on the same horizontal line. The ellipse of the complete shade line can be drawn through the eight points which have been located. These are a sufficient number of points for accuracy if the draftsman will remember to round out the small ends of the ellipse so that they are tangent to the sphere.

The shadow of a sphere is an ellipse with both axes at 45°. In front view the major axis is down and to the right. The simplest method of locating the shadow is to find the shadows of a number of parallel circles in the sphere. The shadow of the sphere is the outline around the shadows of the circles. The circles are cut through the sphere parallel to the surface on which the shadow falls. The shadows of these circles are circles of the same size and can be drawn easily.

In the right side view of Fig. 189 II line J-K represents an edge view of a circle cut through the sphere. This circle is parallel to the wall Y-Z on which the shadow falls. J-K is the diameter of the circle and J-O and K-O its radii. The shadow of the center O of this circle is found by 45° projection. With a center at O and a radius J-O, the shadow of the circle is drawn in front view. Line L-M is the side view of a second circle. The shadow of its center is found at X. Its radius N-L is then used to draw its shadow with X as a center. By drawing horizontally across from L and M in side view a second circle P-R with same diameter is located. These two equal circles have shadows of the same radius. They are equidistant from circle A-B which passes through the center of the sphere. Find as many circle shadows as necessary to provide the required accuracy in the outline of the shadow of the sphere. The circles can be located at any desired positions in side view. The use of equal pairs of circles provides symmetry and order in the construction.

Irregular Circular Forms. The most common irregular circular form has a vertical axis and horizontal circular elements. Such a shape is shown in Fig. 190. Four types of shade or shadow points can be located on these forms.

A. Points can be located on the edges by 45° tangents. Point A1 is the shadow point at the top left located by the tangent to the overhanging edge above. Point A2 is the shade point on the convex surface on the left. Point A3 is the shade point on the right edge at the top.

B. Because of the symmetry of the object and the direction of light there will be a shade or shadow point on the vertical center line of the object at the intersection of the horizontal from each A point. These points are lettered B1, B2, B3. Point B3 is on the hidden shade line.

C. Where the profile of the curving shape is vertical the shade point C will be the same distance in from the edge as on the vertical cylinder of the same diameter. This distance is slightly less than ⅓ the radius of the horizontal circle at that point. It is usually sufficiently accurate to estimate these distances. They can be worked out precisely on circles of required diameters when necessary.

D. The smallest width of shade or shadow occurs on the left of the object at the 45° points L. The height of these points can be located on the profile by using the true angle of light (35°–16′ which is the diagonal of a cube instead of 45°) as shown by the dotted lines on the left edge of Fig. 190. Points L are located at slightly less than one third the radius from the points of tangency of the 35°–16′ lines.

The above four types of points are all that can be located on this type of form by 45° projection.

The vertical light plane method can be used to determine shade and shadow points on irregular circular solids. The light planes are at 45° in plan. Their intersections with the object lie in vertical light planes. Any point on an intersection line of a plane and the object will cast its shadow on the intersection line. Therefore 45° projection lines can be used on each profile cut through the object to determine shade and shadow points. The method is long and tedious. There are few projects which justify its use.

M E T H O D   O F   E A S I L Y   L O C A T E D   P O I N T S

F I G . 190   S H A D E   L I N E S   O N   C I R C U L A R   S O L I D S

The direction of light on different views of the same object is often a matter of concern to the draftsman. There are three solutions. Each may be used under conditions where it seems to be the best answer.

A. The direction is chosen for the object as a unit and each view made to conform to that direction. This method is particularly logical if the object will be placed with a constant direction of light on it. However this system leaves two of the elevations in complete shadow, Fig. 191 A. These shadowed drawings will not explain the object as clearly as those which have both light and shadow areas.

B. The same direction of light can be used on each elevation as though they are all turned the same way and are in the same plane. In this system the front direction of light may be used on all the elevations. The plan views should conform to the same light direction as the front view when shadows are shown on the plans. This arrangement is usually quite satisfactory and is commonly used on a set of multi-view drawings, Fig. 191 B.

C. A direction of light can be chosen for each view as a separate problem, Fig. 191 C. This allows the most effective presentation of each individual drawing. If carried to extremes it may cause confusion in understanding the entire object.

If light directions are limited to diagonals of cubes, projections of the same horizontal and vertical elements will give equal shadows on all elevations and keep the shadows simple. The light may come from either left or right to secure the best shadow effect.

Directions other than the conventional one from the top left to lower right on front view can be used when the draftsman wishes to do so. This may be done to (1) fit a given site or location, (2) avoid unsatisfactory shadow forms, (3) produce a different effect, or

REAR ELEV.   L. ELEV.   FRONT ELEV.   R. ELEV.

(A) SINGLE DIRECTION FOR UNIT

REAR ELEV.   L. ELEV.   FRONT ELEV.   R. ELEV.

(B) SAME DIRECTION ON EACH ELEV.

REAR ELEV.   L. ELEV.   FRONT ELEV.   R. ELEV.

(C) BEST DIRECTION ON EACH ELEV.

FIG. 191 LIGHT DIRECTION SYSTEMS
FOR SHADOWS ON SEVERAL VIEWS

FRONT ELEVATION   R. ELEV.

(I) CONVENTIONAL 45° ANGLE

FRONT ELEVATION   R. ELEV.

(II) LOWER ANGLE OF LIGHT

FRONT ELEVATION   R. ELEV.

(III) STEEPER ANGLE OF LIGHT

FIG. 192 SIMPLE VARIATIONS IN ELEVATION ANGLE OF LIGHT

for other reasons. The location of the object either inside or out of doors may give a constant direction of light or a limited variation of light direction which leaves one or more sides of the object in shadow. The designer may wish to recognize this fact in his renderings and present the object as he expects it to be seen.

Shadow forms are sometimes unsatisfactory with the conventional direction of light. The shadow of an overhang may fall at a bad height. This may give a tiny shadow, one that is too large, one which coincides with the edge of another form or shadow, Fig. 192 I, or is unsatisfactory in some other way. The simplest change that can be made from the conventional direction is to use a larger (60° or 75° perhaps) or smaller (30° or 15°) angle of light than 45° on elevations, Figs. 192 II, III. If the plan angle of light remains at 45° all elevation views will have the same angle of light. This angle can be one of those suggested above which are obtained with standard triangles or any other angle desired. A constant light direction for the entire object must be assumed in working out the shadows on a single view. If the elevation direction of light is 30° and the plan direction 45° then all other elevations must have a 30° angle of light when used to construct front view shadows. When the plan angle of light is not 45° each two opposite elevations have the same light angle. Adjacent elevations have different angles of light.

A lower angle of light, one more nearly perpendicular to the walls in plan, or a combination of the two can be used to decrease shadow areas on the object. A steeper angle of light, one more nearly tangent to walls in plan, or a combination of the two variations from the conventional direction can be used to produce larger elevation shadows. These variations will help change the mood of a presentation.

CHAPTER 27
Shadows on Paraline Drawings

In addition to their value in design, paraline shadows also serve a useful purpose as an intermediate step between the study of multi-view and perspective shadows. The more easily constructed paraline drawing shadows serve as an introduction and aid to understanding three-dimensional shadows on perspective drawings. Characteristics of paraline shadows follow the general characteristics of the type of drawing used. Any parallel lines of the object and its shadows remain parallel in the drawing. The following three rules explain a great many of the shadows on paraline drawings.

1. When a line is parallel to a plane receiving the shadow, the shadow is parallel to the line. In Fig. 194 A the vertical lines cast vertical shadows on the wall planes. The horizontal overhangs make shadows parallel to the direction of the overhangs in the drawings. In Fig. 194 B the horizontal overhang edge *A-B* is parallel to the parts of the shadow from this line on wall at *a-x* and floor at *x-b*. The right top edge *B-C* and rear top edge *C-D* have shadows *b-c* and *c-d* parallel to them on the floor because these lines are parallel to the floor surface.

SHADOWS ARE OFTEN PARALLEL
TO LINES MAKING THE SHADOWS

PARALLEL LINES MAKE PARALLEL SHADOWS
OVER ANY PLANE SURFACE

FIG. 194 SHADOWS ON PARALINE DRAWINGS

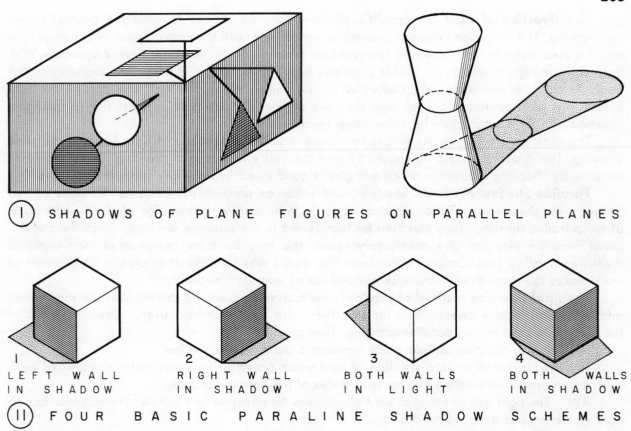

I SHADOWS OF PLANE FIGURES ON PARALLEL PLANES

1	2	3	4
LEFT WALL IN SHADOW	RIGHT WALL IN SHADOW	BOTH WALLS IN LIGHT	BOTH WALLS IN SHADOW

II FOUR BASIC PARALINE SHADOW SCHEMES

FIG. 195 SHADOWS ON PARALINE DRAWINGS

2. Parallel lines make parallel shadows on the same plane or on parallel planes. In Fig. 194 c the parallel lines projecting from the right wall plane make parallel shadows on that plane. The continuation of their shadows on the slanting surface and on the floor are also parallel to each other. The top edges of the triangular horizontal prisms cast parallel shadows on the adjoining prisms and on the floor, Fig. 194 D. The slanting right edges also make parallel shadows on the floor.

3. When a plane figure casts a shadow on a plane parallel to the figure, the drawings of the figure and its shadow are identical, Fig. 195 I. This fact is useful not only for shadows of plane figures but for shapes cut by planes parallel to the surface receiving the shadow as a method of shadow construction as shown in Fig. 195 I, right illustration.

The basic shadow schemes for paraline drawings are designated by the light and shadow conditions of the two visible wall planes and one horizontal plane of the outside of a box shape. When a wall is in light it may have shadow areas over a part of its surface from projections or from sunken areas. When a wall plane is in shadow its surface and all surfaces parallel to it are completely in shadow. These are the basic shadow schemes for paraline drawings, Fig. 195 II.

1. Left wall in shadow with the right wall and top in light.

2. Right wall in shadow with the left wall and top in light.

3. Both walls in light with the top in light also. The direction of light may give larger shadows from projections on one wall than on the other.

4. Both walls in shadow. The light may strike the top and make shadows of projections there. The shadow of the object will extend onto the floor plane in front of the object and be a prominent part of the composition.

The direction of light for paraline shadows can be chosen to give the best effect on the drawing. The simple and obvious procedure would be to use the conventional direction of light which is used on multi-view drawings. This direction is never satisfactory on isometric drawings. With both walls in light there are no visible shadows from projections and no visible shadows on the floor. All shadows are completely concealed by the object. When one wall is in shadow the horizontal tops of projections conceal their shadows on the wall which is in light. The conventional direction of light is satisfactory for some other paraline drawings.

The most satisfactory procedure is to choose a suitable direction of light for each paraline drawing. The direction should be chosen to give the best effect on that drawing. This can usually be done by choosing a direction which will give a good effect in some one main shadow area.

Paraline Shadow Methods. Shadow construction on paraline drawings can be done by two methods. The shadows can first be worked out on the three multi-view drawings which show the areas of the paraline drawing. They can then be transferred to the paraline drawing. Since the conventional direction may not give satisfactory results this may be more complicated than standard multi-view shadow construction. Furthermore the results may be difficult to predict. Duplication of work makes the theoretically easy task become rather long and involved.

The light direction method of shadow construction on paraline drawings is the most direct and most satisfactory one. In this method there are four standard useful directions of light for shadow casting on any paraline drawing. They are:

L   The true direction of light which connects a point and its shadow.

H   The horizontal or plan direction of light which provides the direction for shadows of vertical lines on areas representing horizontal surfaces of the paraline drawing.

RW   The right wall direction of light which gives the direction for shadows of perpendiculars on right wall planes of the paraline drawing.

LW   The left wall direction of light which gives the direction of shadows of perpendiculars on left wall planes of the paraline drawing.

An example of each of these four directions is given on the large block of Fig. 196 c.

When any two of these directions are given or assumed, the remaining two can be determined. In Fig. 196 A the true direction of light L and the plan direction of light H have been assumed for the object. Direction H is made the diagonal of a plan rectangle which has its sides parallel to the horizontal lines of the paraline drawing of the object, Fig. 196 A step I. From one of the two corners of the rectangle which are on the diagonal H a light direction line L is drawn to meet a vertical from the other corner which is located on the diagonal, Fig. 196 A step II. This point establishes the height of the light direction prism which is now completed by drawing parallels to the lines already drawn as shown in Fig. 196 A step III. The LW and RW directions are then drawn on the completed prism as shown in Fig. 196 A step IV which gives all four of the useful light directions for this paraline drawing. The H, RW, and LW directions are the projections of the ray of light A-B (which is the diagonal of the light prism) onto the bottom, right side, and left side respectively of the light prism. These are the paraline representations of the directions which light rays appear to take in each of these views. Any two of the four light directions L, H, RW, and LW determine the proportions of the light prism and the other two directions. The actual size of the prism does not have any effect on the direction of light. When one face of the prism is drawn around the diagonal for that face the size of the prism is established. Since the face of the prism which is drawn first can be made any size, the prism can be made any size but will keep the same proportions regardless of its size. The light prism must be in the same type of paraline drawing as the object, its lines parallel to the axes of the object. This method of shadow construction works on any type of paraline drawing.

In Fig. 196 B the plan direction of light H and the right wall direction of light RW as assumed for the large block are used to construct this light prism.

In the large block shape of Fig. 196 c, LW is the assumed direction of the shadow of D-E which is a perpendicular to the left wall plane. RW is the chosen direction of the shadow of F-G, a perpendicular to the right wall plane.

H AND L GIVEN ON OBJECT   STEP I   STEP II   STEP III   STEP IV

(A) PRISM CONSTRUCTED FROM DIRECTION H AND L

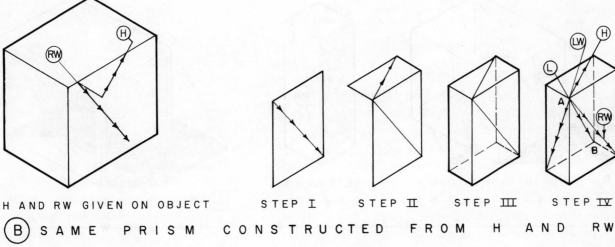

H AND RW GIVEN ON OBJECT   STEP I   STEP II   STEP III   STEP IV

(B) SAME PRISM CONSTRUCTED FROM H AND RW

LW AND RW GIVEN ON OBJECT   STEP I   STEP II   STEP III   STEP IV

(C) SAME PRISM CONSTRUCTED FROM LW AND RW

FIG. 196 LIGHT PRISMS FOR PARALINE SHADOWS

208

Ⓐ S H A D O W S   O F
P E R P E N D I C U L A R S

Ⓑ L I G H T
P R I S M

Ⓒ S H A D O W S   I N   B O X

B O T H   W A L L S   I N   L I G H T

Ⓓ S H A D O W S   O F
P E R P E N D I C U L A R S

Ⓔ L I G H T
P R I S M

Ⓕ S H A D O W S   I N   B O X

L E F T   W A L L   I N   S H A D O W

Ⓖ S H A D O W S   O F
P E R P E N D I C U L A R S

Ⓗ L I G H T
P R I S M

Ⓘ S H A D O W S   I N   B O X

R I G H T   W A L L   I N   S H A D O W

FIG. 197 USES OF THE FOUR LIGHT DIRECTIONS

I DETAILS OF SHADOW CONSTRUCTION

VI WITH L AND H

V WITH L AND LW

II WITH L AND RW

III WITH LW AND RW

IV WITH H AND LW

FIVE DIFFERENT CONSTRUCTIONS FOR SAME SHADOW

FIG. 198 CONSTRUCTION OF PARALINE SHADOWS

In Fig. 197 A the shadows of the perpendiculars to the top, right wall, and left wall are located by drawing the construction lines shown parallel to the direction lines of the prism in Fig. 197 B. Shadows are constructed in the hollow box of Fig. 197 C with the same directions. Different shadow effects can be obtained by using different directions for light as shown in Figs. 197 D, E, F, and G, H, I. It is often convenient to use one or more of the light directions to trace lines where there are no actual shadows. The vertical line C-D of Fig. 197 F does not cast a shadow. However its imaginary shadow D-E can be used to locate point E on the shadow outline. The line A-B does not cast a shadow on the left wall of Fig. 197 D. Nevertheless the left wall direction of light can be traced from B to the ground and then along the ground to locate the visible part of the shadow. From point X a ray of light can be traced back to determine point Y where light and shadow meet. The same point Y can be located by drawing a vertical line from the right corner of the A-B area to the top corner of the object at Z, then drawing a direction RW from Z to locate Y. There are often different constructions which will locate the same shadow point and check on accuracy.

Although it is seldom necessary to have all four of the light directions provided by the light prism construction, it is often convenient to use them. In Fig. 198 I the direction of the shadow G-K is located by extending line A-B to point C then drawing the line from K toward point C. This line C-K is the LW direction. Directions H and L are often adequate for all shadow construction for a drawing. However, the wall directions may provide shorter, more direct construction, and more accurate results.

In Fig. 198 II, III, IV, V, and VI different constructions have been shown for the same shadow. These figures will demonstrate the possible variations in construction for paraline shadows.

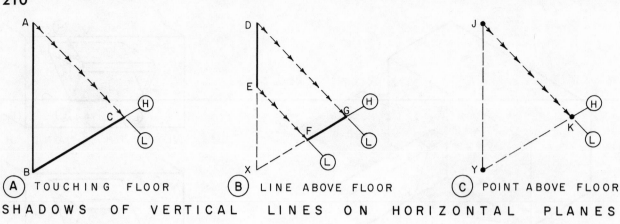

A TOUCHING FLOOR   B LINE ABOVE FLOOR   C POINT ABOVE FLOOR

SHADOWS OF VERTICAL LINES ON HORIZONTAL PLANES

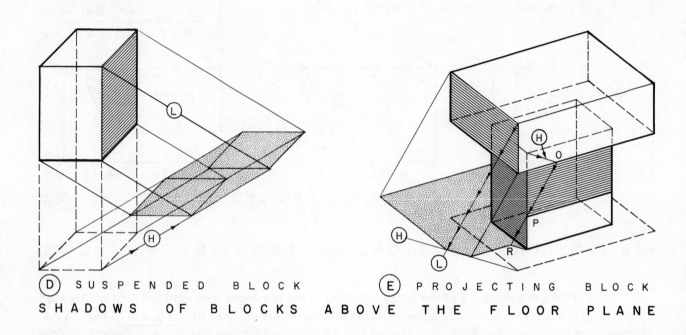

D SUSPENDED BLOCK   E PROJECTING BLOCK

SHADOWS OF BLOCKS ABOVE THE FLOOR PLANE

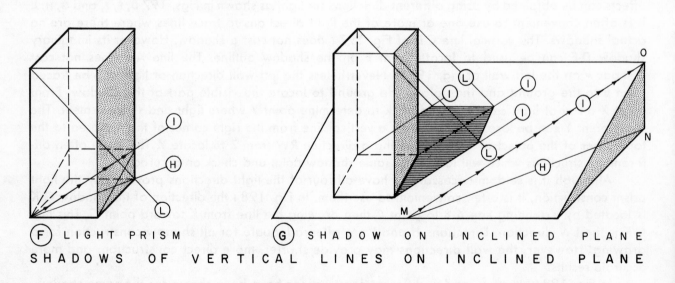

F LIGHT PRISM   G SHADOW ON INCLINED PLANE

SHADOWS OF VERTICAL LINES ON INCLINED PLANE

FIG. 199 CONSTRUCTION OF PARALINE SHADOWS

Shadows of vertical lines on the horizontal planes occur in the shadows of most objects. In Fig. 199 A the shadow of a vertical line A-B extends from the point B where it touches the horizontal plane. The direction of this shadow is the plan or H direction of light. The shadow ends where a light ray L from the top A of the line intersects with the shadow at C. B-C is the shadow of A-B.

When the vertical line D-E is suspended above the horizontal plane on which the shadow falls its extension to point X on this plane must be located, Fig. 199 B. Light ray lines L are then drawn from each end D and E of the line to meet the plan shadow direction line H from X and locate F-G the required shadow.

To find the shadow on a horizontal plane of any point J, a similar construction is used, Fig. 199 C. A vertical line J-Y is drawn from J to meet the horizontal plane at Y. The plan shadow direction line H from Y meets the light ray line L from J at K the required shadow of point J.

This system of locating shadows of vertical lines and points with any chosen plan direction H of light and direction L of light rays can be used to find shadows of areas and solids. In Fig. 199 D a rectangular solid with vertical corners is located above the floor plane on which the shadow falls. Each vertical corner casts a shadow similar to the one of the line in Fig. 199 B. The shadows of the corners are connected to make the shadow area. It should be observed also that the shadows of the top and bottom of the box shape are identical with the shapes of the top and bottom of the object. After one point on each is located these shadows of the top and bottom may be drawn in as directly as possible. These shapes are then connected by tangents to complete the shadow outline. This is an application of the principle that plane figures parallel to the plane receiving the shadows have shadows which are identical with the figures.

In Fig. 199 E a large block is supported by a smaller block. The H direction is traced on the concealed surface of the overhang to locate a point O which casts its shadow at P and also at R.

Shadows of verticals on an inclined plane appear to be difficult. One method of locating these shadows requires the use of an auxiliary inclined plane in the light prism, Fig. 199 F. If this plane exactly parallels the inclined plane of the object the light direction l on the plane in the prism will be the correct direction for the shadows of vertical lines on the inclined plane of the object. The l direction can also be found on the object as shown by triangle M-N-O of Fig. 199 G.

Shadows of circular objects can usually be located by the point method. The H and L light directions are used to locate points on the shadows in the examples of Fig. 200. In number I the top and its shadow on the floor are the same shape.

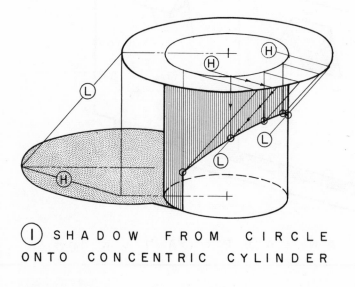

Ⓘ SHADOW FROM CIRCLE
ONTO CONCENTRIC CYLINDER

Ⓘⓘ SHADOW ON FLOOR
FROM VERTICAL CURVE

FIG. 200   SHADOWS   OF   CIRCULAR   OBJECTS

SHADOWS OF BLOCK FORMS

SHADOWS OF AN APPLIANCE

FIG. 201 EXAMPLES OF PARALINE SHADOWS

SHADOW ON FLOOR

SHADOW ON
FLOOR + WALL

SHADOWS OF A LAMP SHAPE

SHADOWS OF A CABINET

FIG. 202 EXAMPLES OF PARALINE SHADOWS

CHAPTER 28

Perspective Shadow Methods

The shadow lines of a perspective drawing are a part of the line system of the drawing. When they are parallel to the picture plane they retain their true directions in perspective. The shadows of vertical lines on vertical surfaces remain vertical in standard one-point and two-point perspectives. This is the most common example of shadow lines parallel to the picture plane, Fig. 203. When the shadow lines are oblique to the picture plane they go to the same vanishing points as lines of the object to which they are parallel, Fig. 203.

Three methods of casting shadows on perspective drawings are described briefly below. The last two of these are variations of the light direction method. They are explained in detail in the next two chapters.

1. Shadows can be worked out on the three multi-view drawings which show areas of the perspective drawing. They can then be drawn in the perspective from their measurements just as other lines are drawn. This does not require any new theory. It does require shadow construction on four drawings to obtain them on one. When the conventional direction of light is not satisfactory, the construction of shadows on the three multi-view drawings is more difficult. Since this procedure is a repetition of multi-view shadows and perspective which have been described previously, no further explanation is given.

2. The light direction method of perspective shadows with light rays parallel to the picture plane makes the constructing of shadows directly on a perspective drawing relatively easy. This method is a simple and effective one for two-point perspective, Fig. 204 A. It requires that one set of wall planes be in shadow and the other in light. The horizontal shadows of vertical lines which are characteristic of this method may appear stiff on some perspectives. The big advantage of the

FIG. 203 CHARACTERISTICS OF PERSPECTIVE SHADOWS

214

(A) TWO—POINT PERSPECTIVE

(B) ONE—POINT PERSPECTIVE

LIGHT PARALLEL TO PICTURE PLANE

(C) TWO—POINT PERSPECTIVE

(D) ONE—POINT PERSPECTIVE

LIGHT OBLIQUE TO PICTURE PLANE

FIG. 204 PERSPECTIVE SHADOW METHODS

method is the use of two sets of parallel lines which remain parallel in perspective for construction purposes. The rays of light L are one of these sets of parallel lines and the plan direction of light H the other. They are adequate for all shadow construction. The parallel lines for the other two light directions LW and RW are oblique to the picture plane and will be drawn to their respective vanishing points in perspective. They are sometimes useful for shadow construction.

This method is not satisfactory for one-point perspectives since light parallels one set of wall planes and produces artificial effects with too much shadow area, Fig. 204 B.

3. The light direction method with light rays oblique to picture plane requires a vanishing point for each of the four useful light directions, L, H, LW, and RW which are used for the shadow construction. Points L and H can be located at random with minor restrictions as to their positions. They are usually adequate for shadow construction. Since light in any direction can be used for the shadows of a perspective drawing by this method, any lighting condition can be represented. Shadows of verticals can be any direction on horizontal planes thus avoiding the stiff effect of horizontal shadows. This method works equally well on both two-point and one-point perspectives, Figs. 204 c and D. It is a very satisfactory method for good shadow effects.

CHAPTER 29

Light Parallel to Picture Plane

A method using parallel construction lines to locate shadows on two-point perspective drawings is provided by light rays parallel to the picture plane. The rays of light *L* and the shadows of vertical lines on horizontal planes *H* (plan direction of light) are both parallel to the picture plane Fig. 205. Both of these sets of shadow construction lines remain actually parallel in the perspective drawing. The plan direction of light must be horizontal in this system. The rays of light can be at any desired angle but must all be parallel. It is convenient to use one of the standard angles given by common triangles when they will provide a satisfactory shadow effect on the object. If 30°, 45°, or 60° will not give suitable results, an adjustable triangle can be set to a better angle for the purpose, or the parallel lines can be drawn at the chosen angle by methods previously explained.

When the two sets of parallel light direction lines *L* and *H* are the only ones used for the shadows, this system is one of locating shadows of vertical lines on horizontal surfaces. Some of these *H* shadow construction lines may be actual boundary lines of shadow areas, others may merely locate points through which the shadow lines are drawn. In Fig. 205 A, vertical line *A-B* casts an *H* direction shadow line *B-C*. Vertical line *D-E* does not cast a shadow but its *H* direction imaginary shadow *E-F* may be used to locate point *F* on the shadow outline. *C-F* is drawn to *VR* and a line is drawn from *F* to *VL* to continue the visible shadow outline. The rays of light *L* connect points and their shadows. An *L* line is not used for the direction of actual shadow lines. The *H* lines give the plan direction of light and are the shadows of vertical lines of the perspective on horizontal planes.

A vertical line *G-H* of Fig. 205 B is suspended above the plane on which its shadow falls. It is necessary to find point *I* where *G-H* extended would meet the floor plane in order to construct the

Ⓐ VERTICAL LINE
TOUCHING FLOOR

Ⓑ VERTICAL LINE
ABOVE THE FLOOR

Ⓒ POINT HELD
ABOVE THE FLOOR

FIG. 205 BASIC SHADOW CONSTRUCTION METHOD

I LEFT SIDE IN SHADOW   II RIGHT SIDE IN SHADOW

ONLY TWO SHADOW SCHEMES ARE POSSIBLE

shadow *J-K* of this line. The same is true of any form which is above the horizontal plane receiving its shadow. The box shape in Fig. 205 B and the large circle of Fig. 205 C are both projected vertically onto the horizontal or floor plane receiving their shadows. The projection of point *M* of Fig. 205 C is at *N* on the floor plane and its shadow is at *O*.

Line *P-T* is an example of tracing a plan light direction line which is not a shadow line in order to locate a shadow. The shadow of point *P* is located on the vertical below *T* where the *L* line from *P* intersects it at *R*. A series of constructions like *P-T-R* can be used to locate any number of points on the shadow of the large circle on the vertical cylinder.

Limitations of shadow effects secured with light parallel to the picture plane are a disadvantage of this system. (A) Horizontal shadows of vertical lines may give a stiff and unnatural effect. (B) One set of wall planes must be in shadow and the other in light. They cannot both be in light, Fig. 206 I and II. (C) Change of direction of light rays L has no effect on size of vertical shadows which remain constant. When the shadow areas of overhangs are increased by using a steeper angle of light the shadow of the object on the ground plane becomes shorter. With a lower angle of light the overhang shadows decrease and the shadow of the object lengthens, Figs. 206 III, IV, and V.

Nevertheless this method is often entirely satisfactory. It is the easiest direct method of locating shadows on two-point perspective drawings. A clear understanding of its scope and limitations will help the delineator to use it effectively.

III STEEP ANGLE OF LIGHT

IV MEDIUM ANGLE OF LIGHT

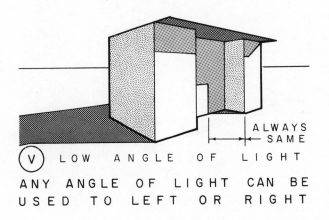

V LOW ANGLE OF LIGHT

ANY ANGLE OF LIGHT CAN BE USED TO LEFT OR RIGHT

FIG. 206 SHADOW VARIATIONS
LIGHT PARALLEL TO PICT. PL.

218

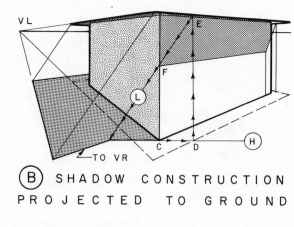

(A) SHADOW CONSTRUCTION
ON BOTTOM OF OVERHANG

(B) SHADOW CONSTRUCTION
PROJECTED TO GROUND

(C) SHADOW OVER A
SIMPLE OFFSET

(D) SHADOW CONSTRUCTION
ON CONCEALED OVERHANG

(E) SHADOWS OVER SLANTING
AND OFFSET SURFACES

FIG. 207 SHADOW CONSTRUCTION
WITH L AND H LIGHT DIRECTIONS

SHADOW WIDTHS FROM ORTHOGRAPHIC PLAN

SUBSTITUTE LINES ABOVE PERSPECTIVE

VL   VR

THE PERSPECTIVE

SUBSTITUTE LINES BELOW PERSPECTIVE

FIG. 208 SUBSTITUTE LINES FOR ACCURACY IN DETERMINING WIDTHS OF SHADOWS

Although shadow construction in two-point perspective is relatively simple with light parallel to the picture plane, it does often require a great deal of ingenuity in working out the shadows. In Figs. 207 A, B, and D the shadow of the overhang has been constructed on different surfaces of the drawings. In Fig. 207 A the bottom surface of the overhang is a visible and adequately large area for this construction with line A-B in the plan direction of light H. In Fig. 207 B the bottom surface of the overhang is too thin and its lines too nearly horizontal for accurate construction with a horizontal line. The projection of the overhang on the ground plane provides an adequate representation of the overhang for construction of the shadow. Line C-D is drawn on this surface and a vertical line from D locates point E. A light ray from E locates the shadow F of point E on the nearest vertical corner of the walls. The shadow of the overhang is drawn from F to VR. In the perspective view from above in Fig. 207 D the concealed surface of the overhang is used for the shadow construction.

Figs. 207 C and E provide examples of constructions of other types of shadows. In Fig. 207 C the shadow line G-I from the top left edge J-M of the large block on the vertical surface of the lower block is constructed in two ways on the example. The shadow of the long vertical corner M-N can be used to locate the shadow on the lower horizontal surface and find point I. The shadow construction from the left vertical corner on the middle horizontal surface locates point G. Then line G-I is drawn. The second method of locating G-I may be more accurate, especially when the vertical surface on which G-I is located is small. After point I is located, the vertical wall above I is assumed to extend to point J. Then the line J-M will cast a shadow J-I of which G-I is a part.

Accuracy in casting shadows directly on a perspective drawing depends on having adequate representations of horizontal lines and areas on which to work out the shadows. When the horizontal lines and areas in a part of a perspective drawing are too horizontal and thin the method of a substitute area on the ground plane used in Fig. 207 B can be extended to areas above or below the perspective. In Fig. 208 neither the tops nor the bottoms of walls provide sufficiently definite forms for shadow construction. When their lines are drawn either above or below the perspective better results are obtained. When the orthographic plan which was used for the perspective construction is available, T-square lines can be drawn on it to trace the direction of light, Fig. 208.

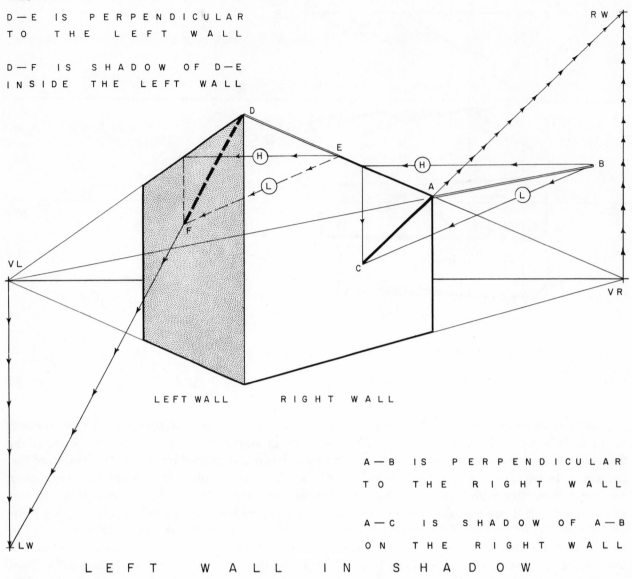

D—E IS PERPENDICULAR
TO THE LEFT WALL

D—F IS SHADOW OF D—E
INSIDE THE LEFT WALL

LEFT WALL   RIGHT WALL

A—B IS PERPENDICULAR

TO THE RIGHT WALL

A—C IS SHADOW OF A—B

ON THE RIGHT WALL

LEFT WALL IN SHADOW

FIG. 209 LOCATING WALL SHADOW VANISHING POINTS

Wall shadow vanishing points. The directions of shadows of perpendiculars on the wall surfaces are given by the wall vanishing points of light LW and RW. These wall shadow vanishing points are useful for actual shadows of perpendiculars to the walls and also in tracing construction lines for other shadows. The two wall directions of light are actually parallel inclined lines in each of the two sets of wall planes. Since each set of lines is oblique to the picture plane the lines of the two sets will converge to their respective vanishing points.

Wall shadow vanishing points are not necessary for shadow construction by this method. Most shadows can be worked out rather directly by use of the L and H light directions. However, the wall shadow vanishing points sometimes provide an easier, more direct, and more accurate construction. This is especially true when there are a great number of perpendiculars casting shadows on wall planes. In such a case it is very convenient to be able to draw all these shadow lines to a single vanishing point directly and also avoid minor inaccuracies in line directions.

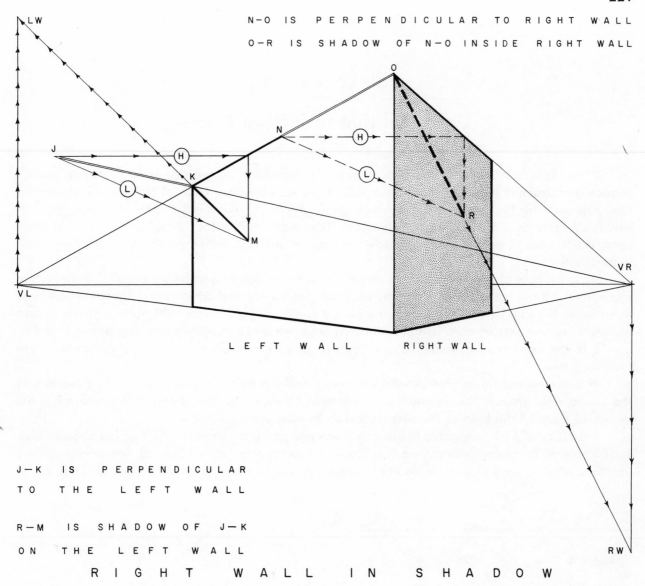

N—O IS PERPENDICULAR TO RIGHT WALL

O—R IS SHADOW OF N—O INSIDE RIGHT WALL

LEFT WALL   RIGHT WALL

J—K IS PERPENDICULAR
TO THE LEFT WALL

R—M IS SHADOW OF J—K
ON THE LEFT WALL

RIGHT WALL IN SHADOW

FIG. 210 LOCATING WALL SHADOW VANISHING POINTS

Wall shadow vanishing points are sometimes inconveniently far away. They may be so far that it is impractical to locate and use one or both of them. The farther apart the vanishing points of the perspective and the steeper the angle of light the more distant the wall shadow vanishing points will be.

A simple method of locating the two wall shadow vanishing points is to construct a large shadow of a perpendicular on each of the two wall planes. These large shadow lines are extended to meet the verticals through the vanishing points of the perspective and locate the required points, Figs. 209 and 210. The shadow line from the perpendicular to a left wall plane is extended to meet the vertical through *VL* to locate *LW*. Point *LW* is the vanishing point of all shadows of perpendiculars on left wall planes. It is also therefore the left wall direction of light vanishing point. The shadow of the perpendicular to a right wall plane is extended to meet the vertical through *VR* to locate *RW*. This method is easily understood by most draftsmen. It is usually sufficiently accurate.

CHAPTER 30

Light Oblique to Picture Plane

When light is oblique to the picture plane in two-point perspective drawing, there are no shadow construction lines parallel to the picture plane. Therefore each of the groups of parallel lines representing the light directions which are useful for working out shadows converges to its vanishing point as other perspective lines do. Thus each of the four groups of parallel shadow construction lines of paraline drawing now becomes a group of lines to a shadow vanishing point in perspective.

As in the case of paraline shadows and of perspective shadows with light parallel to the picture plane, two of these light directions may be adequate for the shadow construction. These two are in all three cases the true light direction and the plan direction of light. With light oblique to the picture plane, these two sets of parallel light direction lines vanish to shadow vanishing points L and H.

L is the light rays vanishing point. Lines to point L connect points of the perspective and their shadows.

H is the horizontal or plan direction of light vanishing point. This point gives the directions of the shadows of vertical lines on horizontal planes of the perspective drawing. Therefore it is the vanishing point of shadows of the perpendiculars to plan planes.

It is especially advantageous to use only these two points for shadow construction because they can be located at random wherever they will give a good shadow effect. The only limitations on their positions are: (1) point H must be on the horizon, (2) point L must be on the vertical through H.

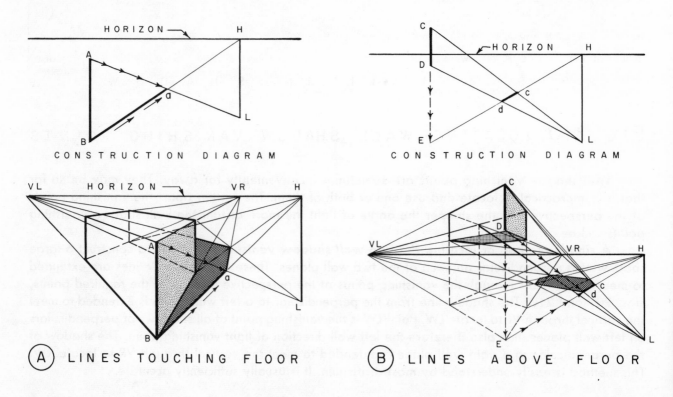

FIG. 211 BASIC SHADOWS WITH OBLIQUE LIGHT

Ⓘ SHADOWS OF AN OVERHANG

ⒾⒾ SHADOWS OF BLOCK SHAPES

FIG. 212 SHADOW DETAILS WITH OBLIQUE LIGHT

Practically all shadow construction by this method depends on the locating of shadows of vertical lines on horizontal surfaces of the perspective drawing. The diagrams and simple drawings of Fig. 211 show the basic shadow construction procedure. These figures are similar to those previously used for shadows of paraline drawings and shadows in perspective with light parallel to the picture plane. In the previous examples all construction was done with two sets of parallel lines, one for the plan direction of light and the other for the true direction of light. Here vanishing point *H* is used for the plan direction and point *L* for the true direction of light.

The diagram of Fig. 211 A shows the routine procedure for constructing the shadow *B-a* of line *A-B* when point *B* touches the horizontal or floor plane on which the shadow falls. The procedure of this diagram is used for construction locating shadows of three of the vertical corners of the block below the diagram. The form taken by the lines of the diagram may vary greatly in different positions on a perspective drawing. It may be narrow or spread out. It may have point *H* either to the right or left of the line *A-B* which makes the shadow. The diagram has no constant proportions or direction. It may locate an actual shadow of the object or an imaginary one which falls in an area in shadow. In Fig. 211 B the line *C-D* is extended to meet the floor plane at *E* in order to locate its shadow *d-c* on the floor plane.

In Fig. 212 Ⓘ a line is drawn from *H* through point *G* to meet the overhang at *F*. Point *F* will cast its shadow on the vertical line below *G*. The line from *F* to point *L* traces a ray of light to locate the shadow *f* of point *F*.

The working out of shadows on a perspective drawing requires a great deal of ingenuity and careful drafting. Shadows should appear to be logical and consistent. If they do not there is usually an error in the construction.

(A) L BELOW HORIZON
H LOCATED TO THE LEFT OF VL

(I) L ABOVE HORIZON
H LOCATED TO THE LEFT OF VL

(B) L BELOW HORIZON
H LOCATED BETWEEN VL AND VR

(II) L ABOVE HORIZON
H LOCATED BETWEEN VL AND VR

FIG. 213 BASIC SHADOW SCHEMES WITH LIGHT OBLIQUE TO THE PICTURE PLANE

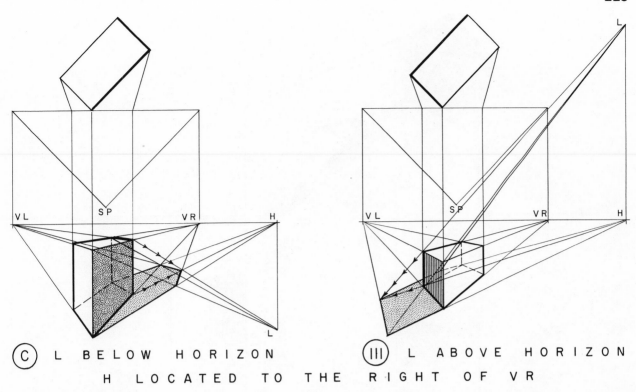

$\overset{C}{\bigcirc}$ L   B E L O W   H O R I Z O N $\overset{III}{\bigcirc}$ L   A B O V E   H O R I Z O N

H   L O C A T E D   T O   T H E   R I G H T   O F   V R

The location of point H on the horizon determines the plan direction of light on the object. In Fig. 213 B, H is given between the vanishing points of the perspective. A vertical from H to the picture plane locates point A. SP-A is the multi-view plan direction of light with the given location of H. When the light source is behind the SP the plan direction of light will be from SP toward A and both visible walls will be in light. Then point L must be below the horizon and below point H. If the light source is beyond the object and in front of the SP the plan light direction will be from A toward SP, Fig. 213 II. Both visible walls are then in shadow with the ground plane shadow extending in front of the object toward the observer. Point L must then be above H.

Study of Fig. 213 will show that with L below H and light from SP to A:

A. When H is to the left of VL left walls are in shadow and right walls in light, Fig. 213 A.

B. When H is between VL and VR both walls of the object are in light, Fig. 213 B.

C. When H is to the right of VR the right walls are in shadow and the left walls in light, Fig. 213 c.

With L above the horizon and light behind the object:

I. When H is to the left of VL the left wall planes are in light and right wall planes are in shadow, Fig. 213 I.

II. When H is between VL and VR both visible walls are in shadow, Fig. 213 II.

III. When H is to the right of VR the right wall planes are in light and left wall planes are in shadow, Fig. 213 III.

These statements assume plain wall surfaces. Overhangs may overshadow part or all of the wall which would otherwise be in light.

When H and VL or VR coincide, light is exactly parallel to one set of wall planes. In most cases this produces an unsatisfactory shadow effect. In fact the results are usually better when H is at a considerable distance from either vanishing point.

The illustrations of Fig. 213 show that: (1) when L is below the horizon the light is from behind the observer, (2) when L is above the horizon light comes from in front of the observer and shadows come toward him. The light ray through SP always intersects the picture plane at point L.

VL   D   E   H   VR   RW1   L1   L2   RW2   L3

B SHADOW VARIATIONS CAUSED BY
DIFFERENT DISTANCES FROM H TO L

H,L

A H AND L SAME—LIGHT HORIZONTAL

FIG. 214 PLANNING THE SHADOW EFFECT

The distance of point L from H determines the amount of shadows visible under overhangs and on floor planes. When *L* is at *H* on the horizon, rays of light are horizontal and there will be no shadows under overhangs. Light is parallel to horizontal surfaces which will be in shadow (shade) on both top and bottom surfaces, Fig. 214 A. This is seldom a satisfactory light direction.

When *L* is close to *H* there are small shadows under overhangs and large shadows on ground planes, Fig. 214 B. As *L* moves farther from *H* the shadows under overhangs become larger and shadows on ground planes become smaller. This has been shown in Fig. 214 B by using three distances of the *L* point below *H*. Point *L1* is closest to *H* and *L3* is farthest from *H*. Shadows have been worked out and shaded in a different way for each of these points *L1*, *L2*, and *L3*.

Point *L2* is on the line from *VL* along the edge *D-E* of an overhang on the left side of the object. The shadow of *D-E* coincides exactly with the line so there is no visible shadow below the overhang. With *L* in this position, or any position closer to the horizon, the shadow of the edge of the overhang will be concealed. The shadow may be visible beyond the right end of the overhang as shown for points *L1* and *L2* but not below it. When *L* is below the line from *VL* extended along the edge *D-E* of the overhang, the shadow of *D-E* will be visible below the line as shown from *L3*. The farther *L3* is below *L2* the larger this shadow becomes.

By varying the position of *H* on the horizon and the distance of *L* from *H*, the shadow areas can be adjusted to give the best effect for an object. When the possible results from shadows obtained by light parallel to the picture plane and light oblique to the picture plane are combined, any lighting effect can be secured on a perspective drawing.

The simple method of locating LW and RW explained for light parallel to the picture plane can be used here also. Construct a shadow *A-Y* of a perpendicular *A-C* on a left wall plane, Fig. 215. Extend the shadow line *A-Y* to meet the vertical through *VL* and locate *LW*. Repeat on a right wall for *RW* which is located on the vertical through *VR*. The larger the shadows used for this purpose the more accurately the points *LW* and *RW* will be located. Fig. 215 illustrates the locations of *LW* and *RW* when both walls are in light. The general positions of these point for either left wall in shadow or right wall in shadow with L below the horizon would be the same as illustrated for light parallel to the picture plane in Figs. 209 and 210. These vanishing points of shadows of perpendiculars to wall planes are sometimes very useful. However, they may be too far away for practical use and are a convenience, not a necessity.

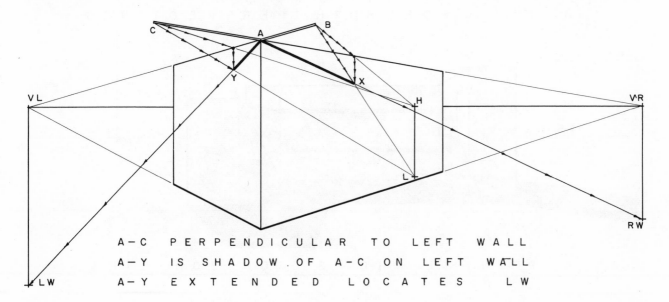

A-C PERPENDICULAR TO LEFT WALL
A-Y IS SHADOW OF A-C ON LEFT WALL
A-Y EXTENDED LOCATES LW

FIG. 215 LOCATING LW AND RW — BOTH WALLS IN LIGHT

228

HORIZON

A POINT L BELOW HORIZON LINE

PICT. PL.

B PLAN FOR BOTH PERSPECTIVES

HORIZ.

C POINT L ABOVE HORIZON LINE

FIG. 216 SHADOWS IN ONE-POINT PERSPECTIVE

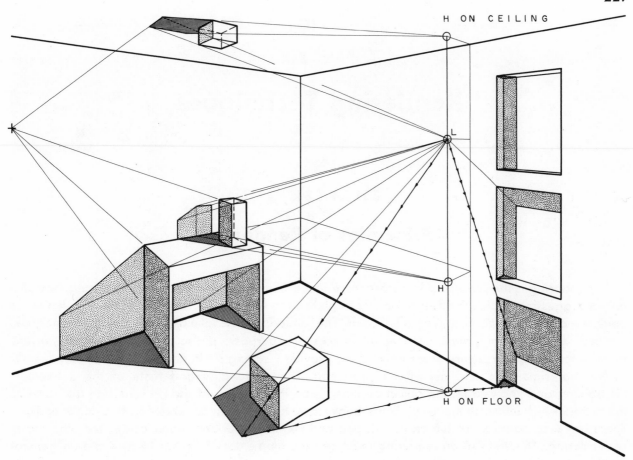

H ON CEILING

L

H

H ON FLOOR

FIG. 217 SHADOWS FROM A POINT SOURCE OF LIGHT

One-point perspective shadows are constructed by the system used for two-point perspective with light oblique to the picture plane, Fig. 216. Since one set of wall planes is parallel to the picture plane it will have parallel lines for the light direction A-C on those walls, Fig. 216 A. The other set of wall planes, which is perpendicular to the picture plane, will have a vanishing point W for its light direction as shown by lines D-E and F-G. This point W will be on the vertical through V. One side of walls perpendicular to the picture plane will be in shadow. When H is to the right of V and L is below H, the right sides of walls perpendicular to the picture plane are in shadow, Fig. 216 A. When H is to the left of V and L is below H, the left surfaces are in shadow. These light and shadow conditions reverse with L above the horizon. When L is below the horizon the walls parallel to the picture plane are in light, Fig. 216 A, and when L is above the horizon they are in shadow, Fig. 216 C. A vertical line through H locates point X at its intersection with the picture plane in plan view. Line SP-X is the plan direction of light. Lines parallel to SP-X can be used to trace light rays on the multi-view plan. This procedure is used for greater accuracy when the perspective represent- ations of horizontal areas are too small for good construction. An alternative is to provide a larger perspective substitute area as described for light parallel to the picture plane on page 219.

Shadows from a point source of light are shown in Fig. 217. The projection of the point light source onto the floor plane is labelled H on floor. Lines radiating from this point trace the shadows of verticals on the floor. Lines from L represent light rays and terminate the shadows of verticals. A new point H must be used for each horizontal plane on which a shadow is located. These H points are all on the vertical through L at its intersections with the various horizontal planes on which the shadows fall.

PART SIX

Rendering Techniques

CHAPTER 31

Principles of Rendering

Rendering is the process of transforming a line drawing into a picture. The rendering may give only a suggestion of picture effect or be so complete as to approach photographic realism. It may be done in monotone, in part color, or in full color. The rendering material may be dust, spray, pencil, ink, applied sheet material, paints, or other substances. The purposes are to clarify the drawing, give a more or less complete picture of the object, and provide a setting for it. Renderings may vary greatly in the materials used and the effects produced. The personality and taste of the delineator, his training and knowledge, the object depicted, and the purpose of the presentation are some of the factors which influence the result. Entire books have been written on rendering in a single medium. There are such books available on pencil, pen and ink, scratchboard, water color, and other types of rendering. This treatise on rendering must be very elementary in order to give a brief general treatment of the subject.

Although there is great variety in media, techniques, and results in rendering, many devices are useful for rendering in any medium. The discussion of a number of these will be given in the following pages of this chapter. The reader should realize that it may not be practical to use all of the devices described in a single rendering. The delineator must choose the ones best suited to his problem. A good assortment of such tools enables him to secure better and more varied results in his rendering.

Intensity of light and shadow are important elements of rendering. Shadow casting is concerned with only the quantity or areas of shadows. Rendering often represents the qualities of shadow areas also. When the conventional direction of light is used for rendering of multi-view drawings, an octagonal prism will demonstrate variations of light and shadow intensity. The drawing of Fig. 218 A shows the relation of the plan light direction to each visible surface of the prism. Light rays, as seen from above, are perpendicular to the left area which consequently receives the greatest possible quantity of light and is called the *high light,* (HL). Light rays are at 45° to the center area which receives less light than the left area. This center surface is parallel to the front view plane and is called a *light area,* (L). Light rays are parallel to the right side of the prism leaving it in shadow, (S). Gradation of the flat areas of the octagon from side to side may be used to make the effect brighter and more contrasting, Fig. 218 C. When gradation of areas is employed their correct relative tones should be kept. If desired, the overall effect can be kept light for the entire octagon with adequate separation of areas when this device is used, Fig. 218 D. This shading of flat areas increases contrast and adds life to the rendering of these surfaces.

The application of the high light, light, and shadow tones of the octagon to beveled surfaces is shown in Fig. 218 E and F. It is a powerful means of separating areas and expressing form.

A LIGHT IN PLAN

HL   L   S

B FLAT TONES

HL   L   S

C DARK TONES
BRIGHT EFFECT

D LIGHT TONES
CAN BE USED

L S   L   HL   L

E SIMPLE BEVELS

L
S

L

HL
L

HL S   L   HL S   L

F DOUBLE BEVELS

L
HL
S

L

HL
S

TONES ON FLAT AND BEVELED SURFACES

FIG. 218 HIGH LIGHT, LIGHT, AND SHADOW TONES

B SHADING ON CYLINDER

C GRADATION AT RIGHT
HELPS EXPRESS FORM

A PLAN RELATION OF
LIGHT TO A CYLINDER

D SHADING ON SPHERE
IN THE FRONT VIEW

FIG. 219 SHADING ON CYLINDERS AND SPHERES

When the system of high light, light, and shadow of the conventional direction of light is used on a cylinder, the high light, *HL,* is at the 45° point on the left, Fig. 219 A, B. There are two lights, *L,* one at the extreme left edge and the other at the exact center of the visible surface of the cylinder. At both these positions in plan the light rays are at 45° to the tangents to the curved surface. From the 45° tangent point of light on the right to the right edge, the surface of the cylinder is in shadow, *S.* When this area is made the same darkness throughout its width the cylinder seems flat on the right side, Fig. 219 B. A better treatment is to lighten the shadow area from the shade line to the right edge of the cylinder. This makes the darkest tone on the shade line and helps to model and express the cylindrical shape, Fig. 219 C. The sphere of Fig. 219 D is shaded in a similar manner. However it should be noted that the high light is located at the top left on the 45° diagonal through the center of the sphere. Light rays are actually perpendicular to the tangent surface at this point.

Reflected light is used to produce variations in tone in areas which are in shadow. It is a means of expressing form, separating areas, and adding details to shadow areas. The octagonal prism of

I OCTAGON SHADOW TONES

II SHADOW GRADATIONS

THE EFFECTS OF REFLECTED LIGHTS ON SHADOWS

III REFLECTED SHADOWS
FROM SMALL OFFSETS

IV REFLECTED SHADOWS
AND LIGHTS ON BEVELS

FIG. 220 REFLECTED LIGHTS AND SHADOWS

Fig. 220 I has a shadow across the top from a projecting block. *Reflected light, RL,* is assumed from the right and slanting up and back as shown by the arrows in plan and elevation. This is the commonly used direction of reflected light. Its effect is to make each visible plane in shadow a different darkness. The right plane receives the most reflected light, is lightest in shadow, and is called a reflected light, *RL.* The left area receives no reflected light, and is darkest. It is called a *reflected shadow, RS.* The center area receives a little less reflected light than the right area and is slightly darker. It is called shadow, *S.* The effect of reflected light on the shadow on a cylinder is shown in Fig. 220 II. The sequence of the shading here reverses the shading on the area of the cylinder in light. It expresses the round form of the cylinder in shadow. Reflected shadows are usually limited to small details in shadow areas, Fig. 220 III. They provide a means of showing shapes in large shadow areas which would often be blank and uninteresting without them. The small reflected shadows can be made crisp and sharp. Larger ones are sometimes suggested near the form causing the shadow reflection and then faded out from it. Their complete representation may be more confusing than helpful.

FIG. 221 SEPARATION OF PLANES IN RENDERING

Separation of planes can be done in three simple ways, Fig. 221 A, B, C. (A) By use of high lights on corners toward the source of light and shade lines on the corners away from light. This method assumes that there is no visible shadow. (B) By use of difference of tones on the adjoining areas. (C) By use of shadows when the areas are so related that the shadows are visible. Shadows form separations on one or two sides. The edges toward light can be outlined by high lights or separated by tones, or by a combination of the two methods, Fig. 221 D, E, F.

These devices for separating planes are useful in perspective and paraline renderings as well as on multi-view renderings. The high lights and reflected lights are however usually at the meeting of two visible planes on pictorial drawings and not at an edge made by a visible and concealed plane as in multi-view, Fig. 221 G, H, I.

High lights and shade lines are actual elements of the surfaces represented in rendering. Few persons observe these parts of objects. High lights are especially prominent on almost everything

(I) LIGHT TO DARK SEQUENCE

(II) DARK TO LIGHT SEQUENCE

(III) DARK TO LIGHT TO DARK

(IV) LIGHT TO DARK TO LIGHT

FIG. 222 EXPRESSION OF DEPTH BY SHADING

we see. The use of these light and dark lines without any consideration of direction of light produces an artificial effect and should be avoided.

Expression of depth or distance away from the observer is often accomplished partially by use of tones. The tone sequence depends on the forms of the object and the effect to be achieved. Four simple tone sequences for this purpose of expressing depth are shown in Fig. 222 I, II, III, IV. They are: (I) Nearest surface lightest and each succeeding more distant surface darker. (II) Nearest plane darkest and each plane lighter as the distance away increases. (III) One of the middle planes lightest with distances from this plane expressed by increasing darkness in both directions. (IV) A middle plane darkest and distance from this plane in both directions expressed by lighter sequences of tones.

These schemes for tone sequences to express depth assume the same material throughout the design and no variations of tone caused by colors of different materials.

Shadow areas alone are a very effective means of expressing, by their shapes, positions, and sizes, the distances perpendicular to the plane of the paper.

Ⓐ INTEREST FOCUSED BY CONTRAST VARIATIONS

Ⓑ GRADATION OF TONE SEPARATES ADJACENT AREAS

FIG. 223 USEFUL DEVICES OF RENDERING

The focusing of interest on one part of a rendering by extreme contrasts is a very effective device. This may be accomplished in monotone rendering by extreme contrast of shadows and light at the center of interest, Fig. 223 A. Other areas have less contrast between light and shadow. In color rendering brighter colors and greater contrasts are used in the center of interest area than in other parts of the rendering.

Gradation of tone over an area is useful for several purposes. It is effective in obtaining contrast where two planes meet without making a definite difference of tone over their general areas, Fig. 223 B. It is a means of increasing the contrast at the top and bottom of an object where one end of the area has a light background and the other end a dark one, Fig. 224 I, II. Gradation of tones is a useful device in expressing receding surfaces of ground, roof, walls, or other areas.

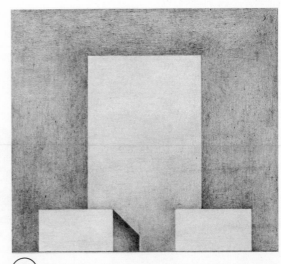

Ⓘ LIGHT BACKGROUND   Ⓘ DARK BACKGROUND

SILOUHETTE EMPHASIZED BY VERTICAL GRADATION

Ⓘ GRADATIONS EXPRESS RECEDING PLANES

FIG. 224 USEFUL DEVICES OF RENDERING

Reflected light from horizontal surfaces sometimes causes the vertical surfaces of objects to be lighter at the bottom and darker toward the top. The reflected illumination is strong near the reflecting surface and quickly fades out. Few people observe closely enough to see the effect of reflected light. Experimenting with objects and good reflecting surfaces such as white cardboard in a strong light will help the reader understand the power of reflected light. When you are wearing white clothing on which the sun is shining walk up near some person or object faced away from the sun and watch the increase of light in the shadow area.

Some of the gradations of tone used in rendering can readily be explained, but others seem to be used for effect without having an obvious foundation in fact. Their use often makes the rendering clearer and more interesting.

238

(A) LONG SHADOWS DARK AT THE TOP LIGHT AT BOTTOM

(B) TWO SHADOWS RUN TOGETHER ON SAME SURFACE

(C) THIN SHADOWS APPEAR DARKER THAN WIDE ONES

FIG. 225 GRADING AND TONE RELATIONS OF SHADOWS

Shadows take on life and sparkle when the edges away from the shape making the shadow are darkened. This gives the effect of a dark shadow without making an opaque dark blot of the entire shadow area. Long vertical shadows are often faded out lighter at the bottom because of reflection from horizontal surfaces on which the object rests. In some paintings and illustrations the edges of light areas adjoining shadows are made lighter as well as the edges of the shadows darker. Overemphasis of these devices can dominate the entire picture. More restrained use of them is normal for rendering to add life and brilliance to the effect.

Small bands of shadow appear darker than large areas on an object. Perhaps this is due to extreme contrast on the two edges in a very limited space. There is not sufficient dark area for the eye to adjust to see details within it, and thus makes it appear to be less intense. It is usually necessary to make these small bands darker than the large shadow areas of a rendering in order to get them to show up correctly. A rendering should be viewed from a distance at intervals as the work progresses. The tone relations can then be seen more clearly than from the close position from which the work is done.

Adjoining shadow areas all run together. There should not be a line of tone difference from shadows caused by different objects or different parts of the same object on the same plane.

Surroundings of the main object in a rendering are used for several purposes. They may be used in foreground and background to give the effect of distance. Their primary purpose may be to suggest a setting of time and place for the object. In all cases they should be considered as design elements. As such they can add interest in shapes and positions and are sometimes useful in focusing the attention at the correct place. Their locations, forms, and effects on the composition should be studied as carefully as the design of the object depicted is studied.

AIR BRUSH RENDERING BY MEL O'BRIEN
MANN AND HARROVER—ARCHITECTS

TEMPERA RENDERING BY ROBERT E. SCHWARTZ
KEMPA AND SCHWARTZ-ARCHITECTS—J. H. LIVINGSTONE ASSOC.

FIG. 226 SURROUNDINGS ARE A PART OF RENDERING

CHAPTER 32

Rendering With Pencil or Ink

Pencil and ink renderings require very little in the way of materials. However, these methods can be used to secure a wide variety of results which range from very simple to more elaborate presentations. Although the necessary materials are owned and used in some ways by almost every draftsman they are also employed by expert delineators, who may be draftsmen or other persons, to obtain highly artistic results in rendering.

Pencil rendering requires only paper and a pencil as the essential materials. A smooth-surfaced paper is best for fine details and smooth tones. An assortment of pencils from soft to hard is also helpful in producing bold or fine lines and dark or light tones. The flat chisel point is very useful for pencil rendering. The bevel is made at an angle to give a broad stroke on the paper. Erasers

STUDENT RENDERING BY RONALD LOWRY

FIG. 227 EXAMPLE OF PENCIL RENDERING

PENCIL SKETCH BY EERO SAARINEN
EERO SAARINEN AND ASSOCIATES—ARCHITECTS

FIG. 228 EXAMPLE OF PENCIL RENDERING

which will erase clean, and an erasing shield are very useful. One of the most difficult things in pencil rendering is to avoid smudging or smearing of lines when working on the drawing. This is especially true when individual sharp strokes are used. The pencils should be kept clean of dust from sharpening and the drawing protected by paper under the hand when working over a part of the rendering. The experienced person often plans the sequence of work to avoid having to rest the hand on any part of the finished rendering. When the rendering is completed a coat of fixative spray will help to prevent smudging.

The simplest type of pencil rendering employs tones for background, object, and shadows. The tones may be made with lines ruled mechanically parallel and close together or by going over the areas freehand with many strokes to produce a smooth even tone. With care high light corners or bands can be erased out clean. They add crispness and polish to a simple tone rendering.

The indications of materials and textures add greatly to a pencil rendering when these elements are present in the object depicted. Bricks, stone, wood graining, and rough textured rugs or upholstering materials may be indicated. Reflections on polished surfaces express their characteristics. More detailed and elaborate pencil renderings use the individual strokes of the pencil to produce a pattern and give a bold effect.

STUDENT RENDERING BY RONALD L. WENDLANDT

STUDENT RENDERING BY J. J. SONDERMAN

FIG. 229 EXAMPLES OF PENCIL RENDERING

STUDENT RENDERING BY M. PINTO

STUDENT RENDERING BY P. L. BROOKSHIRE

FIG. 230 EXAMPLES OF PENCIL RENDERING

RENDERING BY FRANCIS MAH
OFFICE OF WALK C. JONES JR., ARCHITECTS

FIG. 231 EXAMPLE OF INK LINE RENDERING

Pen and ink rendering is similar to pencil rendering in some respects. Since darks are more intense with ink, a more contrasting effect can be produced. The medium does not allow modelling of form as simply and easily as pencil rendering. The example of Fig. 231 has tones produced by many ruled ink lines. These tones are used to separate areas of the building and surroundings and to represent shadows. All renderings are conventionalized and simplified representations of the object to some degree. This example of professional work is an effective simple presentation.

Pen strokes and ink areas must be given time to dry before working over them. An ink rendering can be cleaned with a soft eraser when it is finished. Care must be taken to avoid removing so much ink that the blacks are faded and become grays. A good assortment of pens from the finest Cro-quill to the coarse Speedballs will give variety of stroke widths. Waterproof drawing ink should be used. A number of penholders will at least partially avoid the inconvenience of changing pens. The pens should be kept clean. Wash and dry them before the ink has a chance to harden.

Scratchboard provides a variation of pen and ink technique for rendering. The materials required are the board itself, pens and ink, a brush for applying ink on areas, and a number of sharp pointed or edged tools for scratching the ink off. Some of these tools can be made to produce various combinations of multiple lines with one stroke. The drawing is usually made for scratchboard rendering by tracing and transferring with a pencil which will make the lines visible on both the ink and the white paper areas.

The board for this type of rendering has been coated with a thin layer of white chalky material by the manufacturer. When there are small areas of black or small black lines and comparatively large areas of white the ink is applied with a pen where it is to remain. When there are large areas of black and small amounts of white the entire area is coated with ink and the whites are scratched out. Fig. 232 focuses the interest in the central area by strong contrasts of blacks and whites.

The effects produced with scratchboard offer wide variation. Some drawings are fine in detail and resemble the delicacy of engravings. Others are bold and coarse in effect. There are entire books published on the scratchboard method of rendering. These books range from ones with simple examples and text to those with very expert, detailed, and artistic professional work.

RENDERING BY DALE C. BYRD
MARCEL BREUER AND ASSOCIATES ARCHITECTS

FIG. 232 EXAMPLE OF SCRATCHBOARD RENDERING

246

STUDENT RENDERING BY RICHARD A. BAXTER

STUDENT RENDERING BY RINALDO PEREZ
INK WITH LIGHT WATER COLOR WASHES

FIG. 233 EXAMPLES OF PEN AND INK RENDERING

STUDENT RENDERING BY C. VAN WINKLE

STUDENT RENDERING BY WERNER LOUIS FEIBES
HOUSE AT BEAR RUN, FRANK LLOYD WRIGHT, ARCH.

FIG. 234 EXAMPLES OF SCRATCHBOARD RENDERING

CHAPTER 33

Wash Rendering

The term wash rendering is used for illustrations made with any mixture in water which is applied with a brush and gives transparent tones. The medium used may be any of a number of materials. These include Chinese stick ink, transparent water colors, or a semi-transparent mixture of opaque white and water colors. Even strong coffee solution can be used for wash rendering.

There are two general characteristics of wash rendering. (A) The paint materials for the washes are sufficiently transparent to allow lines and tones to show through them. (B) The materials used are capable of gradual change in tone. This quality allows gradation of an area with wash, and modelling to show the shapes of curved objects. The paint must allow repetition of washes.

Materials for Wash Rendering. All of the materials listed below can usually be obtained at an art supply store.

1. Illustration board
2. Water color brushes
3. Water color paints
4. Small dishes or pans
5. A large pan for water
6. Small blotters

1. Illustration board is used for most wash renderings. It is thick cardboard with a surface coating of good paper. The surface should not be very smooth or slick. A slightly rough surface takes wash better. Illustration board with a surface of cold pressed water color paper is excellent for most wash renderings. Common illustration board is less expensive and is satisfactory. The illustration board should be attached firmly to the drawing board with heavy thumb tacks or drafting tape to prevent warping from the large washes.

2. Brushes of red sable or other materials which retain their shapes when wet are best suited for water color rendering work. Some types of brushes become soft and flabby when dipped in paint solution or water. They do not spring back to shape but stay bent until straightened out by hand. Get three round pointed brushes of varying size if they can be obtained and are not too expensive for the use to be made of them. The large size is usually number 12 and has bristles about 1¼ inches long. The medium size should have about ⅞ inch bristles and the small one ⅝ or ½ inch bristles. If only one brush is bought it should be the medium sized one. Flat red sable brushes with chisel edges are also very useful for water color rendering.

3. Paint should be limited to monotone while learning the technique of handling washes for rendering. The simplest procedure is to use a tube of ivory black or lamp black water color for this purpose. A constant mixture of one color and black is also easy to prepare and use. Any single color or mixture of two or more paints used for monotone wash rendering should be capable of producing a dark tone.

4. The small pans or dishes should be white so that it is possible to see what they have in them. It is very convenient to have about six of the small pans or dishes. Do not use a muffin pan or other connected small pans. They are a nuisance when it is necessary to empty one or pour from one to another of the small divisions.

5. A larger flat pan or small pail holding about a quart should be used for water supply. Do not attempt to use a soft drink bottle. When a person is in a hurry to wash out a brush he does not have time and patience to aim at the small opening in a bottle.

6. Small white blotters are very useful for emergencies. Keep one under the hand while running a wash. Do not use colored blotters which will fade and discolor the illustration board.

Preparations for Wash Rendering. Precautions are necessary in preparing for and making a wash rendering. The drawing surface should be kept clean and free from damage. Avoid getting

FIG. 235 MATERIALS FOR WASH RENDERING

grease or dirt from hands or elsewhere onto the paper. It will prevent the wash from coating the paper evenly. Erase cautiously, remembering that roughened paper absorbs wash and becomes darker while polished spots will be lighter when the wash is applied.

The drawing can either be made with neat pencil lines and left in pencil or it can be inked with diluted black ink. The diluted ink should give a light gray line. It will require a great deal of water and a little ink in the mixture. The paper must be kept clean when pencil lines are used. Inking the lines allows cleaning with a mild eraser after inking.

Scrap paper or illustration board of the same general type as that used for rendering is very useful for testing washes.

New pans may have an oily film on them. They should be washed with soap and water. Some brushes have been treated with a starchy material which should be washed from the bristles. Remove all lint and eraser particles from the drawing before starting a wash rendering.

To prepare the solution for the wash, squeeze about one-half inch of paint from the tube into an empty pan. Add some water and mix thoroughly with a brush. This mixture will probably be too dark to use. Pour part of it into another pan, add water and mix. Continue to dilute until it is light enough to use. The paint often settles to the bottom of the pan in a short time. It must be kept mixed when it is being used.

When beginning a rendering the paper is often very dry before the first wash is run over an area. Keep the solution for the first wash quite pale as it is more likely to streak than later washes when the paper is slightly moist. Darker washes can be used later if that seems desirable and if they can be handled successfully. There is safety from streaks in using a number of light washes instead of one dark one. However, do not go to the extreme of using such light washes that they do not produce a perceptible darkening of the area.

Incline the board at an angle of about 1½ to 2 inches to the foot with the length of the area which is to receive the wash in the direction of the slope. See that the board is supported securely so it will not tilt when work is done on it. Place the pan of wash near the board but on the table. For a right-handed person it should be on the right side. Do not set a pan of wash on the board where it is easy to spill over the drawing. Remove other pans of wash to a distance so the brush will not be dipped into the wrong one.

(A) BEGINNING WASH (B) MIDDLE OF WASH (C) FINISHING WASH

FIG. 236 TECHNIQUE IN RUNNING A FLAT WASH

Flat Washes. The flat wash is the simplest to apply. It requires a uniform darkness over an entire area. It is best to use a simple rectangular area of moderate size for a first exercise. The size may be about three or four inches wide and five or six inches long, Fig. 236 A, B, C.

The procedure in running the flat wash is to apply a small puddle of the mixture to be used across the top of the area with the brush. Fill the brush as full as possible without dripping. Hit the line exactly. Now guide the puddle down over the area about ¼ inch at a time. Add wash with the brush when necessary in order to maintain a uniform small puddle at the lower edge of the wet area.

As the wash is guided down over the area to be treated, keep the lower edge level so the puddle is uniform all along the edge of the wash. If the board is tilted too much or the puddle is large and collects at one side, the water mixture may start running in a stream over the paper and continue until it hits the floor. If this happens, blot the run immediately and firmly. Then start at the edge at once with a smaller puddle and lower the board a little if necessary. Speedy use of the blotter will often prevent streaks entirely. Do not go back into a partly dried area of the wash with the wet brush. To do so will almost always cause streaks.

Move the wash at as uniform speed as possible. If the puddle remains longer in one place it will make the wash darker. If the wash runs over the edge, move the puddle below the place, then blot to the line and press the edge of the blotter firmly. Do not attempt to blot at the edge of the puddle. An experienced person sometimes pushes the edge of the wet wash back firmly beyond the line with the finger. Since the fingers are slightly oily the wash usually stays back and is then guided over to the line with the brush. If a drop of wash gets on the dry paper, blot it instantly. The sooner it is blotted the less it will stain the paper. Turn the brush so the part of it which is running the wash to the line can be seen clearly.

As the wash approaches the bottom of the area reduce the puddle a little then guide it to the bottom line. Remember to turn the brush so it is easy to see the edge of the wash. After the wash covers the entire area, remove the fluid from the brush and touch the moist brush to the puddle at the lower end of the area. It will pick up a little of the puddle. Repeat cautiously until the puddle is removed without changing the darkness of this area. If it is permissible to do so, remove the fluid from your brush by flipping it on the floor. The brush can also be emptied by squeezing the bristles lightly at the ferrule then pulling them between the fingers. The third method is to touch the wet brush to a cloth or paper towel to remove the paint solution.

After the wash is finished, allow the board to remain tilted as it is until the moistened area has dried. As soon as the area no longer shines from being wet, the board can be moved. The area should feel dry before running another wash over it or an adjoining area.

A little thought will often prevent a great deal of trouble in running washes. Remember that the puddle runs down the slope. Turn the board so the wash can be run the easy way across the small dimension of the area. It is almost impossible to run a smooth wash over a long thin area by starting on a long edge.

Skill in handling a brush can be acquired by almost anyone with normal coordination of hand, eye, and mind. People frequently say, "I am just too nervous to do that." Most persons can control their nerves to do this type of work. It usually takes a great deal of effort and concentration for a beginner to run a wash neatly to a line. After a reasonable amount of practice this operation becomes routine and semi-automatic with many delineators. Without worry or any conscious effort the hand of the experienced person just places the brush in a correct spot and moves it along. This is difficult for a person who hasn't experienced it to believe. It is a case of doing something with the intuition or subconscious mind much better than it can be done by conscious effort.

The sequence of washes in making a rendering may reduce the amount of effort required and provide less opportunity for bad edges. A good procedure is to cover all possible areas with one wash. When a light, medium, and dark area adjoin each other run the light tone over all three areas. Then run the medium tone over both the medium and dark areas. Finally run the dark area only. This system avoids unnecessary repetition of washes and unnecessary repeated running of washes to lines. It assures a definite difference in the tones of the areas, Fig. 237.

In some renderings there is one important part which should be just right. In such cases this area may be rendered first and other areas rendered to suit it. There is often a tendency to put off until last the very important part of the rendering. This may result in a bad practice of the renderer waiting until he is tired and rushed for time to do the essential part of the rendering.

Borders offer their problems in avoiding streaks. If the border extends around three sides only, or is interrupted, the technique is simple. Turn the board to start the wash at one end or at the break in the border. When the corner is reached turn the border to slope diagonally so the puddle runs around the corner. After the corner is cleared so there is no danger of a run back, turn the board farther, always allowing for the puddle to run down the slope. When the border is continuous around the plate, turn the board with the slope on the diagonal and run both sides at once. Start at top and end at bottom corner.

| (I) LIGHTEST WASH OVER ALL AREAS | (II) MEDIUM TONE ON MEDIUM + DARK AREAS | (III) THE DARK AREAS ARE DARKENED LAST |

FIG. 237 A SUGGESTED SEQUENCE FOR WASHES

FIG. 238 EXAMPLES OF GRADED WASHES

Graded Washes. Graded washes change gradually and smoothly from dark to light. They are applied in the same general manner as flat washes. The important difference is that the darkness of the wash solution is gradually changed as the puddle is guided over the paper.

The simplest method for running a graded wash requires the use of a sequence of mixtures in a number of pans. It is best to have at least five or six pans so that the difference in darkness of wash in adjacent pans is slight. The pans are arranged in the order in which they are to be used. They are placed conveniently near the right edge of the board for a right-handed person. The change in darkness of the puddle is secured by using the mixture in each pan in order as the wash progresses.

A second good method of grading a wash is to start with a small quantity of the darkest mixture to be used at this time in a pan. Start the wash at the dark end with this mixture. Then dilute the mixture by adding a small amount of water to the pan with the brush at regular intervals as the wash is moved along over the area. When water is added stir the mixture thoroughly before using it. Good judgment is needed for this method of running a graded wash. If too much of the dark paint solution is used to start the wash, the addition of a small amount of water will not change it enough. The resulting wash will not vary sufficiently from dark to light. Part of the mixture in the pan can be poured out in order to get a more rapid change when the small amount of water is added.

The graded wash can be run from light to dark if that procedure is preferred. This method requires starting the wash with a small quantity of very light mixture or water in the pan. A darker mixture which is assumed to be right for the dark end of the wash is then added a little at a time. The solution in the pan should be practically the same as this dark mixture when the wash is ended. Some persons get better results running graded washes from dark to light, and some prefer the light to dark procedure. Often the board can be turned to run the wash either way.

In running graded washes the change in darkness of the mixture must be made a little before the corresponding change is desired on the paper. This is due to the floating down of the puddle.

A third method is used by some skillful and also by some reckless persons. The darkness of the mixture for the graded wash is changed in the brush entirely by dipping back and forth between the dark to be used and water. This procedure is not a safe one for a beginner. Try it if you wish to live dangerously, but try it first on scratch paper. It is a better method for relatively short washes than for long ones. Better results are obtained with any method by using several light washes.

FIRST WASH

FIFTH WASH

LAST WASH

FOR SMALL SHADOWS

GRADING IN 2 DIRECTIONS

GRADING IN ALL DIRECTIONS

I FRENCH METHOD FOR SMALL BANDS

II SMALL PUDDLE AND MOIST BRUSH METHOD

FIG. 239 GRADING WASHES IN SMALL AREAS

Grading Washes in Small Areas. The modelling of shading on curved surfaces requires the grading of washes in small spaces. Sometimes they must be graded in more than one direction.

The French method of grading a wash over a narrow band is useful for shading in one direction only. The procedure is to apply a sequence of flat washes over one or more of the equal small spaces into which the band is divided. These washes change so gradually and are spaced at such short intervals that the change of tone may seem to be smooth and continuous. The process is rather tedious and mechanical. It requires good judgment of the tones.

The small puddle and moist brush method is used to fade a small wash in one or more directions. Two brushes are required. One is used to supply a small puddle of the dark wash, the other to dampen the paper at the edge of the puddle with water so the wash spreads and fades out into the moist area. This technique is illustrated in its simplest form at the top of Fig. 239 II. The second brush is dipped into water then flipped out until it will leave only a film of moisture on the paper. This film is brought to the edge of the puddle. The puddle then runs onto the moist paper and fades out. This technique requires skill and judgment to obtain good results. If the moist brush carries too much water, the water runs into the dark puddle and control of the shading is lost. This method usually works better on a level board than on an inclined one. It can be used to shade in more than one direction. In the lower left illustration of Fig. 239 II it is used to shade in two directions. In the lower right illustration of Fig. 239 II the fadeout is in all directions from a round puddle. Shading of this type is likely to be more successful when light washes are repeated several times to darken the areas.

Ruling pen washes are a means of producing neat narrow bands. It is surprising to some people that a paint mixture for rendering can be used in a ruling pen. The pen should be clean so that ink particles will not change the darkness or color of the fluid. Small shadow bands can be ruled in much more precisely than they can be put in with a brush. Shade lines at the shadow edges of projections can also be used to trim the edges.

High lights on corners toward the light source can be ruled with a mixture of water color and white. The mixture must be thick enough to cover the paint below it. It should in most cases be tinted to harmonize with the area of which it is a part.

Erasing of high lights is satisfactory when the erased band is kept narrow and trim.

Streaks in Washes. Streaks seem to be an inevitable part of wash rendering. In their worst form they disfigure the plate. Some are often so pale as to be noticed only under careful scrutiny of details. Occasionally a streak occurs where it adds to the effect. It takes a very skillful delineator to make planned streaks as desirable additions to water color technique. For the great majority of persons who do water color rendering, streaks are undesirable blemishes which should be avoided. The following paragraphs describe some of the more common causes of streaks. It is hoped that a knowledge of the causes may help the reader to avoid making undesirable streaks.

The fan or runback streak is caused by having a part of the puddle run back the wrong direction into the partly dry area above the puddle edge of the wash. This may be caused by careless use of the brush in adding the wash solution to the puddle, by allowing a drop of wash to fall in the partly dry area, or by tilting the board the wrong direction before the wash has dried. It may also be caused by using the wet brush to try to correct some defect in the damp area.

Varying the speed at which the wash moves over the paper will cause streaks with most paints. When the wash edge moves slowly or the puddle is allowed to remain too long in one position, a dark band will be formed. The wash should progress down over the area to be darkened at as uniform a speed as it is possible to maintain. This requires rapid work at the beginning of a wash where lines and corners must be met as precisely as possible. It also requires patience to maintain a slower pace in the middle of an area since too-rapid progress of the puddle will cause light streaks.

Varying the amount of puddle will cause light and dark streaks. The greater the amount of puddle the darker the tone applied and the smaller the puddle the lighter the results from the wash. Dark streaks are sometimes made at each side of the wash by carrying those parts of the puddle lower and larger.

Texture produced by a wash is influenced by several things. Almost all water color paints settle out and will produce a texture effect under certain conditions. Some pigments are more noted for this characteristic than others. A rough-surfaced paper increases the rough-textured effect from the wash, while a smooth paper minimizes it. A large puddle run slowly helps to produce texture by settling of the pigments. A small puddle run rapidly over the paper will decrease the texture effect from the wash.

Imperfect mixing of the paint is the cause of some streaks. Most paint pigments do not dissolve in water. They are finely ground particles of earth, charcoal, metal, etc., which are held in suspension when mixed with water. They gradually settle to the bottom. After the mixture has partly settled, a light solution is obtained by dipping the brush part way down. By dipping the brush deep so it rubs over the bottom of the pan, a darker mixture is obtained. The wash in the pan must be stirred every time the brush is dipped into it in order to get a uniform darkness.

Patching Defective Washes. Patching is just as much a part of the technique of rendering as the running of washes. Skill in correcting defects and mistakes is an essential part of the training in drafting and rendering. Care and thought should be devoted to avoiding streaks in washes. It usually takes a great deal of time and effort to correct such defects. Since very few renderings are made without the necessity of some patching it is essential that skill be acquired in this necessary part of the work. Patching usually requires more skill than other phases of rendering.

Edges of washes require precise skill with the brush if they are to be neat and trim. There are very few persons who do not have some slight irregularities in the edges of the washes which they run. Even with repairs by blotting when the area is still wet there are sometimes small places where the wash extends over the line. These areas can be lightened so they are less conspicuous and often removed entirely by using a scrubbing and blotting technique. For this procedure use a small or medium sized brush. The brush should not be soft. If an old one with a somewhat blunted point is available, use it. Dip the brush in clear water, then remove most of the water, leaving enough to wet the paper but not enough to make a puddle. Scrub the dark area, which is to be removed, with the moist brush for two or three seconds, then blot. Repeat until the edge is straightened. Observe carefully to see that the scrubbing is not removing the surface of the paper. When this begins to occur the paper should be allowed to dry before proceeding with the process.

Dark spots in a wash area can be treated by the scrub and blot method described for edges of washes. When there are two or more spots, work on the worst one first so that progress can be noted by comparison with the other spots which have not been treated. Each spot usually requires several careful scrubbings with the moist brush and blottings to make a decided improvement. Care must be used to scrub only where the wash is too dark. A skillful person can often completely remove a dark spot or streak so that all trace of it has vanished.

Light spots can be darkened by different techniques. One method is to put a puddle of wash over the small light area then blot. The blotting softens the edges. This is a method for small spots. The number of applications is determined by the darkness of the mixture used. It is better to try a light mixture first so that the spot is not made too dark.

A second method for light spots is to put the wash puddle over the lightest area then fade the edge with a moist brush. This is the technique of grading a small wash. Remember to use just enough water in the brush to moisten the paper up to the edge of the puddle.

A third method is to use a light mixture and stipple (make small dots) over the area. Allow these dots to dry then repeat. Try to stipple on the very lightest places each time. When a light wash is used for stippling and a number of applications are made, the result should be a gradual darkening of the light spot to match the surrounding area. Sometimes it is preferable to use parallel strokes with an almost dry brush. These fine strokes are allowed to dry before repeating the process.

Camouflage is defined as an expedient to deceive or hide. Sometimes it is much easier to hide or at least lessen the effect of a streak than to remove it. Streaks are made prominent by contrast between near areas. A dark streak in the middle of a wash can be made much less conspicuous. This is accomplished by darkening the light areas near the streak and fading away from it.

A wash over a large area of a rendering often seems quite streaked. The delineator should keep in mind that when such a wash is broken up by later and darker washes over parts of the area, the streaks will be less prominent. There are three reasons for this subordination of the streaks. (1) Part of them have been covered by the darker washes and made less conspicuous. (2) The continuous length of some of the streaks has been shortened or interrupted. (3) The contrast caused by the addition of darker areas attracts attention away from them.

Streaks which at first seem bad in areas which are later broken up into units of stone, tile, or other material may actually be beneficial. They may prevent a hard mechanical feeling.

Scrubbing. Work and a great deal of it is required to do satisfactory patching of washes. If there are many streaks, patching just isn't a reasonable answer. As a final resort, scrubbing of the entire plate can be tried. The most efficient procedure is to take the board to the sink and slope it so water will run from it into the sink. Then get the large pan full of clear water. Start at the top of the rendering and go over it gently and quickly with a dripping sponge. Then go back and scrub lightly with the sponge where needed. Do not scrub hard enough to remove the surface of the paper. Remove water from the paper with the sponge. Then stand board on end until paper dries.

Do not attempt to scrub a partly dry rendering. Some of the moist areas may wash down to white paper. The dry areas may be faded only a little. Wait until the entire rendering is dry.

If the scrubbing is successful the rendering will now be very pale. The streaks will be less prominent and the drawing will still be in good condition. After the paper is dry start in again building up the washes of the rendering. If the scrubbing does not give satisfactory results the only answer is to get new illustration board or paper and start over.

Scrubbing is not the answer to all the ills of rendering. It is an emergency operation which is used as a last resort to save the life of the patient. It should be avoided if possible.

Scrubbing over a limited area of the rendering is sometimes a satisfactory procedure. Cover the surrounding area with white note paper to the exact edge of the area to be scrubbed. Use a minimum amount of water in a sponge. Make all strokes start on the paper covering the surrounding area and move into the wash area. This helps prevent water from running under the masking paper. Turn the sponge to a new part of its surface for each stroke. Clean the sponge in clear water when necessary. The masking paper must be held firmly as the sponge is moved over it.

CITY LIBRARY—PALO ALTO—CALIFORNIA
EDWARD DURELL STONE—ARCHITECT

FIG. 240 DRY PAPER WATER COLOR TECHNIQUE

Paints for Wash Rendering. The following are three common classifications of pigments for wash rendering. These classifications sometimes overlap.

1. Monotone wash rendering is done with any paint or other substance which can be used for this technique. Either a single pigment or material or a combination of two or more colors or pigments in a constant proportion can be used. Constant mixtures can be made of paints alone or of ground and filtered Chinese stick ink tinted with a paint. When a mixture of two or more matericals is used, precautions should be taken to see that the color contents of the washes remain the same throughout the rendering. A sure way to obtain this result is to mix at one time enough dark solution for the entire rendering. This mixture should be at least as dark as any wash required. It will be the source of supply for all washes. In most cases a small amount of it will be diluted with water for use. If the dark mixture must be kept for several days a small quantity of ammonium hydroxide should be added to keep it from spoiling.

A less reliable method is to make as accurate an estimate as possible of the proportion of each material used. The same proportion can then be used to make more wash solution.

2. Transparent water colors are obtained in tubes at any art supply store. They are made by several manufacturers. Some brands are made in two qualities. One is called scholastic water colors and is intended for school use. The other labelled artist's water color is intended for professional use. It is of higher quality and is a more expensive product. Some colors are like dyes and others are more opaque. These characteristics are derived from the materials used.

The selection of colors of paints to use is pretty much an individual problem. The answer varies with the objects and colors to be represented in the renderings to be done. The smallest number of paints which can be used for full color rendering is three. They are yellow, red, and blue. It is possible to get more or less perfect versions of all other colors including orange, green, purple, brown, grays, and black from mixtures of these three. For this purpose one of the following three-color palettes can be used with good results:

RENDERING BY GEORGE C. RUDOLPH
KETCHUM AND SHARP—ARCHITECTS

FIG. 241 WET PAPER WATER COLOR TECHNIQUE

A. Cadmium yellow light
Alizarin crimson (purplish)
Ultramarine blue (purplish)

B. Cadmium yellow light
Cadmium red deep
Phthalocyanine blue

C. Cadmium yellow light
Burnt sienna (red brown)
Phthalocyanine blue

While it is difficult if not impossible to get perfect results in all secondary colors with a three-color palette, it is possible to get very satisfactory results. With the use of only three paints a person must become expert in mixing colors. This is very useful training. Some delineators do not like to use prepared black for rendering. If it is to be used, ivory black is satisfactory.

3. A semi-transparent effect is secured by mixing opaque poster white with transparent water color paints. The general effect is better if some white is mixed with all washes. This mixture gives a more solid and less transparent rendering. It still retains the characteristics of wash rendering but requires more cautious handling. A mixture containing white is not the same color when it is wet as after it has dried. Care must be used to avoid disturbing pigment already on the paper when one wash is run over another or the blotter is used. Edges of washes which touch or cross an area containing a large proportion of white have a tendency to creep. Do not use much puddle in such cases. Try to plan the sequence of washes so that any areas containing a lot of white paint are run last when possible. When ruling lines over washes use as thick a mixture as practical. Do not put too much in the ruling pen. Thin mixtures have a greater tendency to run when lines are ruled.

Wet paper technique is useful in rendering some larger areas in a free style. The paper or illustration board is wet over its entire area at the beginning of such a plate. When paper is used for this purpose it is soaked and then laid over oilcloth on the board. Water color paint is applied to the wet paper with a brush and allowed to spread out. This is a very effective technique for skies, masses of trees, foliage, and other large areas. As the paper begins to dry smaller areas are rendered. Finally, when practical to do so, small details and accents are put in with a brush or ruling pen.

AMERICAN PAVILION—BRUSSELS WORLDS FAIR
EDWARD DURELL STONE—ARCHITECT

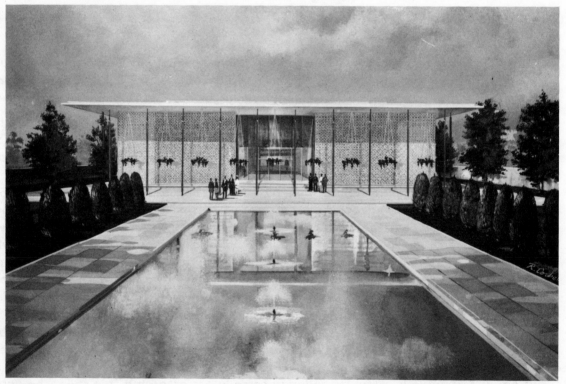

AMBASSADOR'S RESIDENCE—NEW DELHI—INDIA
EDWARD DURELL STONE—ARCHITECT

FIG. 242 EXAMPLES OF PROFESSIONAL RENDERING

A CONTEMPORARY RESIDENCE

STUDENT RENDERING BY FRANK DOST
AN INTERIOR DESIGN PROBLEM

STUDENT RENDERING BY ROBERT MARTIN
PROBLEM IN ARCHITECTURAL DESIGN

FIG. 243 EXAMPLES OF WATER COLOR RENDERING

CHAPTER 34

Opaque Water Color Rendering

Opaque water colors are sold under various names which include tempera, poster colors, showcard colors, and opaque water colors. They can be obtained in either jars or tubes in a wide variety of pigments and colors. They are also available in several tones of gray.

Each application of opaque water colors over an area is usually complete in itself. There is little or no building up of one wash over another, although one wash can be used to hide another. Each wash covers and conceals anything on the area where it is run. The same mixture is normally used throughout an area. There is little danger of bad streaks. However, there is also little opportunity for grading washes and modelling shapes. Instead of using a gradual change in the mixture as in transparent water color rendering, opaque washes are graded by using a sequence of bands with slight differences in color or darkness. These bands can be applied by the French method described for water color. In tempera rendering each band is applied separately and allowed to dry before another is applied touching it. In water color rendering the French method is usually employed for small bands only while large areas are also rendered in this way with tempera to give a graded effect. It is also possible with opaque colors to apply each band while the preceding painted area which it touches is still wet.

Opaque water color rendering loses some of the refinements of expression of wash rendering. It also requires a different type of technical facility and craftsmanship. Its principal advantages are simplicity of handling and the solid effects obtained. Wash renderings sometimes have a thin and paper-like tinted quality. Opaque renderings seem much more vivid and real in their presentations of colors and materials.

Short smooth glass rods or wood sticks are useful in transferring paint from jars to the pan or plate where it is to be mixed for use. Do not leave jars open for long periods of time. Even when closed tightly the paints sometimes dry hard in the jars and are then worthless.

Opaque paints are mixed and applied with brushes in much the same manner as the simple washes of transparent water color. It is advisable to use less expensive brushes than those used for water color rendering, since the opaque paints ruin brushes quickly. Flat bristle brushes such as those used for oil painting are useful for mixing opaque paints and are sometimes suitable for applying paint also. All brushes should be washed before the paints have a chance to dry in them. Enough paint mixture should be used to cover the areas of a wash uniformly. There is no necessity for putting a large puddle on the paper. One wash is usually sufficient over an area, although two coats may sometimes be used. Test samples should be allowed to dry before deciding whether the color is right, since the wet and dry paint may be different colors. Opaque paint mixtures can be used in a ruling pen. It is sometimes better to rule a line of the wash mixture around an area before filling it in with a brush. This gives more precise edges.

Opaque paints may be used for either monotone or color renderings. Opaque monotone renderings are usually more effective when the number of tones is limited. White, black, and about three grays provide a reasonable number of tones for some renderings. The use of a small number of tones gives a feeling of order and simplicity to a rendering. The use of unlimited variety of tones may create confusion and cause the rendering to seem fussy and overdone.

The example at the top of Fig. 244 is a simple monotone rendering with only a small number of tones. The example at the bottom of Fig. 244 is rendered with black and grays.

STUDENT RENDERING BY V. H. A. ALVAREZ

STUDENT RENDERING BY JAMES H. PRESTON

FIG. 244 EXAMPLES OF OPAQUE MONOTONE RENDERING

RENDERING BY RICHARD SCHIFF, RUDOLPH ASSOCIATES
J. SANFORD SHANLEY, ARCHITECT

RENDERING BY GEORGE C. RUDOLPH, RUDOLPH ASSOCIATES
JOSEPH WLADECK ARCHITECT

FIG. 245 EXAMPLES OF TEMPERA RENDERING

RENDERING BY ROBERT E. SCHWARTZ
KEMPA AND SCHWARTZ—ARCHITECTS

RENDERING BY ROBERT E. SCHWARTZ
KEMPA AND SCHWARTZ—ARCHITECTS

FIG. 246 EXAMPLES OF TEMPERA RENDERING

KEMPA AND SCHWARTZ · ARCHITECTS · J.H. LIVINGSTONE · ASSOCIATE

RENDERING BY ROBERT E. SCHWARTZ
KEMPA AND SCHWARTZ—ARCHITECTS—J. H. LIVINGSTONE—ASSOCIATE

RENDERING BY ROBERT E. SCHWARTZ
KEMPA AND SCHWARTZ—ARCHITECTS—J. H. LIVINGSTONE—ASSOCIATE

FIG. 247 EXAMPLES OF TEMPERA RENDERING

RENDERING BY J. WOOD
GEORGE L. DAHL, ARCHITECTS AND ENGINEERS

RENDERING BY JOHN RUSSELL, RUDOLPH ASSOCIATES
WARREN ASHLEY, ARCHITECT

FIG. 248 EXAMPLES OF TEMPERA RENDERING

CHAPTER 35

Some Other Methods of Rendering

Spray rendering materials are very good for smooth application of tones. Spray technique can be used for either flat or graded effects. The spray solution may be of any kind of water color paint or of ink. It should be mixed to appear lighter and brighter than the tone and color desired if it is tested with a brush. The drops are darker and duller than the effect secured by brush technique using the same mixture of paints. Illustration board or stretches of either hot or cold pressed water color paper are satisfactory for spray rendering.

Spray renderings require masking around the area to which a tone or color is to be applied. If the shapes of the drawing are at all complex, masking requires more time than applying the paint. Masking over large surfaces may be done with masking tape and sheets of scrap paper. Small areas can be covered with tape only.

Spray of water color paints can be most easily and most perfectly applied with an air brush. The spray method of applying water color paints is usually called air brush technique. An air brush and compressor are expensive equipment. If they are not available other means can be used to obtain similar results. An atomizer or fixative blower can be used for this purpose, or a piece of

RENDERING BY ROY P. HARROVER
MANN AND HARROVER — ARCHITECTS

FIG. 249 EXAMPLE OF SPRAY RENDERING

RENDERING BY HELMUT JACOBY
KETCHUM AND SHARP—ARCHITECTS

FIG. 250 EXAMPLE OF AIR BRUSH RENDERING

window screen and a toothbrush can be used to produce a fine spatter. The tones of the rendering of Fig. 249 were made by applying water color with a fixative blower.

With an atomizer or air brush, do not get too close to the drawing. Tilt the board so the fine spray hits approximately perpendicular to the surface of the paper. When too much spray is applied at one time the tiny drops run together. Apply a reasonable amount, then wait for that to dry before applying more. With spray it is very difficult to tell how dark an application is. Lift a little of the mask in order to see under it and compare tones at intervals as the work progresses. Masks for clouds, trees, and other forms can sometimes be used for repetition of the same details. It is often sufficient to move these masks to new positions and hold them by hand when an air brush is used. Weights of coins or other objects can be used to hold the masks when the board is horizontal. Small areas and accents can be put in with a small brush. These freehand additions often relieve the stiffness inherent in this technique. They may also add very effective darks and bright colors in small areas with a minimum of effort.

R E N D E R I N G   B Y   J A C K   S T.   M A R T I N
M A N N   A N D   H A R R O V E R — A R C H I T E C T S

FIG. 251 INK AND ZIP–A–TONE RENDERING

Printed patterns provide a limited tone variety for rendering to which black can be added. They provide a simple way to obtain mechanically uniform tones and patterns.

The appliqué process employs printed patterns on transparent sheets of thin plastic material. The patterns are made of dots or lines in most cases, and the most commonly used ones are printed black. However some are printed white to be applied over dark surfaces. There are also solid colors available. There are a great many variations of printed patterns. It is sometimes difficult to get distinctly separate tones since many of the available patterns offer little variety in darkness. However, this material is becoming more widely used as more varied materials become available and the advantages and limitations of the material are better understood.

Two layers of the same pattern can be used to make a darker tone or to produce a different pattern. When a parallel line pattern is used one layer can be at right angles to the other to darken and vary the pattern in a simple way. When this parallel line or a regular dot pattern is used in two layers it will be found that rotating the top layer slowly will produce a surprising number of pattern variations.

The bottom surface of the plastic material on which the patterns are printed is coated with an adhesive. This adhesive will keep the material from slipping around over the drawing when it is pressed against the paper by rubbing lightly. The bowl of a spoon, a polished piece of bone, thumbnail, or some other object must be rubbed vigorously over the material to make it adhere tightly to the paper.

After a pattern has been selected to be used on an area of the drawing, the material is laid over the area and rubbed lightly to keep it from slipping. The material is then scored very lightly

STUDENT RENDERING BY MARY T. SCHUMACHER
PROBLEM IN RENDERING TECHNIQUE

FIG. 252 TONES BY DEVELOPER PROCESS

and evenly with a sharp pointed needle or other instrument all around the edge of the area where it is to be applied. The T-square or triangle can be used to guide the cutting tool just as a line would be ruled. The material over the area is held in place and the edges lifted around it to remove the unwanted material. If the material has been scored correctly with a very sharp tool it will separate readily. Lift the material you are removing by beginning at one end of a line so it follows the cut edge along the line from one end to the other. It is not necessary to scratch completely through the material to separate it. Therefore the needle point should not damage the drawing under the material. When the material has been fitted exactly to the area it must be rubbed vigorously over every part of its surface so it will adhere firmly and permanently to the paper of the drawing.

Since the appliqué material is transparent it can be applied over the drawing lines. The pattern has some effect on the lines but usually can be turned so that it does not seriously interfere with them. The material can be applied over washes or other tones as well as over white paper. It may be used for shadows only or for other rendering purposes.

The developer process of printed patterns provides treated paper which has either one or two invisible patterns printed on the paper. The printed patterns can be brought out by applying the developer to the required areas, Fig. 252. The developer can be used in a ruling pen for thin lines. It is applied with brushes on larger areas. When the paper is printed with two tones, two developers must be used—one for the light and the other for the dark tone. Yellowish stains may appear from blotters used on the developers or from other sources. When the drawing is to be photographically reproduced this is not important. However, when the plate is to be displayed as it has been made, these stains mar the rendering and precautions should be taken to avoid them.

STUDENT RENDERING BY LARRY BLACKMAN

STUDENT RENDERING BY G. LIMKE

FIG. 253 RENDERINGS ON GRAY PAPER

White, black, and gray or colored paper can be used to give very effective conventionalized renderings of some subjects. The colored or gray paper or illustration board is usually better when it is medium dark or between light and medium in darkness. In most cases it is more satisfactory to avoid gaudy and brilliantly colored papers. Try to obtain a pleasing but somewhat subdued color. Poster or tempera white is satisfactory for the opaque white paint. Black waterproof drawing ink is satisfactory in most cases for the black.

Basically this technique is limited to three tones: (A) white, (B) the tone of the paper, and (C) black. However intermediate tones can be supplied with either white or black dots or lines on the paper. They can also be provided by leaving thin lines of the paper color with either white or black bands or other shapes between.

This technique is most effective when there are elements of materials to be shown. Wood boards, brick, stone, tile, and other units of materials and their joints add lines, tones, and interest to a rendering. A commonly used system is to make the areas of the units white and the joints the paper color in light. In shadow the treatment is reversed with joints white and the material units the color of the paper. Since the joints are normally relatively small this makes the shadow areas dark. The joints can sometimes be made black in shadow and the units the paper color. Units of materials are sometimes shown in either light or shadow areas only but not in both. A great deal of ingenuity and good judgment are required to get the best results from this simple technique. There are often several possible treatments of a given area.

Rendering of part of the areas of the drawing is a method of simplifying a presentation. This often produces an interesting effect. Three partial rendering methods are described briefly in the next three paragraphs.

Shadows only are sometimes rendered in black with all other areas left white. This is an indication type of rendering or drawing. It depends on the shadows alone to explain the shapes of the design. This same device is used in photography to produce a very simple and effective picture.

Rendering an outlined part of a drawing concentrates the interest on the most important part of the plate and subordinates less important areas. A circle or other simple outline form is made around an important central part of the drawing. The area within this outline is rendered. The area beyond the outline is left in line or perhaps with a little shading. If the drawing is a perspective with a close station point this type of presentation attracts the attention away from the more warped shapes of the drawing. However, it provides a suggestion of these surrounding shapes.

Spot rendering is a term frequently used for one type of partial rendering in which only a number of selected areas are rendered. When colors are used this method may be called spot color rendering. It avoids many of the complications of sky, background, and foreground tones and colors. It is often a bright and very effective way to render. The amount of rendering used depends on the subject and the wishes of the delineator. There may be only two or three rendered spots, or half or more of the areas may be rendered.

STUDENT WORK — T. SARVAY

Index